Quantity Takeoff for Contractors: *How to Get Accurate Material Counts*

Paul J. Cook

Illustrations by Carl W. Linde

R.S. MEANS COMPANY, INC.
CONSTRUCTION PUBLISHERS & CONSULTANTS

100 Construction Plaza
P.O. Box 800
Kingston, MA 02364-0800
(617) 585-7880

This book was edited by Jill Farinelli, Kevin Foley, Neil Smit, and Ernest Williams. Typesetting was supervised by Dianne Messier. The book and cover were designed by Norman Forgit. Illustrations by Carl Linde. Cover photograph by Norman Forgit.

Printed in the United States of America

20 19 18 17 16 15 14 13 12 11 10 9 8 7

Library of Congress Catalog Number 89-189308

ISBN 0-87629-268-6

Quantity Takeoff for Contractors: *How to Get Accurate Material Counts*

Paul J. Cook

Table of Contents

Part III
Miscellaneous Subtrades and Specialties

Part IV
New Technology

Part V
Appendix

Index

Acknowledgments

My sincere thanks to all the staff of R.S. Means Company, Inc. for their hard work in the editing and production of my books. Special appreciation is due to Neil Smit for his expert technical editing.

Two other construction professionals who deserve much credit for this book are G.E. "Shorty" Myrick, Chief Estimator at Aerospace/Electronics, Industrial Section of Fluor Daniel, for his special interest and encouragement. Also, S.L. "Shorty" Haehn, President of Haehn Management Company, San Diego, California, for the opportunity over a period of 28 years to perfect my estimating skills.

Foreword

This book is for the construction professional who is interested in learning how to perform a *quantity takeoff*, the first and most basic step in the estimating process. Quantity takeoff is the process by which detailed lists of quantities are made, based on drawings and specifications, of all the items of material and equipment necessary to construct a project. This itemized list is made prior to cost estimating and bidding. A *quantity estimator* is the individual who performs the quantity takeoff. In some cases the cost estimator performs the takeoff, but most often it is done by a separate individual who specializes in quantity estimating.

Quantity takeoff is difficult work. Several years of hands-on experience are usually necessary to become proficient. The difficulty lies not in the mechanics and arithmetic, but in the development of the skills necessary to interpret written and graphic specifications and to visualize them accurately as completed elements of the project.

During the takeoff process, the quantity estimator builds a mental picture of the project, taking into consideration a multitude of factors related to each structural component. For instance, in taking off a foundation wall, the quantity estimator needs to know the depth below the floor slab, the characteristics of the supporting footing and surrounding soil, the wall above grade, and exposed surfaces that will receive finish treatment.

The material in this book is organized to demonstrate this "visualization" process. Part I, "Introduction," acquaints the reader with the quantity takeoff process by defining the quantity estimator's role and establishing some general rules for performing a timely and accurate takeoff.

Part II, "Major Construction Elements," is a chapter-by-chapter analysis of those building components for which the general contractor's quantity estimator is typically responsible. Using a two-story administrative building as a model structure, each chapter examines the takeoff procedure for one layer or stratum of the project at a time. The components in each of the chapters are taken off in the order in which they are incorporated into the structure. For instance, the takeoff process is demonstrated for mass excavation first, followed by footings, then foundation walls, then slabs on grade, and so forth. In some chapters, construction methods are discussed in a "what if"-type scenario, to give the reader experience with a number of different building possibilities. For example, a takeoff is demonstrated for both piles and caissons, even though these two types of footings would not normally be used in the same building.

This sequence is based loosely on the *Uniformat System*. (See Figure 0.1.) Uniformat is an organizational system that groups building components and procedures according to their placement and sequential order in the construction of the project. The advantage of this method over other methods, such as that based on the divisions of the *Construction Specifications Institute* (CSI) MASTERFORMAT, is that the inexperienced quantity estimator is better able to visualize the construction process from start to finish and, in this way, avoid omissions and duplications in his or her work.

Part III, "Miscellaneous Subtrades and Specialties," concludes the discussion with an examination of the takeoff procedure of nonstructurally-oriented subtrades such as moisture and thermal control, interior construction, and building specialties.

Comparing CSI and Uniformat Systems

CSI MASTERFORMAT		Uniformat System	
Division	**Description**	**Division**	**Description**
1	General Requirements	1	Foundation/Substructure
2	Site Work	2	Substructure
3	Concrete	3	Superstructure
4	Masonry	4	Exterior Closure
5	Metals	5	Roofing
6	Wood & Plastics	6	Interior Construction
7	Moisture Protection	7	Conveying
8	Doors, Windows & Glass	8	Mechanical
9	Finishes	9	Electrical
10	Specialties	10	General Conditions
11	Architectural Equipment	11	Specialties
12	Furnishings	12	Site Work
13	Special Construction		
14	Conveying Systems		
15	Mechanical		
16	Electrical		

Figure 0.1

This book follows the format in *Means Assemblies Cost Data,* but it should be emphasized that the construction trades that are normally sublet, such as the mechanical and electrical trades, are not discussed in this book. Only those trades typically performed by a general contractor are included, although there is a general discussion of the takeoff procedures for masonry and structural steel. When a quantity estimator for the general contractor does take off quantities of a subtrade, the work is done as a rough estimation for budget purposes only, and with less precision than for those trades that are the general contractor's responsibility and that lie within his or her area of expertise. For more information on the quantity takeoff of subtrades, refer to the estimating series published by R.S. Means Company, Inc.

Finally, Part IV, "New Technology" explores some of the hardware and software packages that have been developed specifically for use in electronic or computerized quantity takeoff. Specialists predict that use of these systems can cut the quantity estimation time by as much as 50 percent.

While individual chapters contain details of the related building elements when necessary for clarification, the actual plans for our model administrative building are located in Part V, Appendix A. The reader should understand, however, that these plans are provided for illustrative purposes only, and represent only the major features of the building. In actuality, such a building would require many more sheets of drawings with more plans, details, sections, and elevations. Also included would be a full set of specifications. For our purposes, however, these figures provide sufficient information. The quantities as given in the sample estimate represent realistic conditions. Assumptions have also been made for items not shown in these plans that would normally be included in the plans and specifications for a project of this type.

Part V also contains appendices for reference on abbreviations and symbols, suggested waste allowances, tables of proportionate quantities, and geometric formulas.

A thorough study of the procedures described in this book, followed by practice with actual projects, should enable the reader to become an accomplished quantity takeoff estimator.

Part I

Introduction

Chapter 1

Introducing Quantity Takeoff

Quantity Takeoff and the Estimating Process

Quantity takeoff is the process of taking measurements from architectural and engineering drawings and specifications and converting them mathematically into useful and meaningful quantities for cost estimating. Quantity takeoff is the first ambitious activity a company undertakes when bidding on a new project. It is often the most time-consuming part of the bidding phase, and until the takeoff is performed, very little work can be done on the project. Both cost estimating and bidding directly depend on the completed quantity takeoff. From the list of quantities, the cost estimator is able to calculate how much it will cost to build the project. All bids are based on cost estimations that are applied to the lists of quantities.

This book will examine the takeoff procedure for those areas of construction that are the primary responsibility of the general contractor. This chapter begins by discussing the role of the quantity estimator, the ways in which a quantity estimator breaks the project down into manageable elements, and some general rules that have been proven to save time and increase the accuracy of the takeoff.

The Quantity Estimator's Role

Quantity takeoff is described in this book as it is practiced in a typical medium-sized general contracting company by a full-time specialist—one who does nothing but make lists of quantities. Quantity takeoff is typically performed by one person, but if the project is unusually large or complex, or if time is limited, takeoff may be done by a quantity takeoff team, or the takeoff of the various trades may be relegated to the respective subcontractors. A *quantity estimator, takeoff estimator,* or *quantity surveyor* refer to the professional who performs the quantity takeoff.

The quantity estimator must have a good working knowledge of construction materials and methods as well as an understanding of the cost estimating process in order to produce meaningful and useful lists of quantities. The quantity estimator must also be thorough and accurate in the takeoff process. If the material, labor, and equipment unit costs are accurate, but the quantities are incorrect, the entire estimate will be inaccurate. The quantities should be *minimal but realistic,* taking into account variables such as swelling, shrinkage, waste, stock lengths requiring cutting, and so forth. The takeoff estimator's goal is to produce a list of quantities that will be *handled* (referred to as *gross quantities*), not just those that will *appear in the finished project* (called *net quantities*).

The successful quantity estimator also possesses the following characteristics:

- An analytical and mathematical mind
- The ability to work independently
- Patience, concentration
- Self-motivation
- Must be detail-oriented, methodical, and organized
- The ability to visualize the project based on plans and specifications
- Neat, legible handwriting

The tools and instruments used by the quantity estimator in the takeoff process typically include:

- *Planimeter*—a mechanical device or measuring wheel that is rolled over a map or drawing to measure plane areas
- *Scales*—architectural (graduated in 16ths of an inch) and engineering (graduated in 10ths of an inch)
- *Pencils*—black, draftsman quality (HB suggested)
- *Colored pencils*—yellow, red, and blue
- *Erasers*
- *Calculator*
- *Preprinted forms* of suitable sizes
- *Drafting table* or large desk

For information on hardware and software systems used in electronic quantity takeoff, see Chapter 26.

Breaking Down the Project

The first thing a quantity estimator must do to organize the task ahead is to break the project down into manageable elements. By doing this he or she is able to allocate responsibility for the takeoff of certain building systems and set up a schedule for completing his or her own work. Projects are broken down into *trades*, *categories*, and *items*. These terms are discussed below.

Trade

A *trade* refers to a division of a construction project large enough to create a separate classification of worker. In quantity and cost estimating, trade names are established by *custom of the trade*. (Customs of the trades are traditional guidelines that determine responsibility for items of work and standards of workmanship.) It is standard practice for construction professionals to speak of, for instance, the "concrete trade," or the "carpentry trade." General contractors often sublet certain trade work (such as electrical and plumbing) to individual subcontractors with expertise in those areas.

Subletting

Subcontractors normally take off quantities for their own trades. Therefore, work that is *sublet* (performed by subcontractors hired by the general contractor) is of little interest to the general contractor's quantity estimator, except for the limits that separate this work from the work of the general contractor. A quantity estimator may overlap with certain subtrades to ensure that no areas are omitted in takeoff. For instance, a general contractor's quantity estimator may take off block walls, even though this building component is, by custom of the trade, the responsibility of the masonry subcontractor. **However, any portion of a project that is not taken off by a subcontractor *must* be taken off by the quantity estimator for the general contractor.**

On a new project, a quantity estimator for the general contractor makes a list of trades and portions of trades that he or she will take off. This list is based on experience and/or instructions from the cost estimator. Figure 1.1 is an example of such a list.

The quantity estimator should keep a similar list of instructions close at hand for reference. As the takeoff proceeds, this list may be modified according to the needs of the project. Some trades may be added, others omitted.

Category

A *category* is a significant subdivision of a trade. For example, footings or foundation walls are categories in the concrete trade.

Item

An *item* is a subdivision of a category small enough so that a quantity is useful for cost estimating purposes. For example, formwork is an item in the concrete wall category; floor beams are items in the carpentry category.

Anything that has a unique cost value is considered an item and is taken off. Itemizing is also done when there are structural differences in the building components (for instance, two types of columns, or several sizes of a particular kind of beam) or when there is a time lapse in construction, such as that which exists between construction of the lower and the upper floors. Items may also be listed individually when they appear in different locations on the project. For example, items in the upper stories of a building might differ in cost from items on the ground floor, due to the hoisting or scaffolding necessary to put them in place.

Quantity Takeoff Instructions

Take Off	Include	Exclude
Demolition	Alteration Work	Concrete Pavement
Concrete Footings	Structural Excavation	Rough Grading
All Structural Concrete	Forms and Finishes	Subcontractor's Inserts Reinforcing Steel
Site Concrete	Layout	Surveying
Miscellaneous Metal Installation	Pipe Railing	Structural Steel
Rough Carpentry	Bolts and Inserts	Subcontractor's Blocking
Finish Carpentry	Wall Paneling	Ceiling Hatches
Millwork	Doors and Frames	Casework

(Note: All trades listed under "Exclude" will be sublet.)

Take off the following trades for budget estimates (these are normally sublet):
- Rough (mass) Demolition
- Rough (site) Grading
- Drywall and Steel Studs
- Concrete Masonry

Figure 1.1

Examples of trades, categories, and items are as follows:

• Concrete	(trade)
–walls	(category)
formwork	(item)
–slabs on grade	(category)
fine grading	(item)
finishing and curing	(item)
• Carpentry	(trade)
–wall framing	(category)
studding	(item)
blocking	(item)

Theoretically, it is possible to continue breaking a project into even smaller elements, but there comes a point when it is no longer practical to do so. Elements of a project fall within a limited range of usefulness for cost estimating purposes. Very large elements may be used for preliminary or rough estimates; very small elements may be used for in-depth analytical cost studies.

General Rules

General rules have been established for improving the speed, ease, and accuracy of the takeoff process. Quantity estimators should adhere to these rules. An accurate quantity takeoff is critical to the accuracy of a cost estimate, since no estimate will be reliable if a mistake is made in the quantity takeoff, no matter how precise the unit price information may be. (Note that more specific guidelines are provided in certain chapters when necessary.)

General Rule 1

When taking off quantities, follow the guidelines provided by the person who will be applying unit prices to the quantities (the cost estimator). The takeoff should be clear and informative to prevent misinterpretation. Use symbols, sketches, or footnotes to clarify ambiguities in the takeoff. The quantity estimator should think of him or herself as an assistant to the cost estimator.

General Rule 2

A takeoff list is not just a list of materials, but a list of measurements separated into categories to which unit prices are applied. Measurements and extensions are usually recorded on preprinted forms called *quantity sheets.* R.S. Means Company, Inc. provides various sizes of quantity sheets for this purpose in *Means Forms for Building Construction Professionals.* These forms come in two sizes, as shown in Figures 1.2 and 1.3. Figure 1.2 is used for simple building components that have few associated operations or items. Figure 1.3 is used for more complex components that have many associated items or operations.

The quantity sheets are relatively simple to use. The name of the building component is written in the far left-hand column labeled "Description." The number of components called out on the plans is listed next, followed by their dimensions (such as length, width, and depth or height). Quantities of items that are taken off of the component are listed in the subsequent columns. When taking off strip footings, for example, the associated items include structural excavation, concrete, formwork, backfill, and disposal. Appropriate units of measurement, such as cubic yards of concrete, square feet of forms, and linear feet of pour strips, are applied to each item.

If more than one building component is listed on the same quantity sheet, or if there are several different sizes of the same component, then quantities are listed in the appropriate columns and totalled at the bottom of the page. In this way the quantity estimator can calculate, for instance, the total number of cubic yards of concrete needed for strip footings for the entire building and write it in one sum at the bottom of the column labeled "Concrete." Figure 1.4 illustrates a quantity sheet that has been completed in this manner.

Means Forms

QUANTITY SHEET

SHEET NO.

PROJECT — ESTIMATE NO.

LOCATION — ARCHITECT — DATE

TAKE OFF BY — EXTENSIONS BY: — CHECKED BY:

DESCRIPTION	NO.	DIMENSIONS			UNIT	UNIT	UNIT	UNIT

Figure 1.2

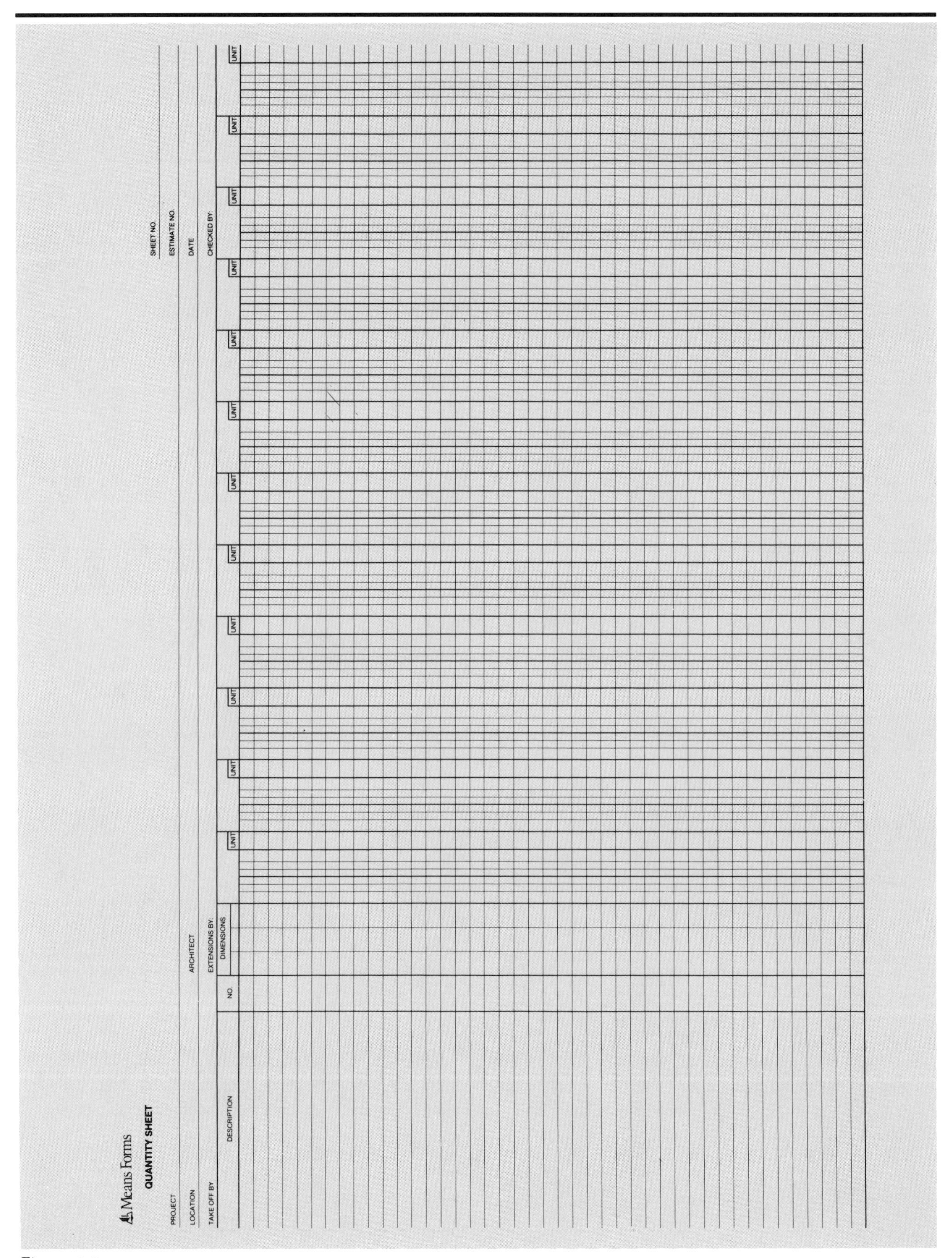

Means Forms
QUANTITY SHEET

PROJECT
LOCATION
TAKE OFF BY
ARCHITECT
EXTENSIONS BY:
SHEET NO.
ESTIMATE NO.
DATE
CHECKED BY:

DESCRIPTION	NO.	DIMENSIONS			UNIT	UNIT	UNIT	UNIT	UNIT	UNIT	UNIT	UNIT	UNIT	UNIT	UNIT	UNIT

Figure 1.3

Means® Forms
QUANTITY SHEET

PROJECT Admin. Bldg.
LOCATION Picacho, Ca.
TAKE OFF BY PC
ARCHITECT Bell & Bell
EXTENSIONS BY: ETW
SHEET NO. 1
ESTIMATE NO. 1017
DATE March 1989
CHECKED BY: NS

DESCRIPTION	NO.	DIMENSIONS l	w	h	MACH. EXCAVA. (UNIT)	HAND EXCAVA. (UNIT)	FORMS (UNIT)	CONC. (UNIT)	REINF. (UNIT)	KEYWAY (UNIT)	B' FILL (UNIT)	DISPOSAL (UNIT)	CORNERS (UNIT)	STEPS (UNIT)	LAYOUT (UNIT)	(UNIT)
Perimeter Footing	512LF		2.67	1.0	5270 CF	1367 SF	1024 SFCA	1367 CF	1536 l.f.	512 l.f.						
					210											
					790											
					1780											
					5170											
Subtotal					13220	1367	1024	1367	1536	512						
Interior Footings	151LF				2275	403 SF		439 CF	453 l.f.	151 l.f.						
Total					15495	1770 SF	1024 SFCA	1806 CF	1989 l.f.	663 l.f.			10 ea.	6 ea.	700 l.f.	
Convert to CY					574 CY			67 CY			507 CY					
Add 10% for compaction											51					
											558 CY	16 CY				
Conv. #5 bars to LBS (1.043 #/LF)									2075 LBS							
Waste Allowances																
conc. 5%								3 CY								
Reinf. 18%									374							
forms 5%							51									
Total					574 CY	1770 SF	1075 SFCA	70 CY	2449 LBS	663 LF	558 CY	16 CY	10 ea.	6 ea.	700 LF	

Figure 1.4

General Rule 3

A quantity estimator may begin the takeoff with any building component and proceed in the order of his or her choice. A good approach is to follow roughly the order of the actual field construction, such as from the footings upward to the roof. This provides the quantity estimator with the clearest mental picture of the project. If a project consists of more than one building, each structure should be taken off separately, since unit costs may vary from structure to structure.

General Rule 4

Check the drawings and details carefully for notes such as NTS (Not To Scale), changes in the scale as it is used throughout the drawings, drawings reduced to one-half or one-quarter their original size, or discrepancies in the specifications and the plans. Be consistent when listing dimensions.

General Rule 5

Always use the dimensions stated in the drawings instead of measuring by scale, but make a habit of frequently checking printed dimensions with a scale or with mental arithmetic to spot draftsman's errors. Always express dimensions in the same order, such as:

length × width × height (or depth)

General Rule 6

Use a systematic procedure when working with the drawings. For instance, take measurements in a clockwise direction around a floor or roof plan, first recording the measurements of items displayed horizontally on the drawings, and then recording those shown vertically. This method is most useful when taking off two-dimensional areas.

General Rule 7

Whenever possible, the items in a quantity takeoff should be identified by their location on the drawings. These drawings are located in Appendix A in the back of the book. Turn to the foundation and footing plan. Note that the footings around the perimeter of the structure can be identified by the *points of the compass* as well as their placement on a grid (called the *column line grid* because its spacing is determined by the placement of the columns). In this example, vertical lines are numbered, and horizontal lines are lettered. Segments of perimeter footings are identified as follows (in the order in which they are taken off): 3D-3B; B3-B4; 4B-4A; A4-A1; 1A-1C; C1-C2; 2C-2D; D2-D3. Note that the footing segments were identified in a clockwise direction, as recommended in General Rule 6. This is particularly helpful when the footings vary in type and size.

General Rule 8

A quantity estimate is not intended to be used for direct purchasing of materials. In fact, many items on a quantity estimate have no material value. These are called *work items* and are simply areas that require labor, such as fine grading gravel or finishing concrete surfaces. Work items may not appear on the drawings but are nonetheless required to complete the job. The quantity estimator should pay close attention to areas that may contain labor requirements. Items that *do* have material value are called *material items*. Both material items and work items are assembled on the same form for eventual pricing out, or cost estimating.

Any item that has a cost value should be assigned a unit of measurement, even if it is only in *lump sum* (LS) form. The term lump sum is used for certain work items that cannot be measured or expressed in any other way. *LS* calls the estimator's attention to an item that requires a judged cost allowance. For example, a quantity estimator can calculate the number of square feet of concrete finish required, but cannot measure or predict how much underground water may have to be drained or pumped from the site. In such a case, the quantity estimator should acknowledge that a cost item exists and label it *Dewater LS.* A column heading labeled LS may be provided on the quantity sheet for such immeasurable items. All quantities listed under this heading are assumed to be work items and are expressed in lump sum amounts.

General Rule 9

Decimals are used in quantity takeoff instead of fractions because they are faster, more precise, and easy to use on a calculator. Drawing dimensions that are given in feet and inches are converted to *decimal feet,* that is, feet and tenths of a foot. Fractions of an inch are converted to hundredths of a foot. The most common decimal equivalents are shown in Figure 1.5. A good rule to remember is that 1/8" is approximately 0.01'.

General Rule 10

Quantity takeoff is performed for cost *estimating* purposes. Since estimating is not an exact science, the lists of quantities need not be overly precise. An example of unnecessary precision is calculating excavation quantities to 1/8 of an inch. However, a reasonable degree of precision is expected, since many bids are lost by narrow margins. No estimator wants to be accused of ballpark estimating.

Decimal Parts of a Foot

Major Divisions	Secondary Divisions	For Added 1/8" Increments
0 = 0.00		1/8" = .01
		1/4" = .02
	1" = 0.08	3/8" = .03
		1/2" = .04
	2" = 0.17	5/8" = .05
		3/4" = .06
3" = 0.25		7/8" = .07
6" = 0.50	4" = 0.33 5" = 0.42	
9" = 0.75	7" = 0.58 8" = 0.67	
12" = 1.00	10" = 0.83 11" = 0.92	

Thus 3' - 7-3/4" becomes:

3' = 3.00

7 = .58

3/4" = .06

3.64 feet

Figure 1.5

In most cases, the use of two decimal places is sufficient for quantity surveying purposes (12′-4-1/2″ = 12.38′) and easy to enter into a calculator. However, when writing the product of the calculation, decimals are usually meaningless. Develop rules for precision that are consistent with measurement capabilities. Below is an example.

Item	Input	Output
Earthwork	Nearest 0.1 feet	Nearest cf or cy
Concrete	Nearest .01 feet	Nearest cf or cy
Formwork	Nearest .01 feet	Nearest sf
Finishing and Precast	Nearest .01 feet	Nearest sf
Lumber	Nearest 0.1 feet	Nearest bf
Finishes	Nearest 0.1 feet	Nearest sf or sy

The quantity estimator must also learn the standards of each industry. For instance, a lumber dimension of 12′-1-1/2″ must be rounded up to 14′ due to standard sawmill cutting practices.

Methods for rounding off measurements will be discussed as the takeoff for each building component is examined. The symbol $\doteq$ used in equations means that the final value has been rounded off and is an approximation.

Finally, do not convert units until all items in a column are totaled. For instance, keep concrete in cubic feet (cf) until all of the quantities listed in the concrete column have been added together. Then convert to cubic yards (cy).

General Rule 11

The quantity estimator should add an allowance for waste to certain quantities. Before the waste allowance is made, the quantities are referred to as *net quantities*. After the allowance for waste is added, the quantities are considered *gross quantities*. Some companies prefer that the quantity estimator refrain from waste speculation and leave that to the cost estimator. However, this book will show examples of waste allowances as a quantity estimator might judge and apply them. Since the quantity estimator works so closely with the drawings, he or she may be best able to determine which items should receive a waste allowance, and by what amount. Likewise, the practice of adding waste by the quantity estimator may prevent possible omission by the cost estimator. Appendix C contains suggested waste allowances for various building materials.

General Rule 12

Ideally, a second quantity takeoff should be performed by a separate individual or team to ensure that no items have been omitted or duplicated. Unfortunately, the personnel to perform a second estimate are usually not available, or the cost to hire additional help is prohibitive. Typically, the quantity estimator systematically must check his or her own work. In fact, the *dimensions* taken from drawings *should* be checked by the quantity estimator while the *extensions* should be checked by someone *other than* the original quantity estimator. Of course this person need not be concerned with anything but the arithmetic.

One way to avoid omissions and duplications is to mark the drawings as items are taken off. Make colored pencil shadings and check marks directly on the drawings as items are taken off. Most quantity estimators have their own methods of marking drawings. Usually a combination of methods is used, rather than a single method, as one kind of mark may be effective in taking off one particular category, and different marks effective for other categories. Figure 1.6 illustrates typical markings.

The quantity estimator may assume that any item on a drawing that has not been marked has not been taken off yet. Shading is useful for expansive areas such as slabs, footings, and foundations. Use light shading for footings and heavy shading for foundation walls. The heavy can be laid over the light.

To avoid confusion on the quantity sheets, place a dash mark or other mark in columns where no quantity will be listed.

General Rule 13

When work is interrupted, for whatever reason, select a natural stopping point and mark it clearly so that when work resumes, no items are missed or duplicated.

Systematic application of these rules will make the quantity estimator's job faster, easier, and more accurate. Refer to the general rules in this chapter whenever necessary.

We now turn to an examination of the quantity takeoff process. In Chapter 2, the fundamentals of mass excavation will be discussed, followed by a step-by-step takeoff demonstration based on a model two-story administrative building. The plans and specifications for this building are located in Appendix A. Turn now to Appendix A to familiarize yourself with the project before reading further.

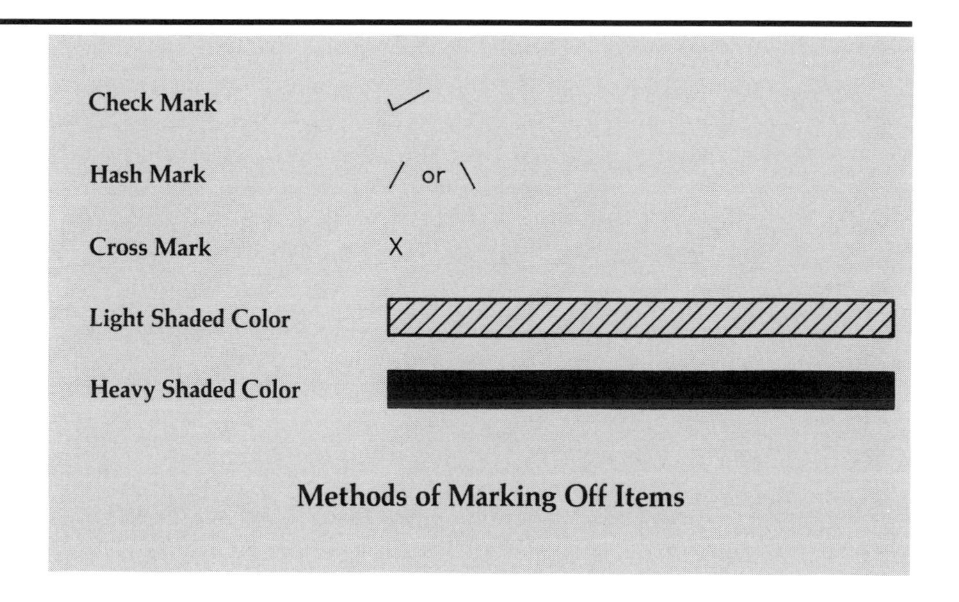

Methods of Marking Off Items

Figure 1.6

Part II

Major Construction Elements

Chapter 2
Clearing, Grubbing, and Mass Excavation

Clearing and Grubbing

Before the mass excavation begins, the general contractor may have to *clear and grub* the site. Clearing and grubbing is the removal of trees, vegetation, and other obstructions from the work site. The takeoff is typically expressed on the quantity sheet in acres. If the site is small and contains only a few large trees, the quantity estimator can simply record the number and size of the trees to be removed.

If large quantities of trees need to be taken off, however, a random count method should be used. First determine the total acreage to be cleared. Then count each type and size of tree for 16′ on either side of a line 340′ long. At least three random counts should be made. Each count will reflect the relative density of one-fourth of an acre. With rising lumber costs (especially hardwood) and the growing use of firewood, the quantity estimator can probably find a company or individual to cut and remove the trees at no cost. The expense of stump and brush removal must still be included, however.

Mass Excavation

Mass excavation, sometimes referred to as *earthwork* or *rough excavation,* is the removal of earth from the existing site contour elevations down to the approximate level of the top of the footings. Mass excavation is sometimes sublet, and sometimes performed by the general contractor. The instructions in this chapter apply to mass excavation for construction projects of all types and sizes.

The quantity estimator should understand the difference between *mass excavation, structural excavation,* and *site grading*. Mass excavation is performed on a much larger scale than structural excavation, which is typically performed for the placement of foundation components (see Chapter 3). Site grading is the final altering of the building site to a desired contour by cutting, filling, levelling, or smoothing. Site grading is performed in preparation for seeding, paving, and so forth. An experienced quantity estimator should be able to distinguish between these three operations. Those who are not well versed in this aspect of construction may choose to consult with an experienced excavation contractor. See Figure 2.1.

Takeoff Items

The items that are taken off for mass excavation include:

- Removal of earth (excavation)
- Temporary shoring or sheeting of banks (if necessary)
- Backfill
- Disposal

These items are discussed below.

Removal of Earth (Excavation)

The first item taken off for mass excavation is the total volume of earth removed or excavated. To calculate this quantity, the quantity estimator must first determine the method of excavation that will be used on the project.

When performing mass excavation for a large concrete foundation, room must be allowed for the workers to erect the forms. If shoring or sheeting is not used to retain the earth, the excavation must be sloped to prevent the excavation walls from caving in on the workers. Figure 2.2 illustrates two basic methods of excavation. Figure 2.2A is a pit that is excavated with vertical sides. Figure 2.2B is a pit that is excavated with sloped sides.

Temporary Shoring (Sheeting) of Banks

Temporary shoring, or sheeting, is installed along the walls or banks of a cut to protect workers and equipment from cave-ins during excavation. Shoring may be constructed of wood or steel, depending on soil conditions and the size and type of the excavation. The total area of shoring is calculated in square feet of exposed area, plus an amount for *toe-in* (driving the shoring in below the excavation line), and an amount for *extension* above the trench. Depending on soil conditions, shoring is usually toed in about one-third of the exposed height and extended above the existing ground elevation about one foot.

Backfill

Backfill is the excavated earth, soil, or other material that is placed around a foundation wall or other substructure to replace previously excavated material. In the simple case shown in Figure 2.1, where the final site grading will be returned

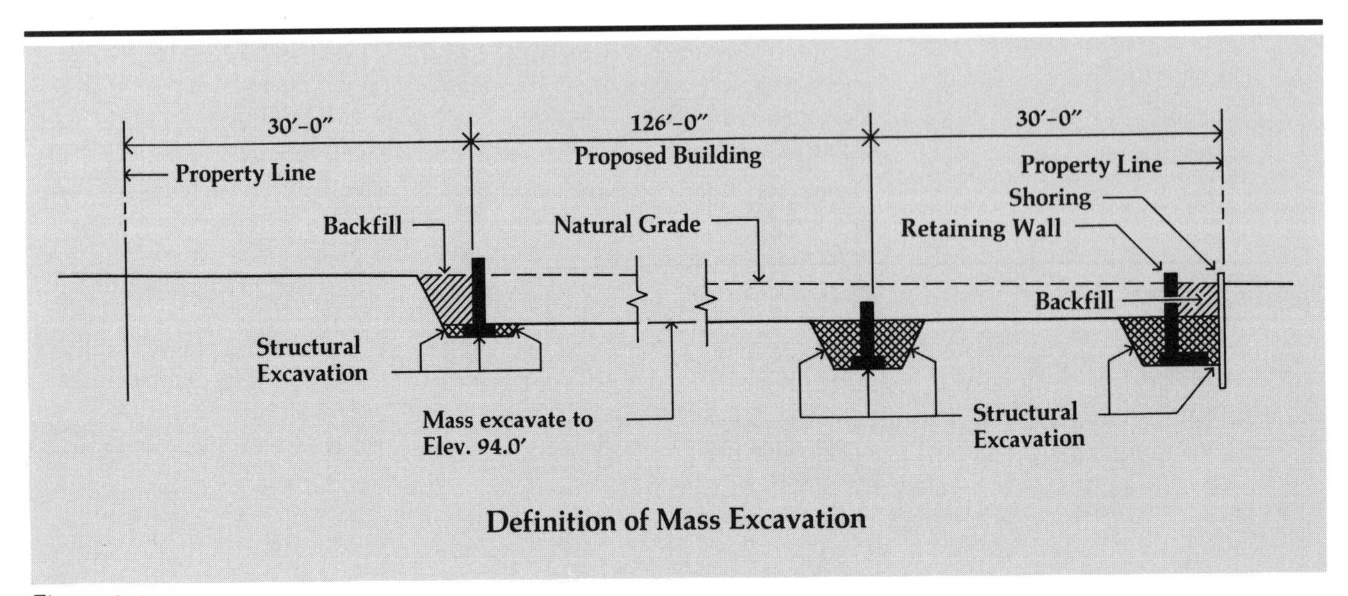

Figure 2.1

to the existing site contour, the total quantity of backfill is found by subtracting the volume of the foundation walls or substructural components from the total volume of excavated material. An allowance for compaction is made consistent with the type of material used for backfill. The volume of backfill is expressed in cubic yards.

Disposal

Disposal is the quantity of excavated material that is not needed (or is unsuitable) for backfill and which must be removed from the work site. The volume of disposal is found by subtracting the volume of backfill from the volume of mass excavation. Disposal is expressed in cubic yards.

Other Variables

There are several other variables to consider when taking off mass excavation. The quantity estimator should convey this information to the cost estimator whenever possible:

- Soil characteristics
- Ground water
- Demolition of existing structures
- Access ramps

Soil Characteristics

First, the handling characteristics of the excavated material should be examined. Borings identify the type of soil, its moisture content, and location of the water table at various points around the site. Certain types of soil may call for additional labor or special equipment. For instance, it may be necessary to blast through solid rock. Or, special vehicles may be required for proper traction and support in sand or mud. Cemented soil, clay, and loam have their own characteristics that may add to the expense of excavation. This information may be valuable to the cost estimator. The quantity estimator should provide separate columns for the different classes of soil, and should include on the takeoff sheet in bold lettering any information that he or she thinks is important for the cost estimator to know.

Identification of soil properties is necessary to determine the amount of backfill and/or disposal. All soil types increase (swell) or decrease (shrink) in volume

Figure 2.2

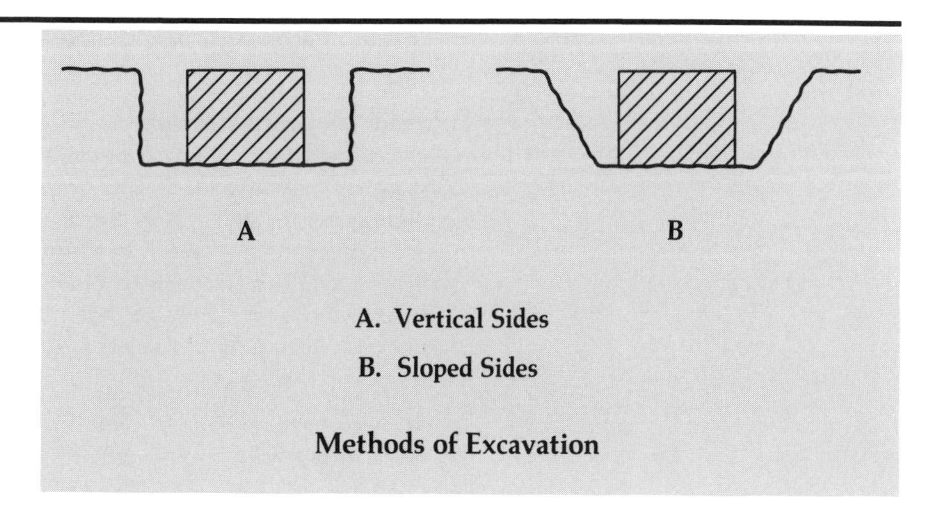

Methods of Excavation

depending on their state. *Bank soil*, or soil in its natural or undisturbed state, is far more compact (smaller in volume) than freshly excavated or *loose soil*. On the other hand, soil that has been used for fill and has been *compacted* has a smaller volume than either bank or loose soil. For instance, one cubic yard of gravel, when excavated, will swell to approximately one-and-a-quarter cubic yards. When then moved to another location and compacted, it will occupy only 90% of its original volume. The amount of swell and compaction varies depending on the type of soil (see Figure 2.3).

Ground Water

The presence of ground water at some predictable elevation is another consideration. This information can be obtained from test borings or pits dug on site. The presence of water might require the use of special equipment, a change in the sequence of excavation, or dewatering. Water affects the property of the soil and may impact the design of the foundation. While the quantity of water cannot be measured, the quantity estimator should alert the cost estimator to the fact that water is present and designate its removal as a work item labeled *Dewater LS* (lump sum).

Demolition of Existing Structures

In reviewing the site plan, the quantity estimator should look for any existing structures, foundations, or foreign objects that will have to be removed to make way for the new construction. He or she should make note of the type and number of structures, their overall size, and the type of construction.

In some instances it may be necessary to remove pavement before excavating. The type and depth of paving material will determine the equipment required to break it up and haul it away. Tar or asphalt pavement, for instance, is faster and easier to remove than concrete pavement. Pavement removal should be listed by the quantity estimator by type and quantity, either in square yards or cubic yards. In addition, the material beneath the pavement as well as objects embedded in the pavement, such as manholes and catch basins, should be listed.

Often the excavator unearths buried junk, chunks of concrete, or other foreign objects during the course of digging. While this cannot always be predicted, the quantity estimator should be prepared for hidden treasures beneath the surface of the ground, since equipment will be required to lift the objects and haul them away. Removal of these objects may also affect backfill and disposal quantities. The quantity estimator should check the site borings for evidence of foreign objects and inform the cost estimator of their presence.

Access Ramps

Finally, depending on the size and depth of the excavation, the characteristics of the soil, and the type of equipment needed, special access ramps may be necessary for transporting trucks and equipment into and out of the pit. The number and size of access ramps, when they are required, are based on the actual quantities of earth moved.

Takeoff Demonstration

In this section, the takeoff of mass excavation will be demonstrated using a two-story administrative building as our model. (This same building plan will be used throughout the book.) Note that the quantities taken off in this chapter apply to mass excavation only; takeoff of structural excavation will be demonstrated in Chapter 3. Using basic mathematical formulas and performing simple calculations, the reader will convert the information provided on the plans to useful lists of quantities, and then record this data on Quantity Sheet 2 (Figure 2.10), located at the end of this chapter.

Because most mass excavations are not executed in simple cubic squares or rectangles, a knowledge of solid geometry is necessary to perform the takeoff. Figure 2.4 is a plan drawing of our model building and provides the dimensions

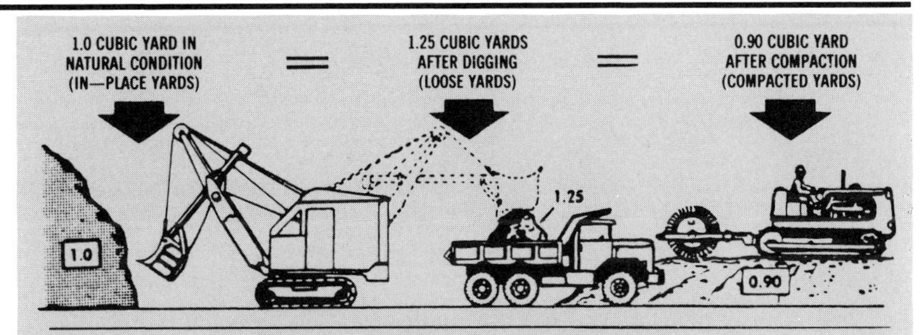

Approximate Material Characteristics*

Material	Loose (lb/cy)	Bank (lb/cy)	Swell (%)	Load Factor
Clay, dry	2,100	2,650	26	0.79
Clay, wet	2,700	3,575	32	0.76
Clay and gravel, dry	2,400	2,800	17	0.85
Clay and gravel, wet	2,600	3,100	17	0.85
Earth, dry	2,215	2,850	29	0.78
Earth, moist	2,410	3,080	28	0.78
Earth, wet	2,750	3,380	23	0.81
Gravel, dry	2,780	3,140	13	0.88
Gravel, wet	3,090	3,620	17	0.85
Sand, dry	2,600	2,920	12	0.89
Sand, wet	3,100	3,520	13	0.88
Sand and gravel, dry	2,900	3,250	12	0.89
Sand and gravel, wet	3,400	3,750	10	0.91

*Exact values will vary with grain size, moisture content, compaction, etc. Test to determine exact values for specific soils.

Typical Soil Volume Conversion Factors

Soil Type	Initial Soil Condition	Bank	Converted to: Loose	Compacted
Clay	Bank	1.00	1.27	0.90
	Loose	0.79	1.00	0.71
	Compacted	1.11	1.41	1.00
Common earth	Bank	1.00	1.25	0.90
	Loose	0.80	1.00	0.72
	Compacted	1.11	1.39	1.00
Rock (blasted)	Bank	1.00	1.50	1.30
	Loose	0.67	1.00	0.87
	Compacted	0.77	1.15	1.00
Sand	Bank	1.00	1.12	0.95
	Loose	0.89	1.00	0.85
	Compacted	1.05	1.18	1.00

Figure 2.3

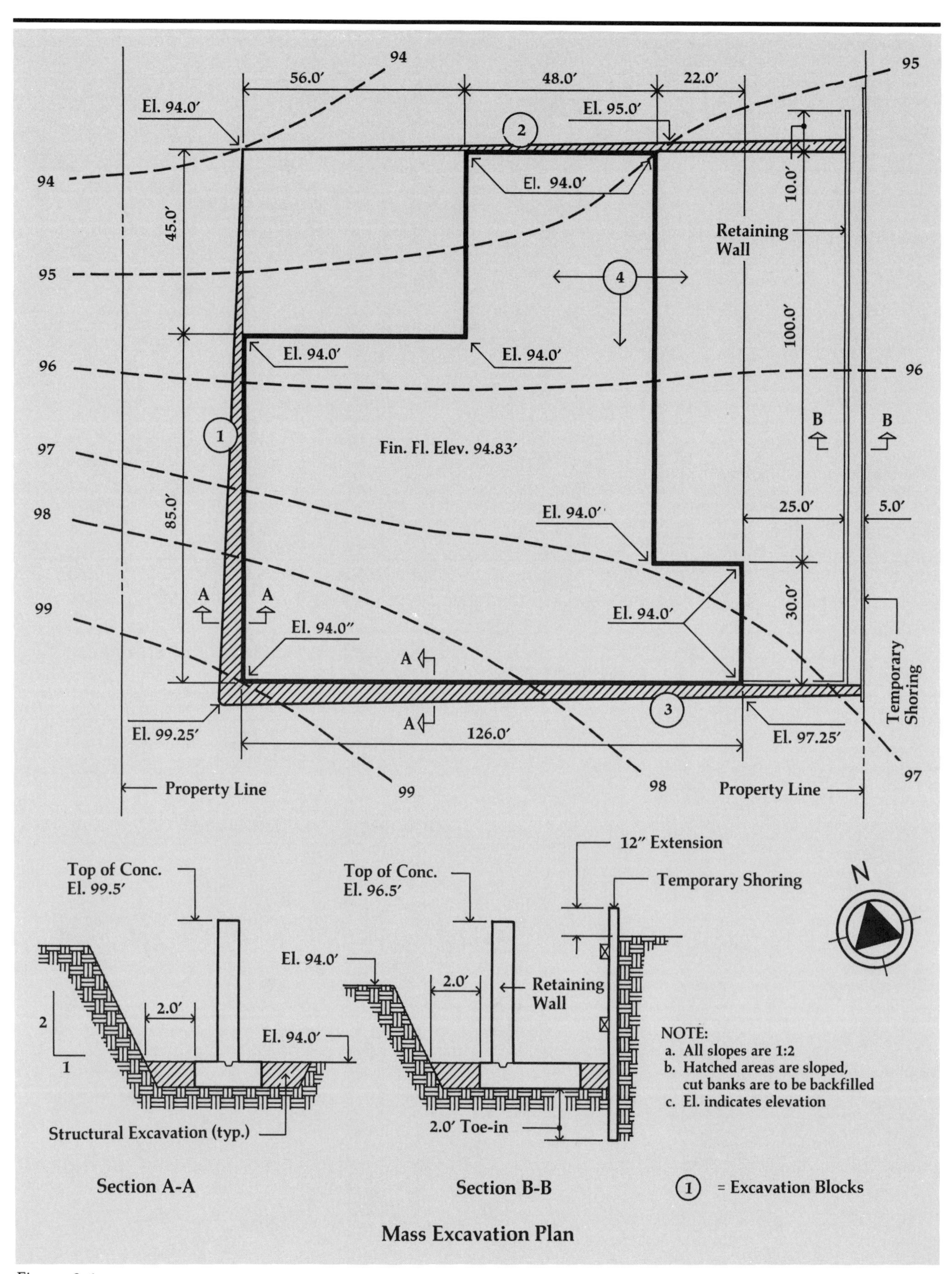
94
95
56.0′
48.0′
22.0′
El. 94.0′
El. 95.0′
2
El. 94.0′
10.0′
45.0′
Retaining Wall
4
100.0′
El. 94.0′
El. 94.0′
96
1
Fin. Fl. Elev. 94.83′
B
B
97
98
85.0′
El. 94.0′
25.0′
5.0′
99
A
A
El. 94.0′
30.0′
El. 94.0″
A
Temporary Shoring
3
A
El. 99.25′
126.0′
El. 97.25′
Property Line
99
98
Property Line
12″ Extension
Top of Conc. El. 99.5′
Top of Conc. El. 96.5′
Temporary Shoring
N
El. 94.0′
2.0′
Retaining Wall
2
2.0′
El. 94.0′
1
NOTE:
a. All slopes are 1:2
b. Hatched areas are sloped, cut banks are to be backfilled
c. El. indicates elevation
2.0′ Toe-in
Structural Excavation (typ.)
Section A-A
Section B-B
1 = Excavation Blocks
Mass Excavation Plan

Figure 2.4

(length, width, and depth or elevation) of our building and the surrounding area. Refer to this plan throughout the procedure.

Step 1: Earth Removal

Calculate the total volume of earth to be removed or excavated, including the area between the building and the retaining wall, starting with the *temporary cut banks* surrounding the proposed mass excavation. The cut banks are represented by the shaded areas in Figure 2.4 and are identified as Blocks ①, ②, and ③. Find the volume of each block, beginning with Block ①. Proceed in a clockwise direction around the perimeter of the building. The mass excavation will be to elevation 94.0.

Block ①: An easy method to determine the volume of Block ① is by using the *Average End Area* formula. This formula is shown in Figure 2.5.

Figure 2.6 demonstrates the volume calculations for Block ① using the Average End Area formula. Allow approximately two feet beyond the footing for work space. Block ① is unique in that the existing contour elevation matches that of the top of the footing at one end of the foundation. Thus, $A_2 = 0$.

The volume of Block ① is 1,445 cubic feet (cf). Record this value on Quantity Sheet 2 in the column labeled "Excavation," in the row for Block ①.

Block ②: Use the same formula to calculate the volume for Block ②. This calculation is illustrated in Figure 2.7.

The total volume of excavation in Block ② is 250 cf. Record this quantity in the row for Block ②.

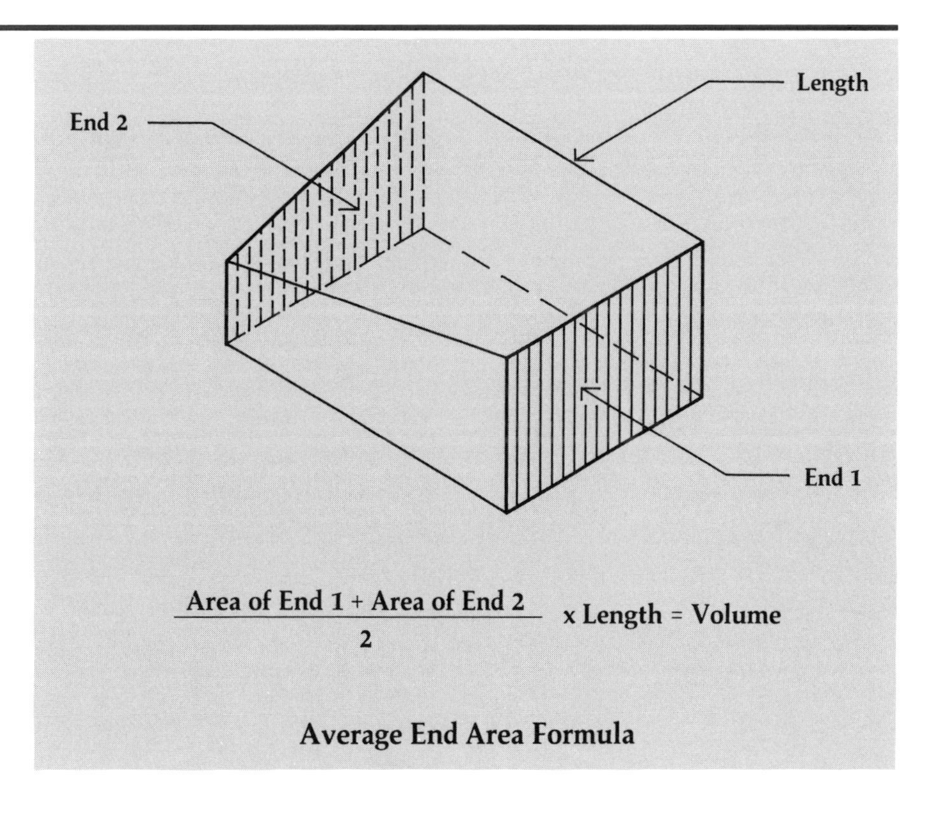

Figure 2.5

Block ③: Calculate and record the volume of excavation for Block ③, again using the Average End Area formula. This is demonstrated in Figure 2.8.

The volume of excavation for Block ③ is 2,615 cf. Transfer this quantity to Quantity Sheet 2.

The takeoff of the sloped banks around the perimeter of the structure is now complete. Do not be overly concerned about the precision of our calculations for mass excavation. The volume of excavation and productivity of excavation equipment in the field will be less precise than our calculations.

The remaining mass excavation can be divided into a convenient rectangular area labeled Block ④. If we know the average depth of each corner of the excavation, we can calculate the volume. Figure 2.9 illustrates the *Average Depth* formula used for finding the volume of this block.

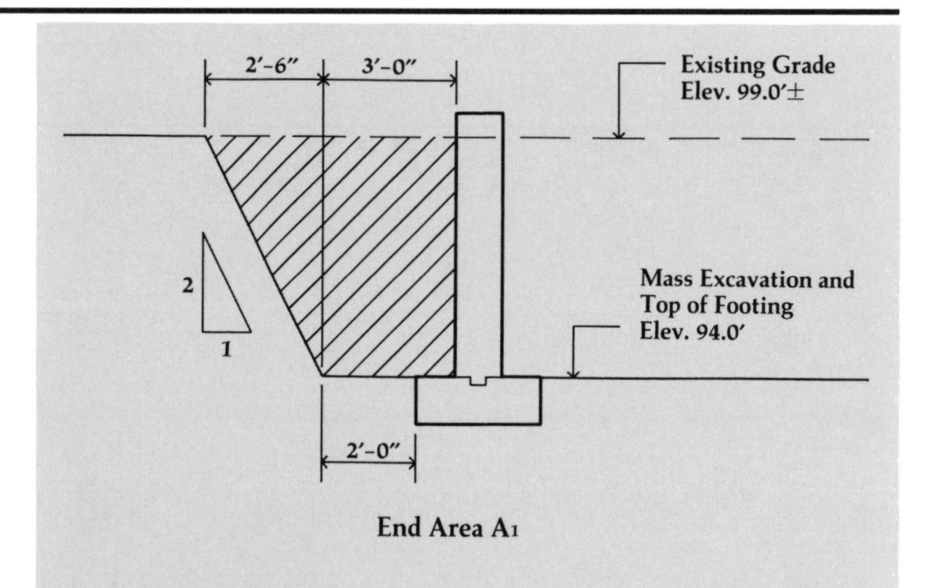

To find the volume of Block ①, apply the Average End Area formula as follows:

$$\text{Volume} = \frac{\text{Area (1)} + \text{Area (2)}}{2} \times \text{Length}$$

$$V = \frac{A_1 + A_2}{2} \times L$$

$$A_1 = (3' \times 5') + \left(2.5' \times \frac{5'}{2}\right) = 21.25 \text{ sf}$$

$$A_2 = 0$$

$$L = 130' + 3' + 2.5' \doteq 136'$$

$$V = \frac{A_1 + A_2}{2} \times L = \frac{21.25 \text{ sf} + 0}{2} \times 136' = 1{,}445 \text{ cf}$$

Volume Calculations for Block ①

Figure 2.6

Add the depth of excavation at each of the four corners of a rectangle and divide by 4. Then multiply this average depth by the area of the rectangle.

Block ④: To find the volume of Block ④, use the Average Depth formula as follows:

$$\frac{h_1 + h_2 + h_3 + h_4}{4} \times \text{Length} \times \text{Width} = \text{Volume}$$

$$\frac{0' + 1' + 3' + 5'}{4} \times 130' \times 156' = 45{,}630 \text{ cf}$$

This completes the takeoff of earth removal, or excavation. Remember to mark off each block as it is taken off, and transfer all quantities to their appropriate place on Quantity Sheet 2.

Step 2: Temporary Shoring

The next item to take off is the temporary shoring of the vertical bank. Figure 2.4 shows the shape and dimensions of the shoring used in our excavation model.

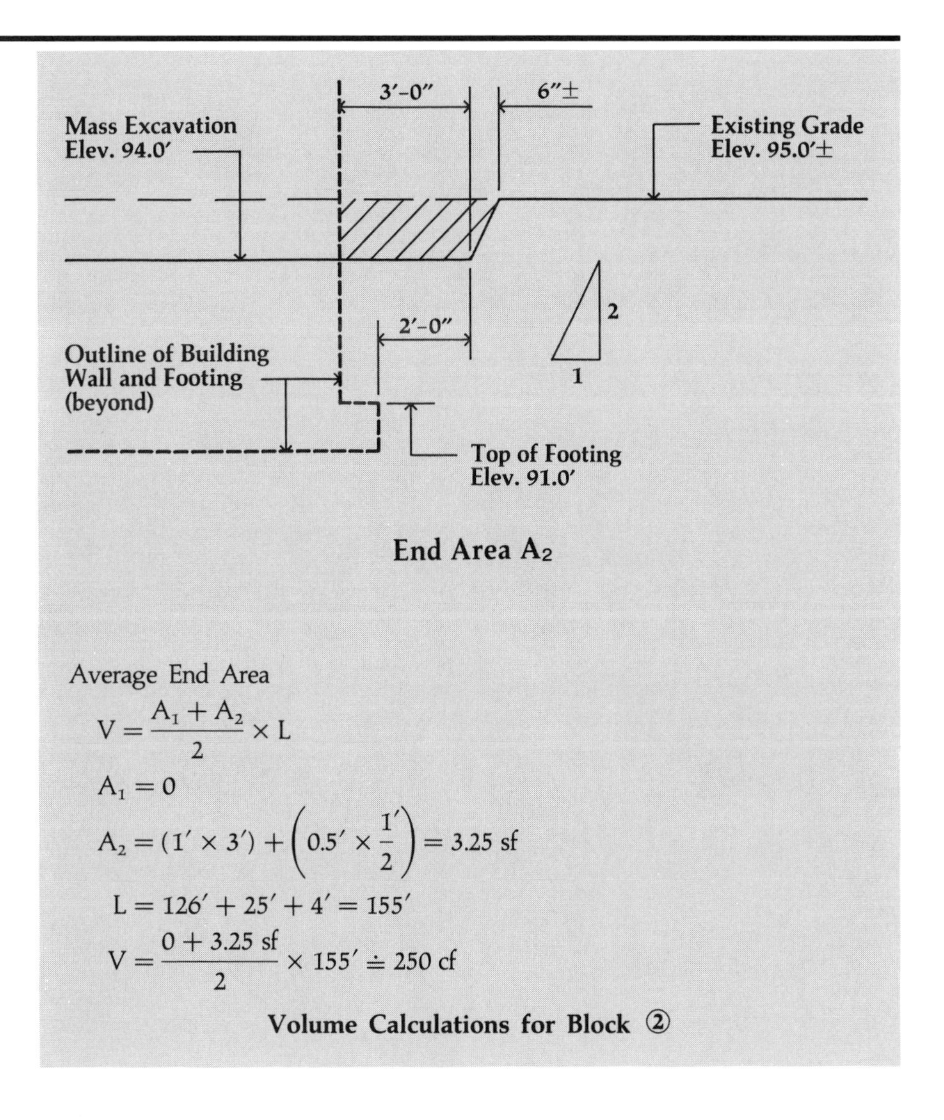

Volume Calculations for Block ②

Figure 2.7

The quantity of temporary shoring is equal to the total length of the embankment, multiplied by the height of the retaining wall plus the depth of toe-in plus 1′ extension of the shoring above the existing ground elevation. To find the area of the shoring, average the two heights at each end of the bank:

$$\frac{7' + 5'}{2} + 2' \text{ (toe-in)} + 1' \text{ (extension)} \doteq 9'$$

and multiply by the length:

$$140' + 13.5' \doteq 154'$$

(The measurement 13.5′ is for the sloped cuts at each end of the wall.)

The total area of shoring or sheeting is:

$$154' \times 9' = 1{,}386 \text{ square feet (sf)}$$

Transfer this quantity to the column and row labeled "Shoring" on Quantity Sheet 2.

Step 3: Backfill

The quantity of backfill is simple to calculate. In our excavation model, backfill will be used to fill in around the foundation once it is in place. We can see from our

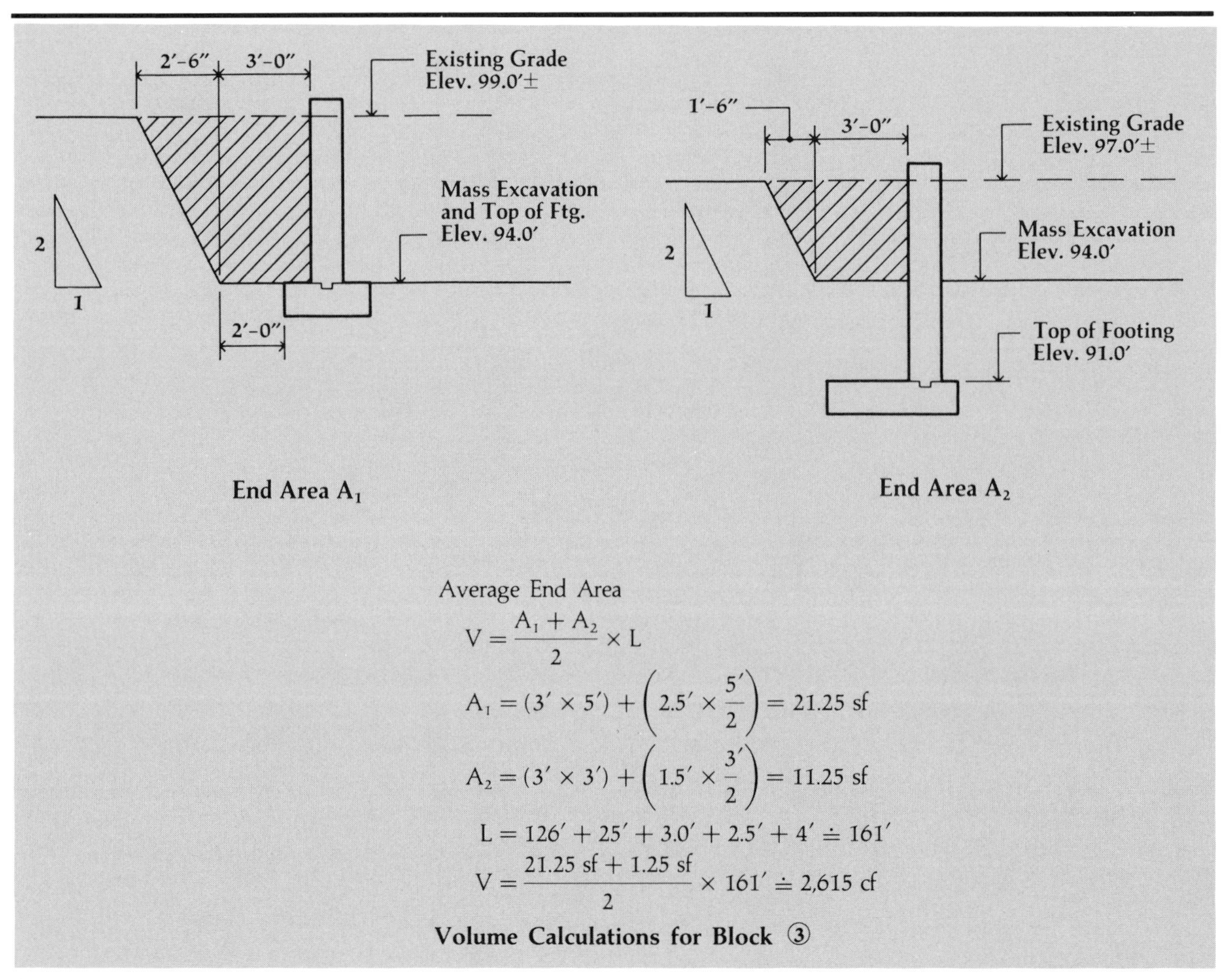

Figure 2.8

plan in Figure 2.4 that this quantity is represented by Blocks ①, ②, ③, and for the area between the shoring and the retaining wall. The backfill quantity for that portion is:

$$\frac{7' + 5'}{2} \times 4' \times 140' = 3{,}360 \text{ cf}$$

Transfer the quantities for these blocks to the column labeled "Backfill."

Step 4: Disposal

The disposal quantity is the amount of mass excavation minus the backfill. These quantities can be found on Quantity Sheet 2. The formula is:

Excavation — Backfill = Disposal

Step 5: Total the Columns

Finally, total each column individually and convert cubic feet to cubic yards by dividing by 27. Next, apply the appropriate factors for swell and compaction. (See Figure 2.3 and Appendix C for these amounts.) If our soil is common earth, it will swell 25% and compact to 90% of its original volume.

This concludes the discussion of clearing, grubbing, and mass excavation. Chapter 3 examines the takeoff procedure for footings.

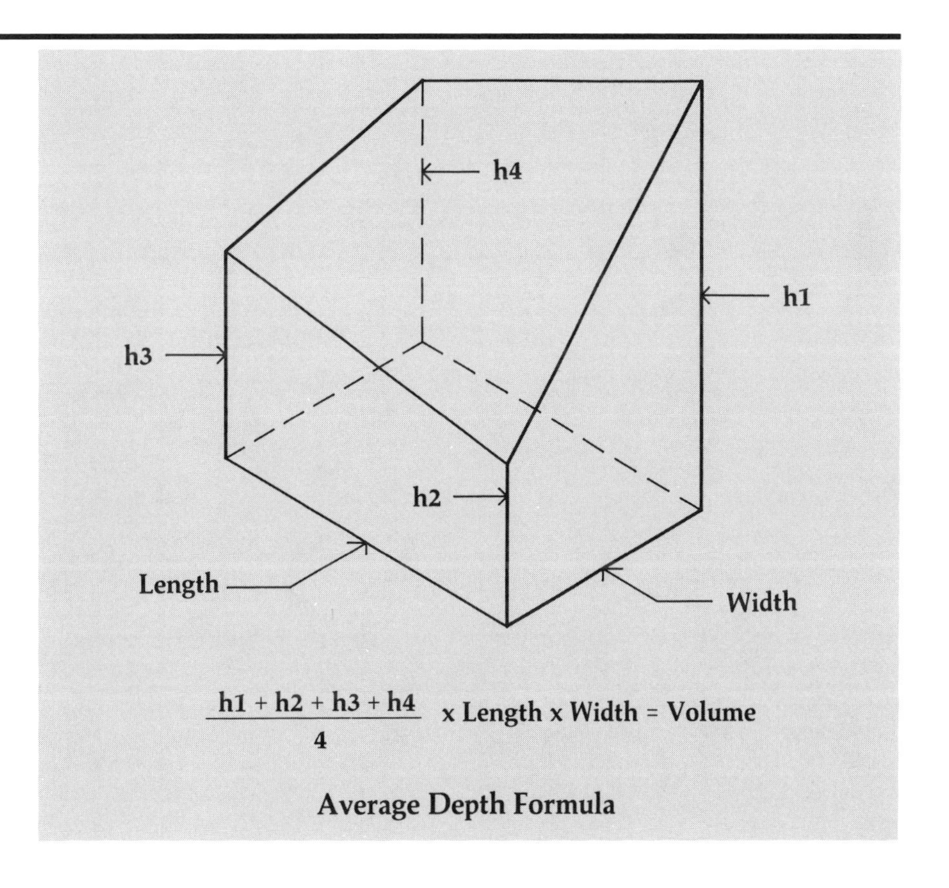

Figure 2.9

Means® Forms
QUANTITY SHEET

PROJECT Admin. Bldg.
LOCATION Picacho, Ca.
ARCHITECT Bell & Bell
TAKE OFF BY P.C.
EXTENSIONS BY: ETW
SHEET NO. QS2
ESTIMATE NO. 1017
DATE March 1989
CHECKED BY: NS

DESCRIPTION	NO.	DIMENSIONS	EXCAVA.	UNIT	B'FILL	UNIT	DISPOSAL	UNIT	SHORING	UNIT		UNIT		UNIT
Mass Excava.														
Block ①			1445	CF	1445									
②			250		250									
③			2615		2615									
④			45630											
B'Fill @ Ret. Wall					3360									
Total			49940		7670		44370							
Convert to CY			1850	CY	284	CY	1643	CY						
Add/Deduct for Compact	10%				+28		-28							
Total			1850		312		1615							
Add for swell	25%		462		78		404							
Total Loose Measure			2312	CY	390	CY	2019	CY						
Shoring									1386	SF				

Figure 2.10

Chapter 3
Concrete Footings

A footing is that portion of the foundation which transmits load directly to the soil. There are two basic types of footings:

- Strip (continuous) footings
- Spread (column) footings

Strip (continuous) footings are typically used under walls of concrete, brick, or block to distribute loads evenly to the supporting soil or to act as a levelling pad to facilitate erection of the formwork for concrete walls. Strip footings usually are no narrower than twice the wall thickness, or less in depth than the wall thickness. Figure 3.1 illustrates a typical strip footing.

Strip footings can be *stepped* to accommodate changes in the elevation of bearing strata, sloping terrain, or building design requirements. Figure 3.2 illustrates a typical stepped strip footing.

Spread (column) footings are used to transfer a concentrated pier, grade beam, or column load to an allowable area load on the supporting soil. Where suitable soil or bearing conditions exist, spread footings are the most widely used type of footing because they minimize the amount of excavation and the quantity of backfill and construction materials. Spread footings may be square, rectangular, or any common polygon shape, and can be used to support single or multiple concentrated loads. Figure 3.3 shows a typical spread footing.

Takeoff Items

The following items are typically taken off for concrete footings:

- Layout
- Structural excavation (machine and hand)
- Formwork
- Steel reinforcement
- Anchor bolts and base plates
- Concrete
- Curing
- Backfill
- Disposal

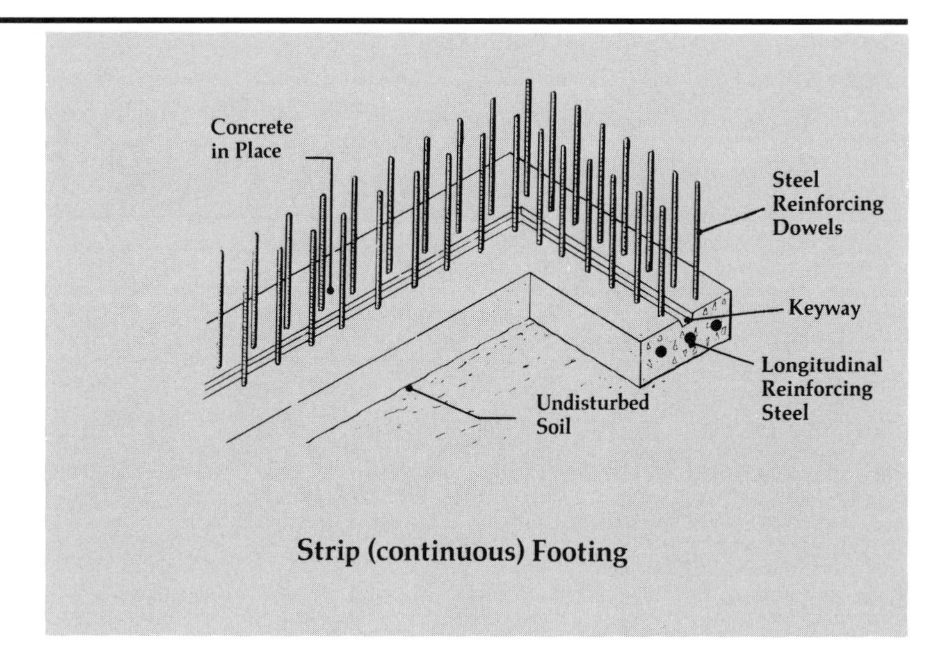

Figure 3.1

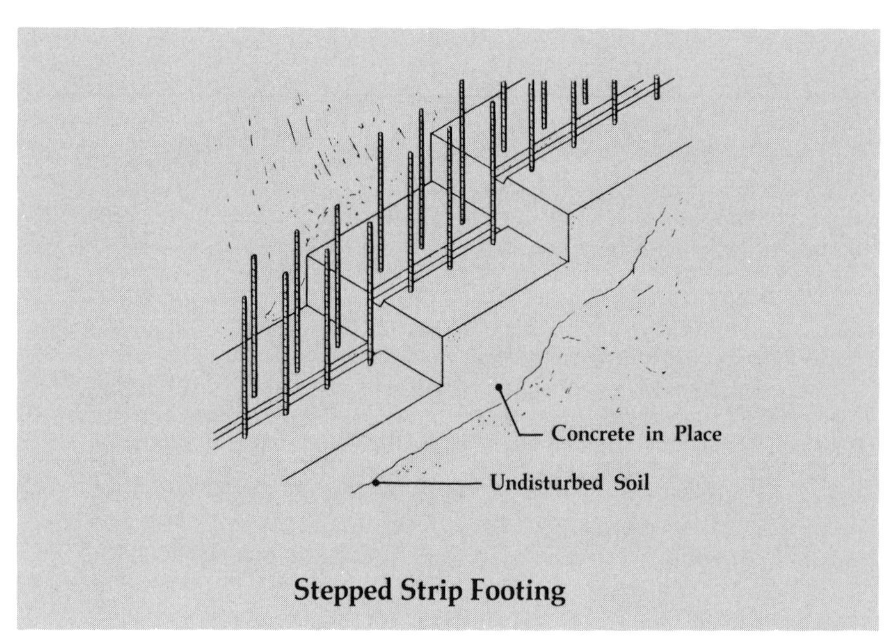

Figure 3.2

Keep in mind that in this and other chapters, the takeoff items are listed in the order in which they would be performed in the field or incorporated into the project. However, this may not necessarily be the best order in which to take them off, because once the dimensions have been determined for one component, it is more convenient to calculate the quantities for all the components that use those same dimensions. This will become evident as the takeoff demonstration proceeds. Below is a brief discussion of each of the items listed above.

Layout

Layout of the lines and grades of a foundation is a cost item that should be noted on the quantity sheet. Included in the cost is the number of manhours required for the contractor's surveyor to stake out the lines showing the edge of the footing and its elevations (grade). For strip footings, list the total number of linear feet and the number of corners and steps. For spread footings, simply note the number of footings.

Structural Excavation

Structural excavation, mentioned briefly in the previous chapter, is the removal of earth directly associated with a foundation. Trenches that are dug for strip footings are considered structural excavation.

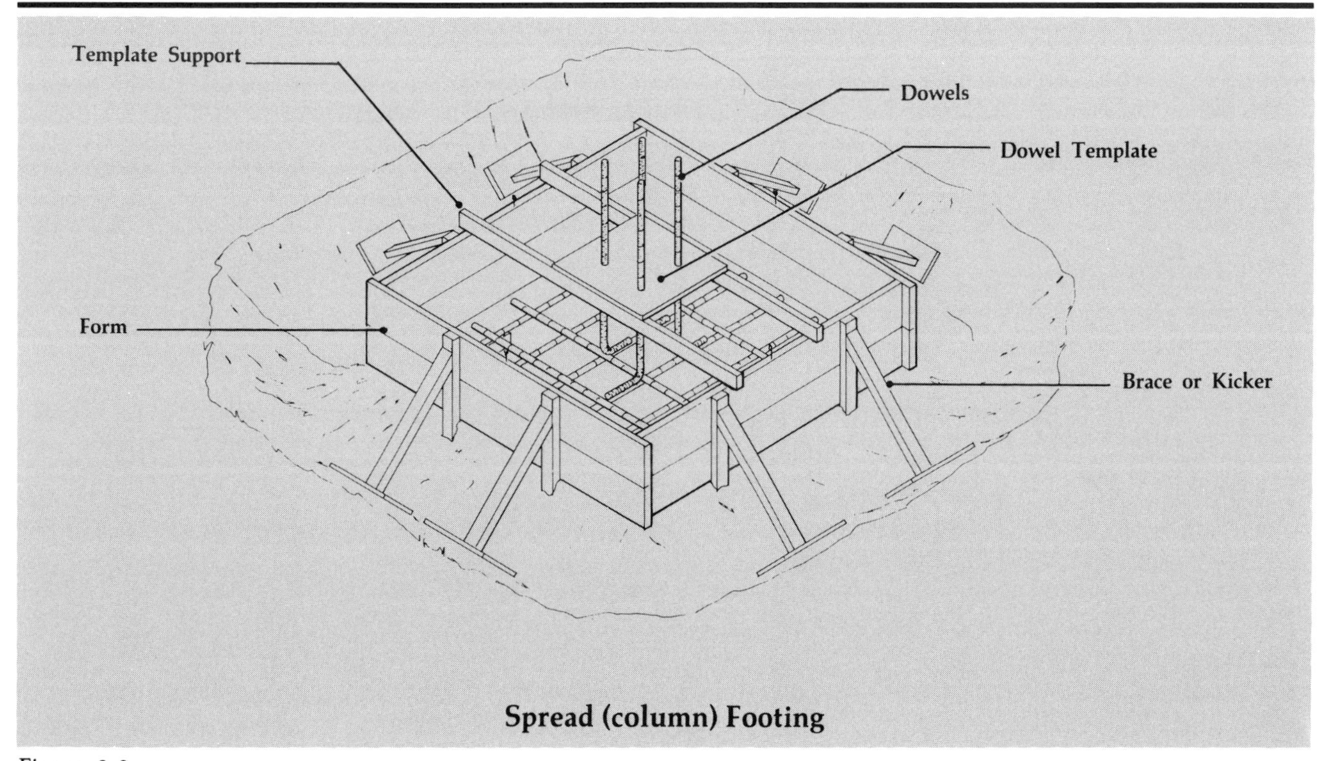

Figure 3.3

Structural excavation is usually done both by machine and by hand. *Machine excavation* is the removal of earth or rock using power equipment such as trenchers, loaders, dozers, and backhoes. *Hand excavation* is performed to trim the bottom and sides of pits and trenches to receive the concrete without the use of forms. The quantity estimator should list both hand and machine excavation in cubic yards (cy) on the quantity sheet, and should state on what basis the hand excavation quantity is derived, since this value is calculated on a subjective basis. When in doubt, the quantity estimator should list the more expensive hand excavation method. In practice, a greater volume of hand excavation is done than is usually estimated.

Structural excavation for footings may be performed *neat* or *overexcavated*. When soil conditions allow, structural excavation is performed neat, or to a minimum trench width so that the concrete fills the trench and side forms are not required. This is usually the most economical method because it requires less excavation and no forms or backfilling. It is customary, however, to increase the width of the trench by several inches, usually 3" wider than the given dimensions, to allow for irregularities in the excavation.

When overexcavation is necessary to allow room to build forms, the quantity estimator should consult the cost estimator for width dimensions, since the volume of excavation will depend on the method of forming that will be used. Figure 3.4

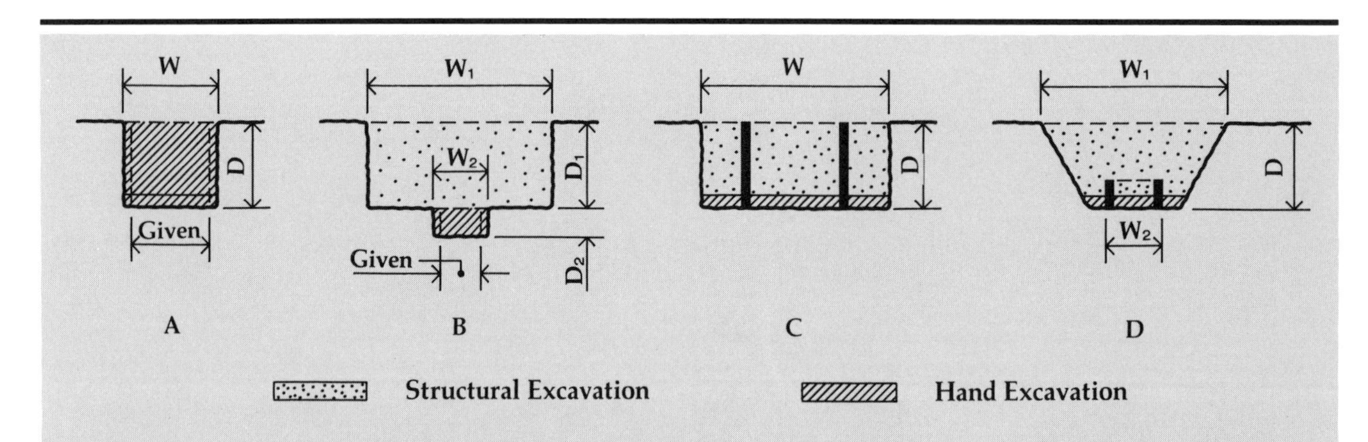

A. Excavate neat approximately 3" wider than given dimensions. End area = W x D

B. Excavate to top of Footing by Machine, then hand excavate lower Trench neat, approximately 3" wider than given dimensions. End Area = $(W_1 \times D_1) + (W_2 \times D_2)$

C. Excavate sufficiently wide to construct and remove Forms. End area = W x D

D. Excavate sloped sufficiently wide to construct and remove Forms. End Area = $\frac{W_1 + W_2}{2} \times D$

Typical Methods of Excavating Strip Footings

Figure 3.4

demonstrates the typical methods for excavating strip footings. This figure also shows how the *end area* (cross-section of the trench) is calculated in neat and overexcavated trenches.

Note that calculations for the depth of excavation are made by subtracting the elevation of the bottom of the footing from the grade left by the mass excavator. The finish grade after mass excavation is the new original grade for structural excavation.

Finally, the quantity estimator should make note of any other considerations of which the cost estimator should be aware. For example, if the trench exceeds a certain depth, the quantity estimator should note that lifts are required. When data from soil boring samples are available, the quantity estimator should separate excavation quantities according to soil characteristics. A good way to express these quantities is in a ratio, as illustrated in Figure 3.5.

Formwork

A form is a temporary structure or mold made from plywood, planks, or other materials, and is used to support concrete while it is setting and gaining sufficient strength to be self-supportive. The quantity estimator should consult the cost estimator for the type of formwork that will be used. Examples of typical footing form designs are illustrated in Figure 3.6 and described briefly below.

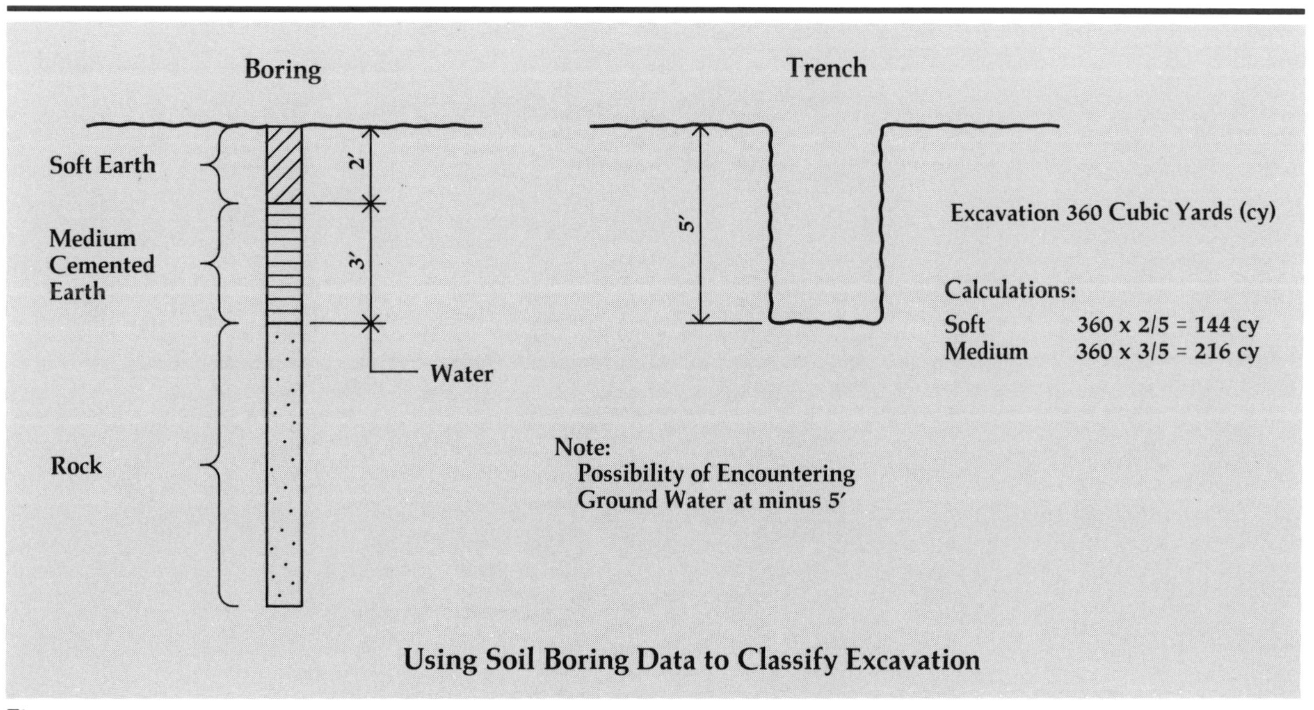

Using Soil Boring Data to Classify Excavation

Figure 3.5

Pour Strips

Pour strips, shown in Figure 3.6A, are planks placed along the top of neat excavation to provide a level form for the top of the concrete footing. The quantity estimator lists pour strips in linear feet (lf).

Side Forms

Figure 3.6C shows side forms that are typically used for strip footings. In this example, the trench is overexcavated by a predetermined amount and the forms are built inside the trench to contain and give shape to the concrete. Side forms are measured in square feet of contact area (sfca):

$$\text{length} \times \text{height} \times 2 \text{ forms} = \text{sfca}$$

This quantity represents the surface area of formwork that comes in contact with the concrete.

Keyway Form

The footings in Figures 3.6A-3.6C are shown with a keyway form. Keyways are placed in the construction joint between the footing and the wall to help the components function as a single unit once they are both complete. The quantity estimator lists keyway forms by the linear foot. Keyways are not provided when a masonry block wall is built on the footings, as in Figure 3.6D.

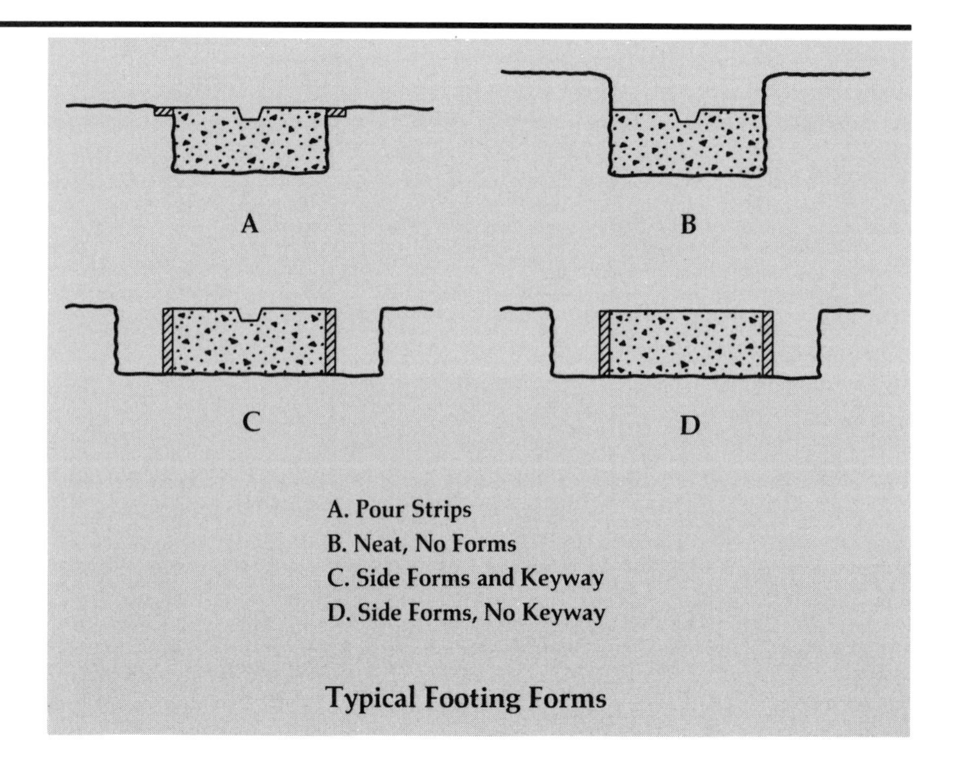

A. Pour Strips
B. Neat, No Forms
C. Side Forms and Keyway
D. Side Forms, No Keyway

Typical Footing Forms

Figure 3.6

Steel Reinforcement

Steel reinforcement is used in strip and spread footings to provide tensile strength and carry stresses caused by shrinkage and temperature change of the concrete. Strip footings contain longitudinal steel reinforcing bars, called *rebar*. Spread footings typically contain a single or double layer of steel bars that are laid in a grid pattern. The quantity estimator should list reinforcing steel bars by size and length, and then convert this quantity to pounds.

Both strip and spread footings may contain *dowels*, which are reinforcing bars that protrude into the next pour of concrete. The quantity estimator should list these by size, length, and number.

See Figures 3.1 through 3.3 for illustrations of steel reinforcement in concrete footings. Refer to Chapter 12, "Reinforcing Steel," for more information on this topic.

Anchor Bolts and Base Plates

Anchor bolts and base plates are used to attach steel columns to spread footings. They are supplied by the steel subcontractor, but are installed and grouted by the general contractor. The quantity estimator should list anchor bolts and base plates by number and size. See Figure 3.7.

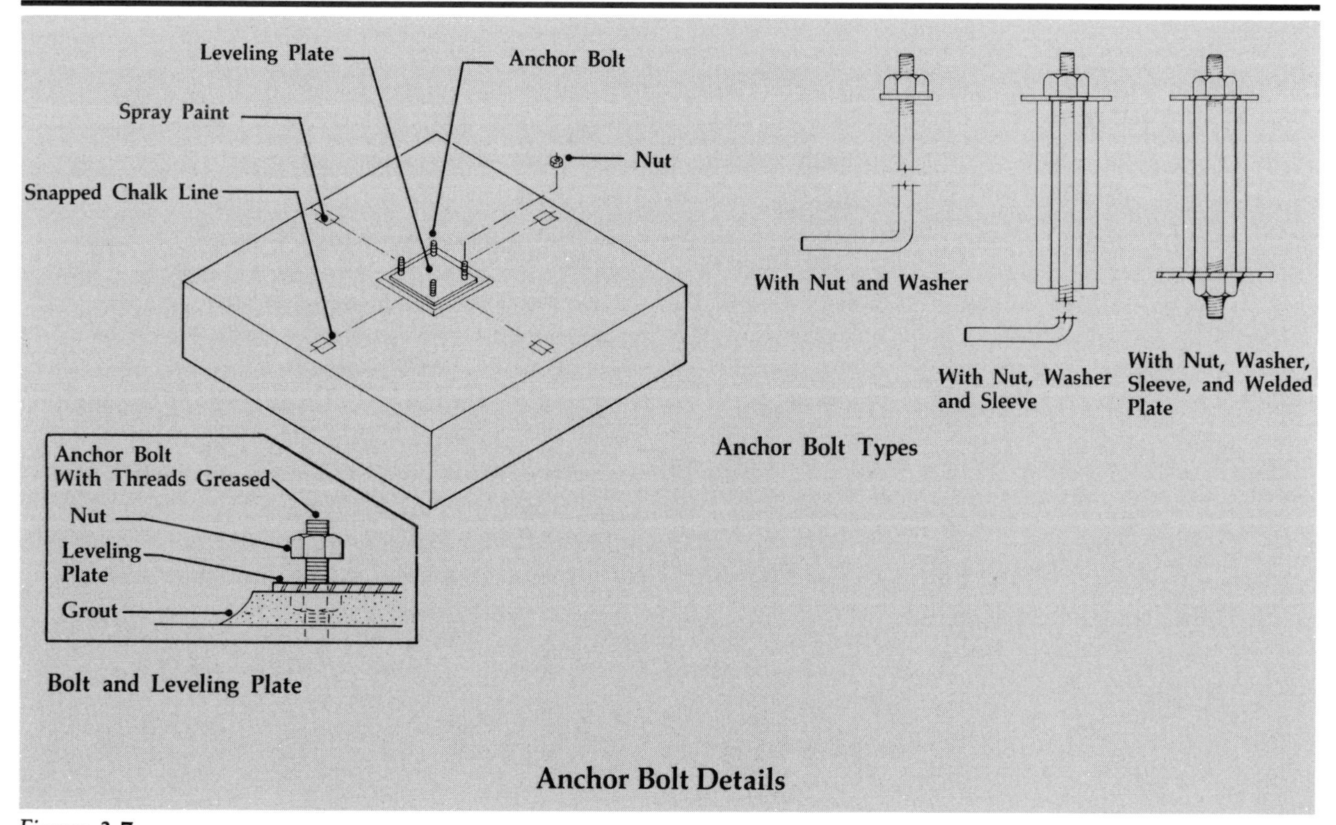

Figure 3.7

Concrete

Concrete is a construction material placed in forms to make footings, pile caps, grade beams, and other foundation components. Information that the quantity estimator should note regarding concrete includes:

- Characteristics of the concrete as specified (such as 28-day strength, aggregate size, admixtures)
- Whether the footing is neat or formed
- The presence of steel reinforcement, since care will have to be taken in placement
- Method of placement (pumping, direct chute, crane and bucket, or wheelbarrow)
- Allowance for waste (see Appendix C)
- Any other special conditions of which the cost estimator should be aware

The quantity estimator calculates the total volume of each strength of concrete by multiplying the length × width × depth of the footing. Concrete quantities are expressed in cubic yards (cy).

Curing

Spread footings that have a large top surface area may require curing. Curing is the process of maintaining the proper moisture and temperature after placing or finishing concrete to ensure proper hydration and hardening. Curing is considered a *work item,* rather than a *material item,* and should be listed on the quantity sheet in square feet (sf). Similarly, in locations where the concrete must be protected from freezing, a cost item should be included for any temporary enclosures and heat sources that are required.

Backfill

Backfill is the soil or other material used to replace excavated material. Backfill quantities for footings are found simply by subtracting the total quantity of concrete in the footing from the total amount of excavation (both machine and hand excavation). A simple formula for finding the quantity of backfill is:

Backfill = (Machine Excavation + Hand Excavation) − Concrete

Remember to allow for the swell of excavated material and the compaction of loose material when calculating backfill quantities. (See Figure 2.4 for swell and compaction factors.) Backfill is expressed in cubic yards.

Disposal

Disposal is the quantity of earth that is not needed (or is unsuitable) for backfill, and which must be removed from the work site. The volume of disposal equals the quantity of earth displaced by concrete and select backfill. When excavated material is used for backfill and is compacted, it occupies less space than in its original state. For this reason, disposal quantities cannot be determined until a compaction factor is added to the backfill. This will be evident on the quantity sheet that accompanies the takeoff demonstration of strip footings.

Takeoff Demonstration of Strip Footings

This section demonstrates the procedure for taking off concrete strip footings based on our model administrative building. (A takeoff demonstration of spread footings will follow.) Note that the examples used in this and all other chapters represent those elements and procedures most commonly encountered by the general contractor's quantity estimator. Almost every job uses footings of one kind or another. Variations of the following examples may be taken off using many of the same procedures.

Turn now to Appendix A, which contains the plans necessary to perform the takeoff of our model building. Refer to the Foundation and Footing Plan. This plan shows the layout of the strip footings for our model building. It also provides footing segment lengths and the location of the steps in the footings. The plan is divided by grid or column lines for easy reference.

A cross-sectional view of the strip footing, showing the various details required for its construction, is shown on the Foundation Detail Sheet. It will be necessary to refer to these details throughout the takeoff demonstration.

Because of the large number of takeoff items, the 12-column quantity sheet will be used and designated Quantity Sheet 3A. Quantity Sheet 3A is shown in Figure 3.9, located at the end of this section.

Step 1: Perimeter Footings

The takeoff demonstration begins with the *perimeter footings*. Start at the northeast corner of the building and move in a clockwise direction until all the footing segments around the periphery of the building have been taken off. Some quantity estimators prefer a counterclockwise direction. The important thing is to be consistent. This will reduce the risk of omissions and duplications.

Assume that all perimeter footings will be excavated to a minimum of 4' below finish grade to the bottom of the footing. The building elevations show the top of footing elevations and the location of the footing steps.

Starting at location D3 and moving in a clockwise direction, the perimeter footings extend from D3-B3 (100'), B3-B4 (22'), B4-A4 (30'), A4-A1 (126'), A1-C1 (85'), C1-C2 (56'), C2-D2 (45'), and D2-D3 (48'). The total length of the perimeter strip footings is 512 lf. Mark off each of these segments on the plan as they are taken off. Note that dimensions on the drawing are to building lines. Using these for footings doubles the inside corner quantity and eliminates the outside corner, keeping the accuracy well within acceptable limits. The calculations for each of the takeoff items (except backfill and disposal, which will be taken off at the end) are listed below.

Concrete: $1' \times 2.67' \times 512' \doteq 1{,}367$ cf
Formwork: $512' \times 1' \times 2$ sides $= 1{,}024$ sfca
Reinforcement: $512' \times 3$ (# 4 bars) $= 1{,}536$ lf of # 4 bars
Keyway: 512 lf
Machine excavation: See Figure 3.8.

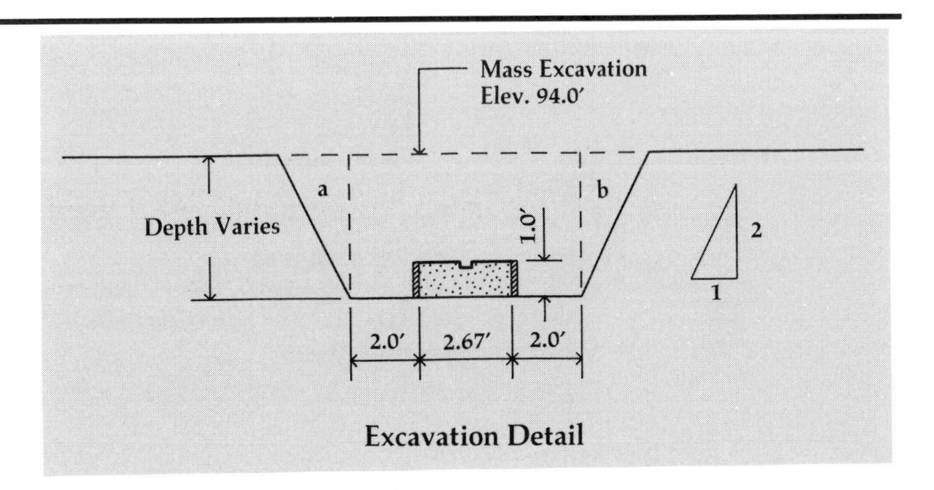

Figure 3.8

Note that in calculating trench excavation with sloped sides, triangle "a" is equal to triangle "b" and can form a rectangular section for easy calculations.

Our mass excavation was performed to Elevation 94.0′. From D3-A4 the bottom of the footing is at Elevation 90.0′. Therefore:

$$"d" = 94.0' - 90.0' = 4'$$

The volume of machine excavation is:

$$[(4' \times 6.67') + (4' \times 2')] \times 152' \doteq 5{,}270 \text{ cf}$$

During excavation in the field, the footing will be stepped to maintain the bottom at 4′ below finished grade. The Average End Area formula produces a close estimate of the actual excavation for footings.

Continuing excavation calculations from A4-A1, note that excavation to 4′ is required for only the first 10′ as the footing steps up to Elevation 94.0′.

a) The volume of machine excavation for the first 10′ is:

$$A_1 + A_2 \times \text{Length} = \text{Volume}$$

$$[(4' \times 6.67') + (4' \times 2')] + [(1' \times 6.67') + 1' \times 0.5'] \times 10' \doteq 420 \text{ cf}$$

b) The volume of machine excavation for the remaining 116′ to A1 is:

$$[(1' \times 6.67') + (1' \times 0.5')] \times 116' \doteq 830 \text{ cf}$$

From A1-C1 is 85′. The quantity of machine excavation for this length of perimeter footing is:

$$\frac{A_1 + A_2}{2} \times \text{Length} = \text{Volume}$$

$$[(1' \times 6.67') + (1' \times 0.5')] + [(4' \times 6.67') + (4' \times 2')] \times 85'$$

$$\doteq 3{,}560 \text{ cf}$$

The final perimeter footing is from C1-D3 at 4′ deep. The volume of machine excavation for this footing segment is:

$$[(4' \times 6.67') + (4' \times 2')] \times 149' \doteq 5{,}170 \text{ cf}$$

Hand excavation: The total length of perimeter strip footings will be trimmed or hand excavated 2.67′ wide for a total hand excavation area of:

$$512' \times 2.67' = 1{,}367 \text{ sf}$$

Step 2: Interior Footings

In our example, interior footings extend from B3-B2 (48′), B2-C2 (55′), and C2-C3 (48′). The total linear feet of interior footings is 151. Calculations for each takeoff item (except backfill and disposal) are shown below. The interior footings will be machine excavated neat and will require no formwork.

Concrete: 1.0′ × 2.91′ × 151′ = 439 cf
Reinforcement: 151′ × 3 ea = 453 lf (# 5 bars)
Keyway: 151 lf
Hand excavation: 151′ × 2.67′ = 403 sf

Step 3: Concluding the Takeoff

Total the Columns

Total each column on Quantity Sheet 3A, Figure 3.9. Convert cubic feet to cubic yards. Convert linear feet of reinforcement to pounds. Add an allowance for waste where appropriate.

Record Layout Quantities

Record the total length of strip footings in our model administrative building (700 lf) under the column labeled "Layout." Count the total number of corners (10) and the total number of steps (6) in the footings and record these values in the proper columns.

Calculate Backfill and Disposal Quantities

The backfill quantity can now be calculated from the excavation and concrete totals, and a compaction factor from Figure 2.4 can be applied:

Machine Excavation − Concrete = Backfill
574 cy − 67 cy = 507 cy
10% Compaction = + 51 cy
Total = 558 cy

The quantity of disposal is:

(574 cy − 558 cy) = 16 cy

This concludes the takeoff demonstration of strip footings. The next section demonstrates the procedure used for spread footings.

Takeoff Demonstration of Spread Footings

Even though the takeoff procedure is very much the same for spread and strip footings, spread footings are taken off separately because they usually are figured with different cost factors.

Again, refer to the Foundation and Footing Plan in Appendix A, which shows the location of the spread footings as they appear in our model building. A clockwise (or counterclockwise) procedure is not applicable. Instead, the spread footings are grouped and taken off by size or type: I, II, and III.

See the Footing Detail Sheet in the Appendix for a cross-sectional view of each footing type. These sections show the depth of the spread footings. This information may be presented in a number of ways, depending on the designer's habits and preferences. A quantity estimator becomes quite adept at locating this information.

Remember to transfer all quantities to Quantity Sheet 3B, Figure 3.10, located at the end of this chapter.

Step 1: Type I Footing

The Type I footing location is shown on the Foundation and Footing Plan in the upper right hand corner of the drawing. As an interior footing, this footing will be excavated neat, so that the top is at the level of the mass excavation. The calculations for each takeoff item are provided below.

Concrete: 2.75′ × 2.75′ × 1.25′ deep × 1 ea = 9 cf
Pour Strips: 3′ × 4 sides × 1 ea = 12 lf
Reinforcement: Reinforcing for these footings should have 3″ of concrete cover to the outside of the footing.
2′ × 5′ × 2′ × 1 footing = 20 lf
Hand excavation: 2.75′ × 2.75′ × 1.25′ × 1 = 9 cf

This footing is too small to take off curing as a cost item. No anchor bolts and base plates are shown. If these items were to be included in the estimate, they would be taken off now before moving on to the next type of footing.

Means® Forms

QUANTITY SHEET

PROJECT Admin. Bldg. SHEET NO. QS 3A

ESTIMATE NO. 1017

LOCATION Picacho, Ca. ARCHITECT Bell & Bell DATE March 1989

TAKE OFF BY PC EXTENSIONS BY: ETW CHECKED BY: NS

DESCRIPTION	NO.	DIMENSIONS l w h	MACH. EXCAVA.	HAND EXCAVA.	FORMS	CONC.	REINF.	KEYWAY	B' FILL	DISPOSAL	CORNERS	STEPS	LAYOUT
Perimeter Footing	512 LF	2.67 1.0	5270 CF	1367 SF	1024 SFCA	1367 CF	1536 l.f.	512 l.f.					
			210										
			790										
			1780										
			5170										
Subtotal			13220	1367	1024	1367	1536	512					
Interior Footings	151 LF		2275	403 SF		439 CF	453 l.f.	151 l.f.					
Total			15495	1770 SF	1024 SFCA	1806 CF	1989 l.f.	663 l.f.			10 ea.	6 ea.	700 l.f.
Convert to CY			574 CY			67 CY			507 CY				
Add 10% for compaction									51				
									558 CY	16 CY			
Conv. #4 bars to LBS (.668 #/LF)							1330 LBS						
Waste Allowances													
conc. 5%						3 CY							
Reinf. 18%							240						
forms 5%					51								
Total			574 CY	1770 SF	1075 SFCA	70 CY	1570 LBS	663 LF	558 CY	16 CY	10 ea.	6 ea.	700 LF

Figure 3.9

Step 2: Type II Footings

Type II footings shown on the Foundation and Footing Plan are exterior footings on good bearing soil. The calculations for each takeoff item are listed below.

Concrete: 3.0′ × 3.0′ × 1.25′ × 4 ea = 45 cf
Formwork: 3.0′ × 1.25′ × 4 sides × 4 ea = 60 sfca
Reinforcement: 2.5′ × 6 × 2 × 4 ea = 120 lf
Machine excavation: 7.0′ × 7.0′ × 4′ deep × 4 ea = 784 cf

Step 3: Type III Footings

Type III footings shown on the Foundation and Footing Plan are interior footings on good bearing soil and will be excavated and formed similar to Type I. The calculations are as follows.

Concrete: 3.75′ × 3.75′ × 1.5 × 4 ea = 84 cf
Pour Strips: 4.0′ × 4 × 4 ea = 64 lf
Reinforcement: 3.0′ × 7 × 2 × 4 = 168 lf
Hand excavation: 3.75′ × 3.75′ × 1.5′ × 4 ea = 84 cf

Again, if curing, anchor bolts, and base plates were to be included in the estimate, the quantity estimator would take them off now.

Transfer all values to Quantity Sheet 3B. Total the quantities in each column and adjust for waste according to Appendix C.

This concludes the takeoff demonstration for footings. Chapter 4 examines the takeoff procedure for concrete piles, caissons, and pile caps.

Means® Forms
QUANTITY SHEET

PROJECT Admin. Bldg. SHEET NO. QS 3B
ESTIMATE NO. 1017
LOCATION Picacho, Ca. ARCHITECT Bell & Bell DATE March 1989
TAKE OFF BY PC EXTENSIONS BY: ETW CHECKED BY: NS

DESCRIPTION	NO.	DIMENSIONS	MACH. EXCAVA.	HAND EXCAVA.	SIDE FORMS	POUR STRIPS	CONC.	REINF.	LAYOUT	B'FILL	DISPOSAL
Spread Footings											
Type I	1	2.75 2.75 1.25		9 c.f.		12 l.f.	9 CF	20 l.f.	1 ea.	21 c.f.	
Type II	4	3 3 1.25	784 CF		60 SFCA		45 CF	120 l.f.	4	739	
Type III	4	3.75 3.75 1.5		225		64	84 CF	168	4	141	
Total			784 CF	234 CF	60 SFCA	76 l.f.	138 CF	308 l.f.	9 ea.	901 CF	
Convert to CY			29 CY	9 CY			5 CY			33 CY	5 CY
14% compact/18% swell										+3 36 +6 42	-3 2 + – 2
Convert #5 Bars to LBS (1.043 #/LF)								321 LBS			
Waste Allowances											
Conc. 5%							1 CY				
Reinf. 18%								58 LBS			
Forms 5%					3	4 LF					
Total			29 CY	9 CY	63 SFCA	80 LF	6 CY	379 LBS	9 ea.	42 CY	2 CY

Figure 3.10

Chapter 4

Piles, Caissons, and Pile Caps

Piles

A pile is a concrete, steel, or timber column-like shaft that is driven or jetted into the ground for the purpose of supporting a load. Loads are received from isolated columns or pier foundations (pile caps), foundation walls, grade beams, or foundation mats. Piles transfer the weight of these loads through poor soil strata to deeper soil of adequate support strength and acceptable settlement. Figure 4.1 illustrates a pile cluster and its associated items.

Piles can be classified in a number of different ways. One is by the way they support their loads. *End bearing piles* have shafts that pass through soft strata to a point at which their ends rest on bedrock and can support the loads above. *Friction piles* have shafts that are embedded in a cohesive strata (moist clay), and develop the required support mainly by adhesion or "skin friction" between the soil and the outside shaft area. See Figure 4.2.

Piles may also be grouped according to the method by which they are introduced into the ground. *Displacement piles* are driven into the ground by a pile driver, forcing the soil out of its path. This can cause compaction, ground heaving, remolding of sensitive soils, damage to adjacent structures, or hard driving. *Nondisplacement* piles either have a hole bored and the pile is cast or placed in the hole, or a hollow, open-ended pipe is driven into the soil and the soil core removed. Use of these types of piles minimizes heaving or lateral pressure damage to adjacent structures or piles.

The placement, or *attitude*, of piles is usually vertical. However, piles are sometimes *battered* (placed at a small angle from vertical) in order to more effectively resist lateral loads.

As a rule, pile driving is sublet to specialists who possess both the equipment and the expertise to perform that task. However, there may be associated responsibilities that belong to the general contractor, making takeoff of piles by the general contractor's quantity estimator necessary.

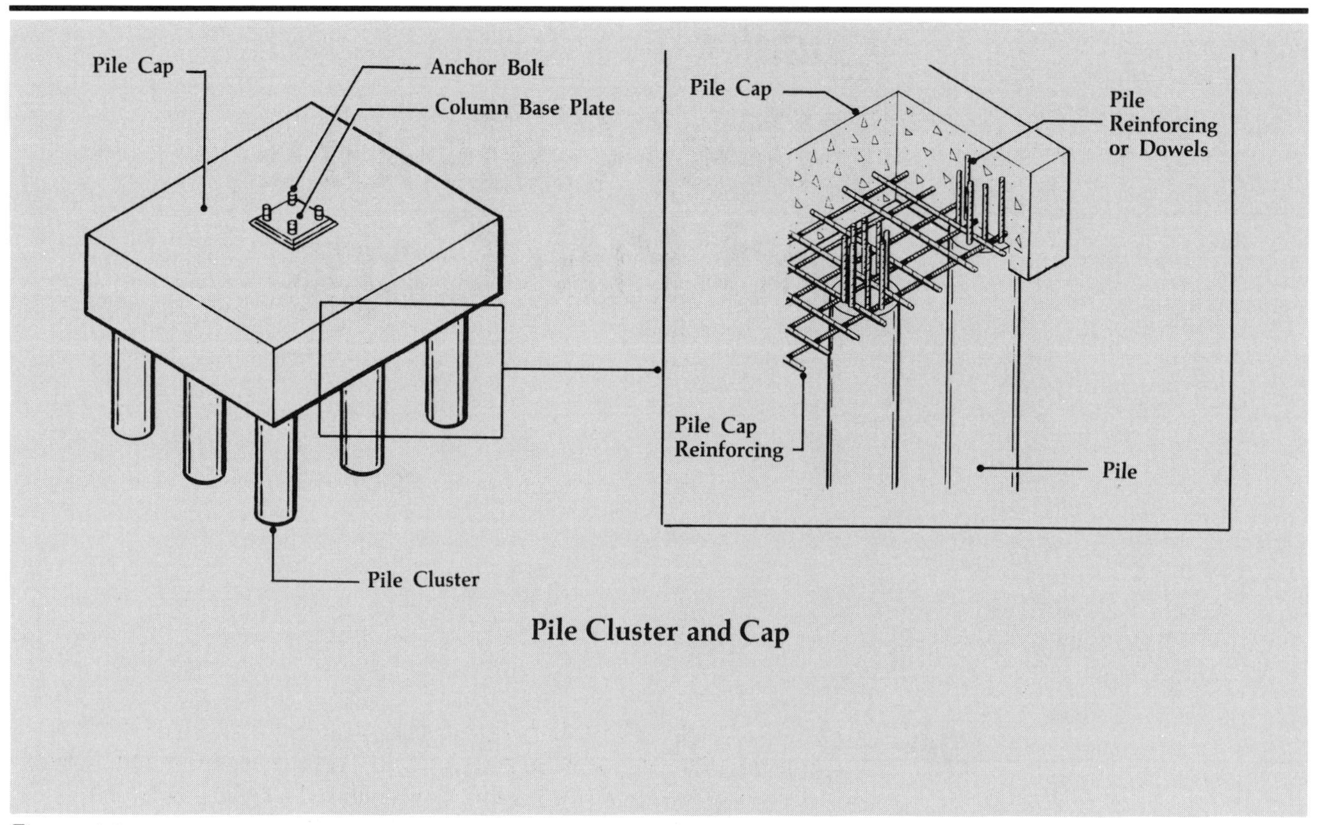

Figure 4.1

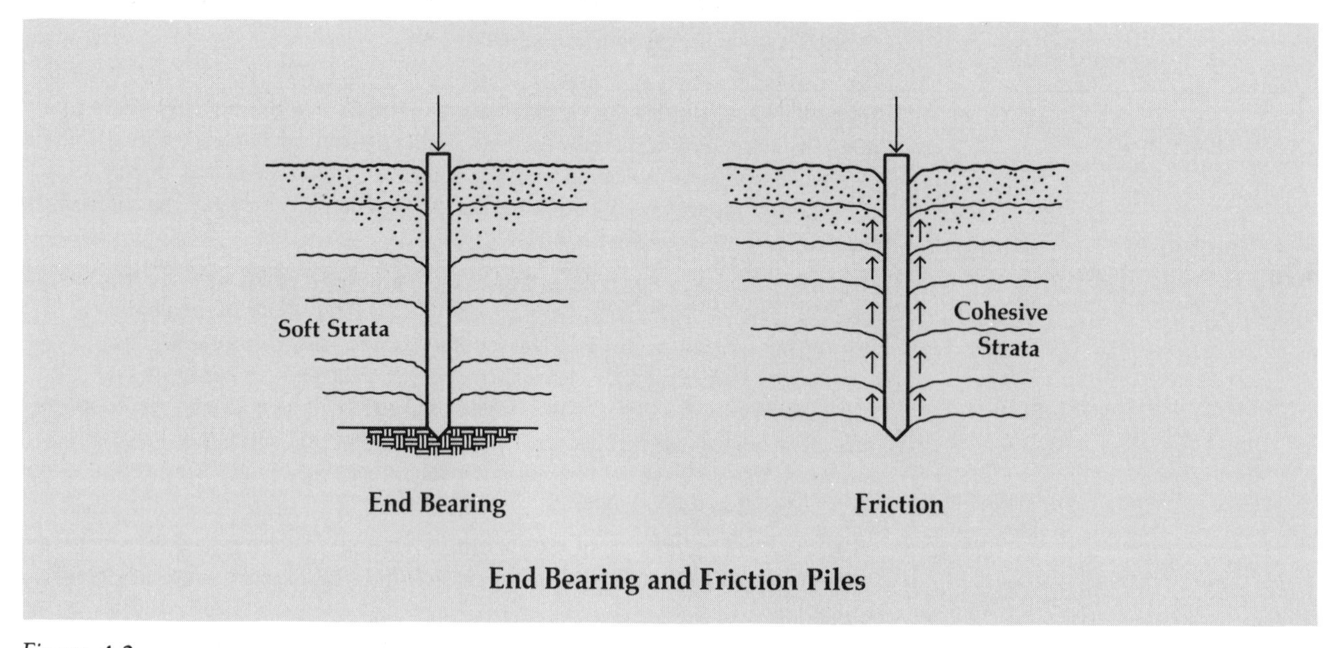

Figure 4.2

Types of Piles

There are five basic types of piles used in construction. The type of pile chosen depends on the soil and foundation conditions of the individual project. The five types of piles are:

- Cast-in-place (CIP) concrete piles
- Precast concrete piles
- Steel pipe piles
- Steel H piles
- Treated wood piles

Cast-in-place concrete piles are formed either by driving steel shells into the ground, then filling them with concrete and reinforcing, or by drilling a hole in the ground and filling it directly with concrete, so that the concrete piles are flush against the earth walls. These piles are often built with a tapered steel shell and horizontal steps or ridges that produce friction against the earth. They are easily spliced.

Precast concrete piles are usually cast to a specific length by a specialty contractor and trucked to the site. They are durable, but difficult and expensive to lengthen, and require heavy equipment to handle and drive. They may be round, square, or hexagonal in shape.

Steel pipe piles have great structural and flexural strength, and are easily cut for adjustment in length. They are usually pre-filled with concrete before being shipped to the site.

Steel H piles are wide flange-shaped rolled steel sections with length and thickness of equal web and flange. They are easily spliced and can withstand rough handling and driving conditions.

Treated wood piles are chemically treated to resist deterioration. They are inexpensive, easy to cut, and easy to handle. Unfortunately, they are prone to driving damage and cannot be used to drive through hard strata. Figure 4.3 illustrates each of these types of piles.

Takeoff Items

After the quantity estimator determines which type of pile has been specified for the project, he or she can identify the items to be taken off. The takeoff *process* is approximately the same for all types of piles, although the *items* that are taken off may vary. The items typically taken off for concrete piles include:

- Layout
- Drill and disposal
- Reinforcing
- Concrete fill (if any)
- Cutoff
- Splicing

Layout

Layout refers to the location, number, approximate length, and types of piles that are indicated on the plan. The number of piles required for a project depends on the type of pile and its capacity, soil conditions, and the building's load and structural characteristics.

Generally, piles are installed in clusters or groups and capped with a reinforced concrete *pile cap*. Building codes require a minimum of three piles per major column load, or two piles per foundation wall or grade beam. Pile capacity is determined by the pile's structural strength and support strength of the soil. Support capacity of a pile cluster is almost always less than the sum of its individual pile capacities due to the overlapping of bearing and friction stresses.

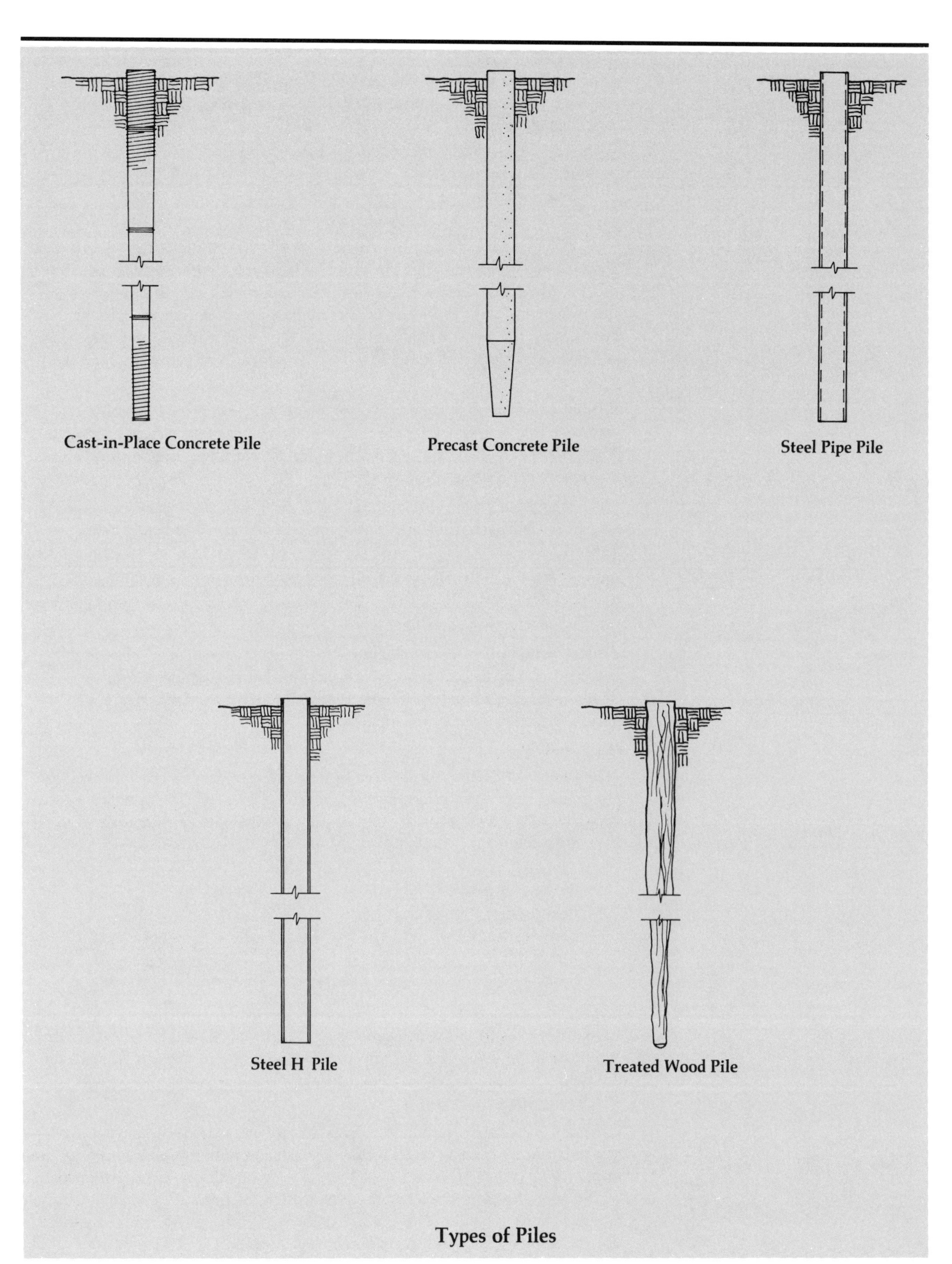
Cast-in-Place Concrete Pile
Precast Concrete Pile
Steel Pipe Pile
Steel H Pile
Treated Wood Pile
Types of Piles

Figure 4.3

Drill and Disposal

Some pile types require predrilling and disposal of displaced earth. The quantity of drill and disposal will depend on the size and type of piles used. This value is expressed in cubic yards.

Reinforcing

Reinforcing bars are generally used in all precast piles and in the upper few feet of CIP piles. In precast piles, the reinforcing is taken off by the subcontractor. In CIP concrete piles, the quantity estimator for the general contractor should take off reinforcing by linear foot of each size and convert this quantity to pounds.

Concrete Fill

Concrete fill is taken off for CIP concrete piles. To calculate the quantity of concrete, use the formula for finding the volume of a cylinder. This quantity should be expressed in cubic yards.

Cutoff

Generally, piles are constructed several feet longer than plan length and are cut off after they are driven. Add approximately 2′ to the length given in the plans to provide for cutoff quantity.

Splicing

All piles except CIP concrete piles are able to be spliced. However, they are usually ordered to the maximum length to be driven and then cut off.

Takeoff Demonstration

Assume, for demonstration purposes, that the piles in our model administrative building are precast concrete piles. When precast concrete piles are used, the general contractor's quantity estimator need not calculate the quantity of concrete in each pile, since the piles will have been cast off site (and taken off) by a specialty contractor and shipped to the work site as needed.

Figure 4.4 is a plan drawing showing the location of the piles in our model building. Figure 4.5 details the typical precast concrete pile, specifying the shape of the pile, the width dimensions (20″), and requests that 2′ of additional length be added for later cutoff. Predrilling is required for the first 30′ of depth. Remember to transfer all values to Quantity Sheet 4A, Figure 4.6, located at the end of this section.

Step 1: *Layout*

Test borings on the site indicate a region of poor soil in the northern portion of the building foundation (see Figure 4.4). An underground bearing strata slopes from Elevation 42.0′ to Elevation 37.0′. The top of the piles will be set at Elevation 94.0′. Therefore, the maximum length of each pile before cutoff is:

$$94' - 37' = 57 \text{ lf}$$

Count the number of precast piles shown in Figure 4.4. (There are 38.) Because precast piles are not easily spliced, the quantity estimator will estimate piles that are 60′ in length. Find the total number of linear feet of piles:

$$38 \text{ piles} \times 60' = 2{,}280 \text{ lf}$$

Record this value on Quantity Sheet 4A.

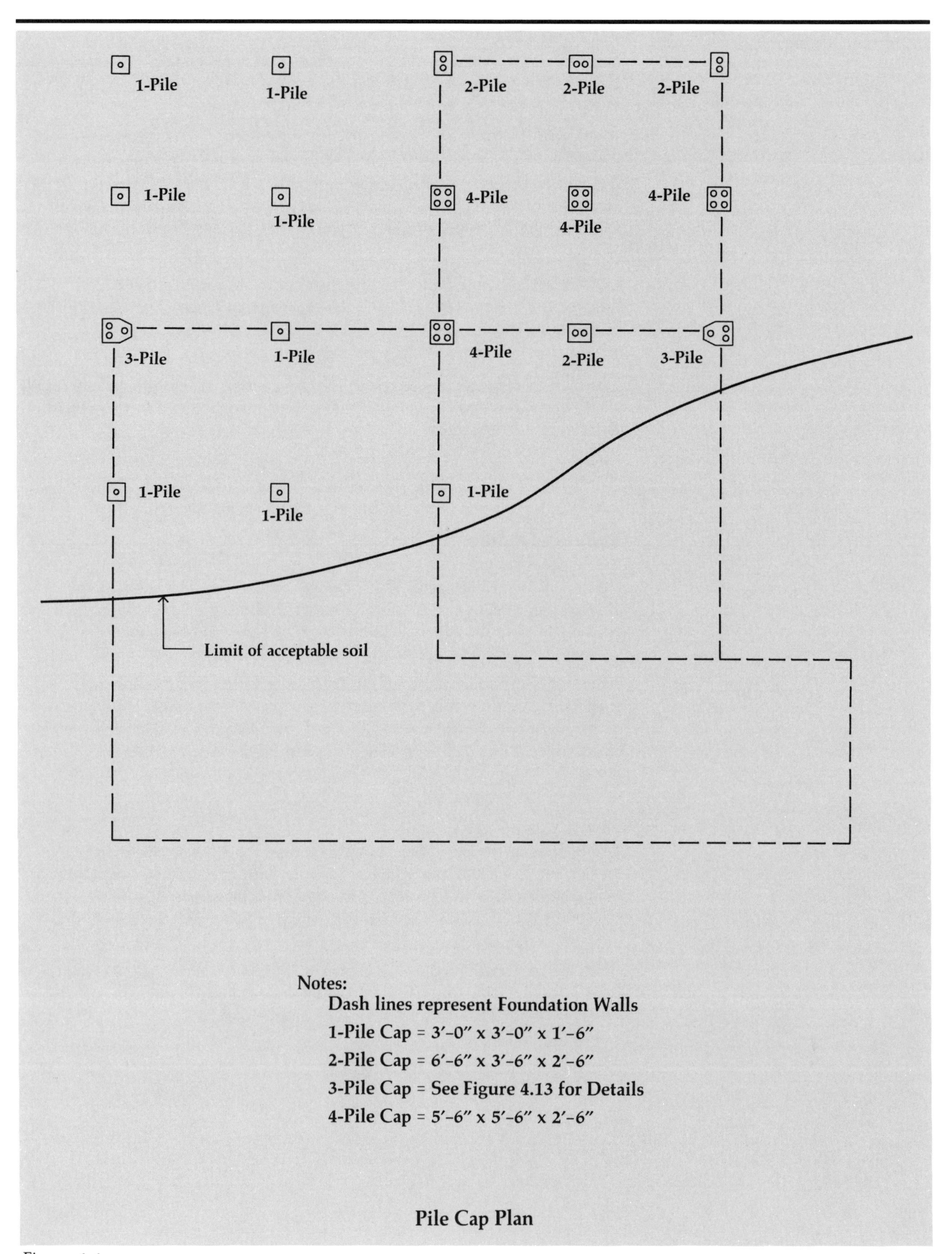
1-Pile
1-Pile
2-Pile
2-Pile
2-Pile
1-Pile
1-Pile
4-Pile
4-Pile
4-Pile
3-Pile
1-Pile
4-Pile
2-Pile
3-Pile
1-Pile
1-Pile
1-Pile
Limit of acceptable soil
Notes:
Dash lines represent Foundation Walls
1-Pile Cap = 3′-0″ x 3′-0″ x 1′-6″
2-Pile Cap = 6′-6″ x 3′-6″ x 2′-6″
3-Pile Cap = See Figure 4.13 for Details
4-Pile Cap = 5′-6″ x 5′-6″ x 2′-6″
Pile Cap Plan

Figure 4.4

Step 2: Drill and Disposal

If these piles are predrilled to 30′ with an auger, the volume of drill and disposal is:

$\pi r^2 \times 30' \times 38 \text{ ea} = 3{,}580 \text{ cf}$

Step 3: Cutoff

The piles will be cut off 6″ above the bottom of the excavated pit in order to receive the pile caps.

Transfer all quantities to Quantity Sheet 4A.

Caissons

A *caisson* is drilled, cylindrical foundation shaft used to transfer a load through inadequate soil to a firm stratum or bedrock. Caissons are similar to piles, but have a much larger diameter. The shaft can be filled with reinforced or unreinforced concrete, and may be either a straight cylinder, "belled" at the bearing level, or socketed (keyed). Figure 4.7 illustrates these three basic caisson shapes.

Think of a caisson as a special type of pile, pier, or footing. Caissons are sometimes used instead of piles and piers because they do not cause the soil heaving and displacement, vibration, and noise that commonly occur during pile driving. Additionally, because caissons are larger in diameter, workers can be lowered into them during installation to visually inspect the bearing strata.

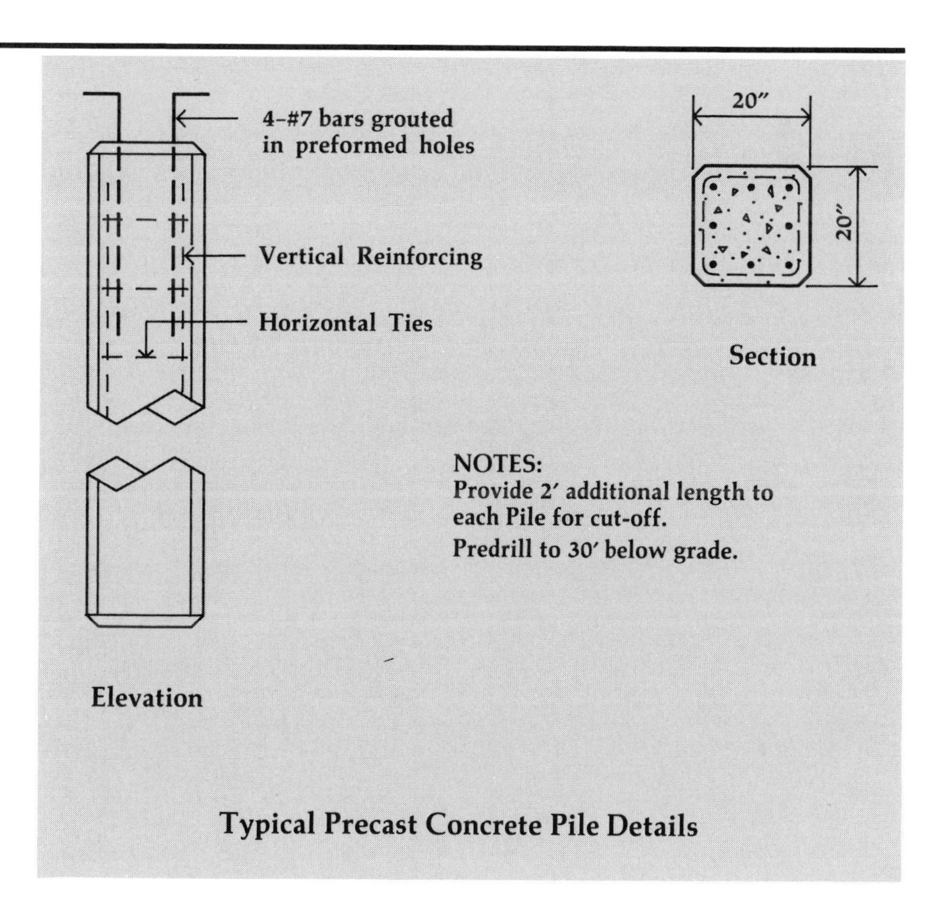

Typical Precast Concrete Pile Details

Figure 4.5

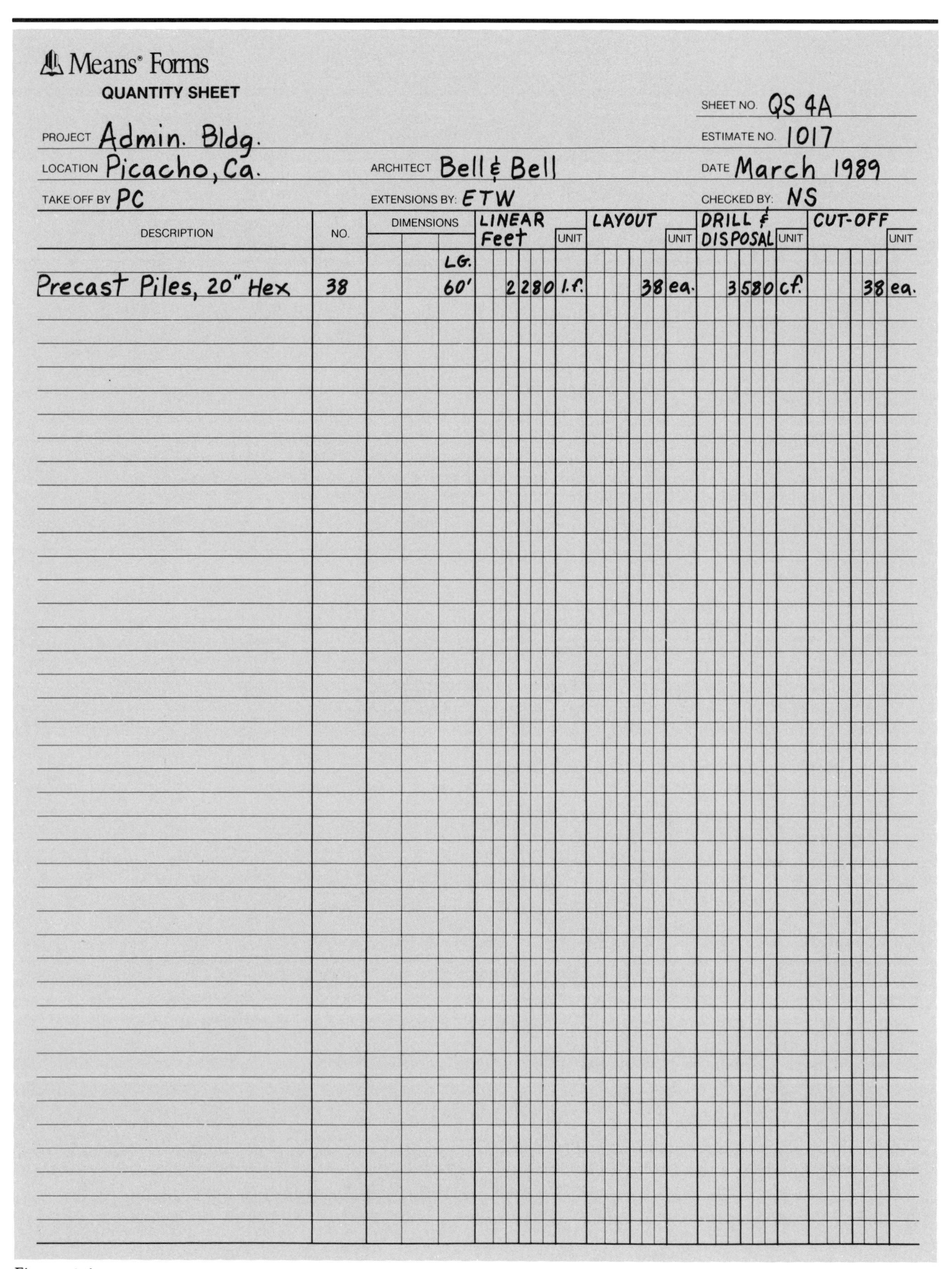

Means® Forms

QUANTITY SHEET

SHEET NO. QS 4A

PROJECT Admin. Bldg. — ESTIMATE NO. 1017

LOCATION Picacho, Ca. — ARCHITECT Bell & Bell — DATE March 1989

TAKE OFF BY PC — EXTENSIONS BY: ETW — CHECKED BY: NS

DESCRIPTION	NO.	DIMENSIONS			LINEAR Feet	UNIT	LAYOUT	UNIT	DRILL & DISPOSAL	UNIT	CUT-OFF	UNIT
				LG.								
Precast Piles, 20" Hex	38			60'	2280	l.f.	38	ea.	3580	cf.	38	ea.

Figure 4.6

A foundation component that is similar to the caisson is the *pressure injected footing*. Often called *bulb end piles*, these foundation units are started in the same manner as CIP concrete piles. Afterward, a plug of concrete is forced down the casing with high-energy blows to form a bulb in the surrounding earth at the base of the pile. The casing may either be left in place or removed. The bulb forms a kind of footing, with the shaft acting as a column or pier. Figure 4.8 illustrates a pressure injected footing.

Takeoff Items

The following items are taken off for caissons:

- Number of each type of caisson
- Length
- Shaft diameter
- Soil type and dewatering (if necessary)
- Drill and disposal
- Plain or reinforced cores
- Concrete

Takeoff Demonstration

Imagine that instead of piles, our model building plan calls for 18 bell caissons of three different sizes. Figure 4.9 is a plan showing the location and top and bottom elevations of each caisson.

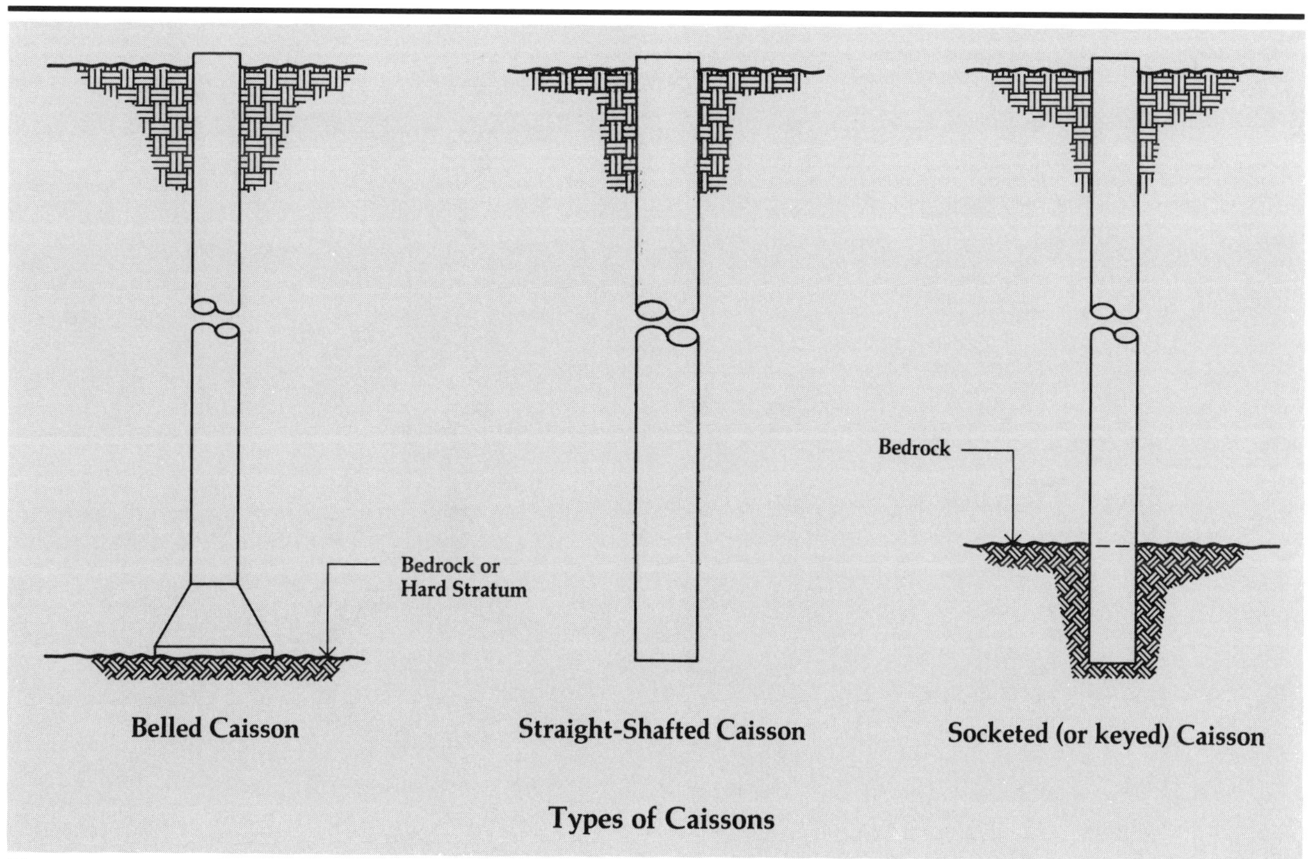

Types of Caissons

Figure 4.7

The most time-consuming part of caisson takeoff is calculating the volume of each size caisson. This quantity will tell us what the drill and disposal and concrete quantities are. The other takeoff items can simply be listed on the quantity sheet (Figure 4.11) under the appropriate columns. This section, then, will demonstrate how to find the volume of a caisson.

Finding the Volume of a Caisson

To find the total volume of each caisson, separate the caisson into two parts: the *shaft* and the *base*. Figure 4.10 illustrates these elements in caissons whose bases are both belled (cone-shaped) and semi-spherical.

Step 1: Calculate the volume of the shaft using the formula:

$V_s = \pi r^2 h_s$

V_s = Volume of shaft

r = Radius of shaft

h_s = Height of shaft

Step 2: Calculate the volume of the base. This can be done in one of two ways:

A. As shown in Figure 4.10a, breaking the cone-shaped base into the *bell* and *band*. First find the volume of the band around the base. Then, using the Average End Area formula, find the volume of the bell.

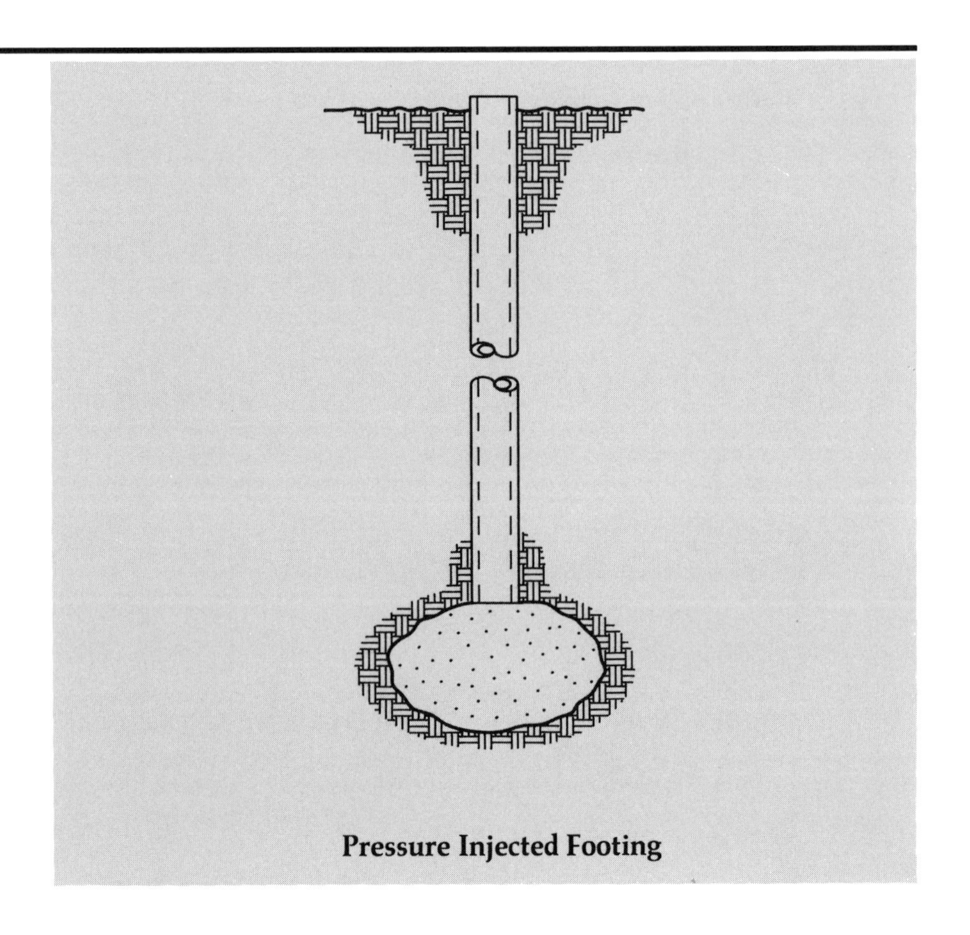

Figure 4.8

Pressure Injected Footing

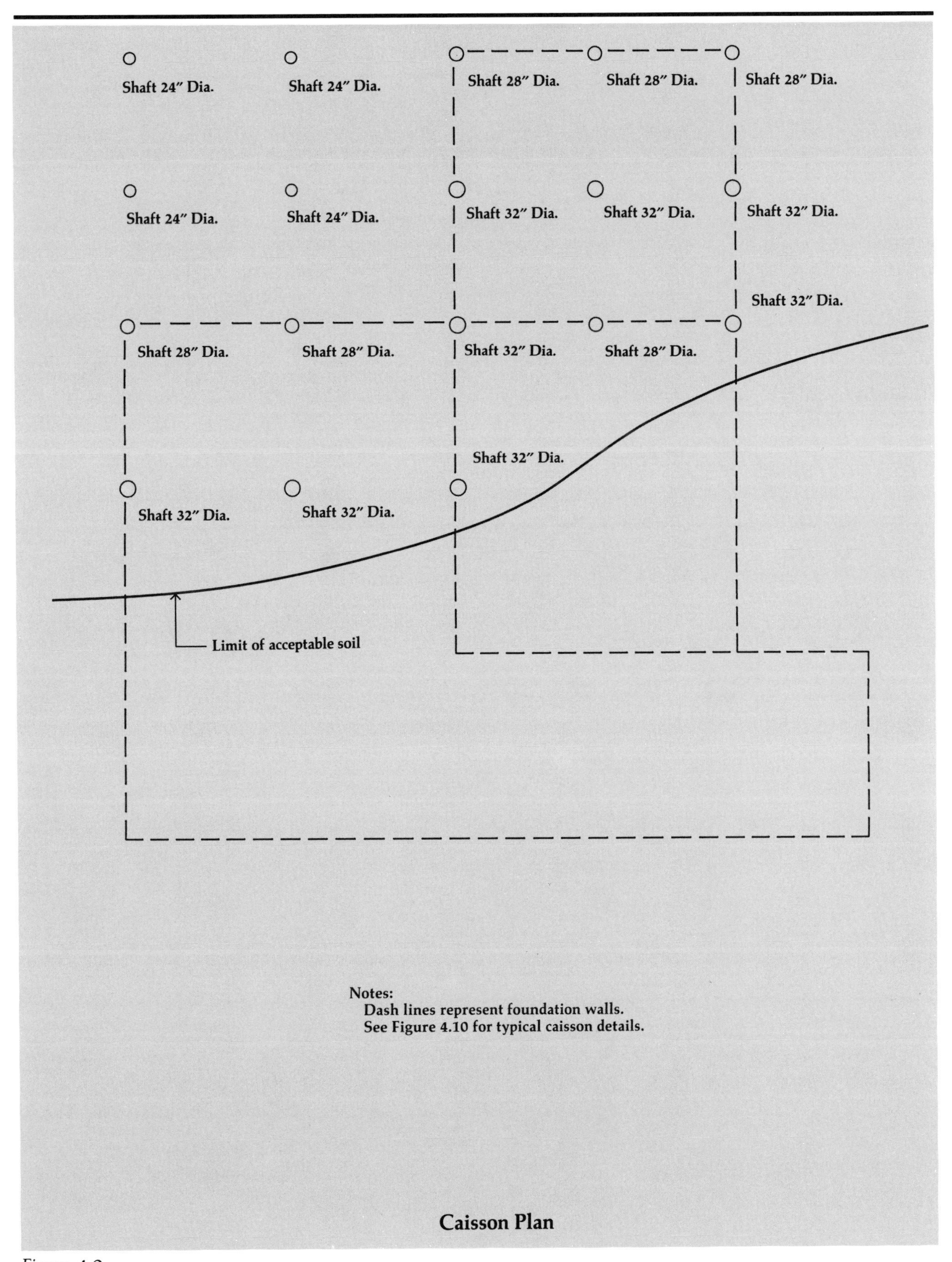
Shaft 24″ Dia.
Shaft 24″ Dia.
Shaft 28″ Dia.
Shaft 28″ Dia.
Shaft 28″ Dia.
Shaft 24″ Dia.
Shaft 24″ Dia.
Shaft 32″ Dia.
Shaft 32″ Dia.
Shaft 32″ Dia.
Shaft 32″ Dia.
Shaft 28″ Dia.
Shaft 28″ Dia.
Shaft 32″ Dia.
Shaft 28″ Dia.
Shaft 32″ Dia.
Shaft 32″ Dia.
Shaft 32″ Dia.
Limit of acceptable soil
Notes:
Dash lines represent foundation walls.
See Figure 4.10 for typical caisson details.
Caisson Plan

Figure 4.9

The formula for band volume is:

$$V_{(band)} = \pi r^2 h_{(band)}$$

$V_{(band)}$ = Volume of band

r = Radius of band

$h_{(band)}$ = Height of band

The formula for bell volume is:

$$V_{(bell)} = \frac{A_1 + A_2}{2} \times h_{(bell)}$$

$V_{(bell)}$ = Volume of bell

A_1 = Area of shaft = πr_s^2

A_2 = Area of band = $\pi r_{(bell)}^2$

$h_{(bell)}$ = Height of bell

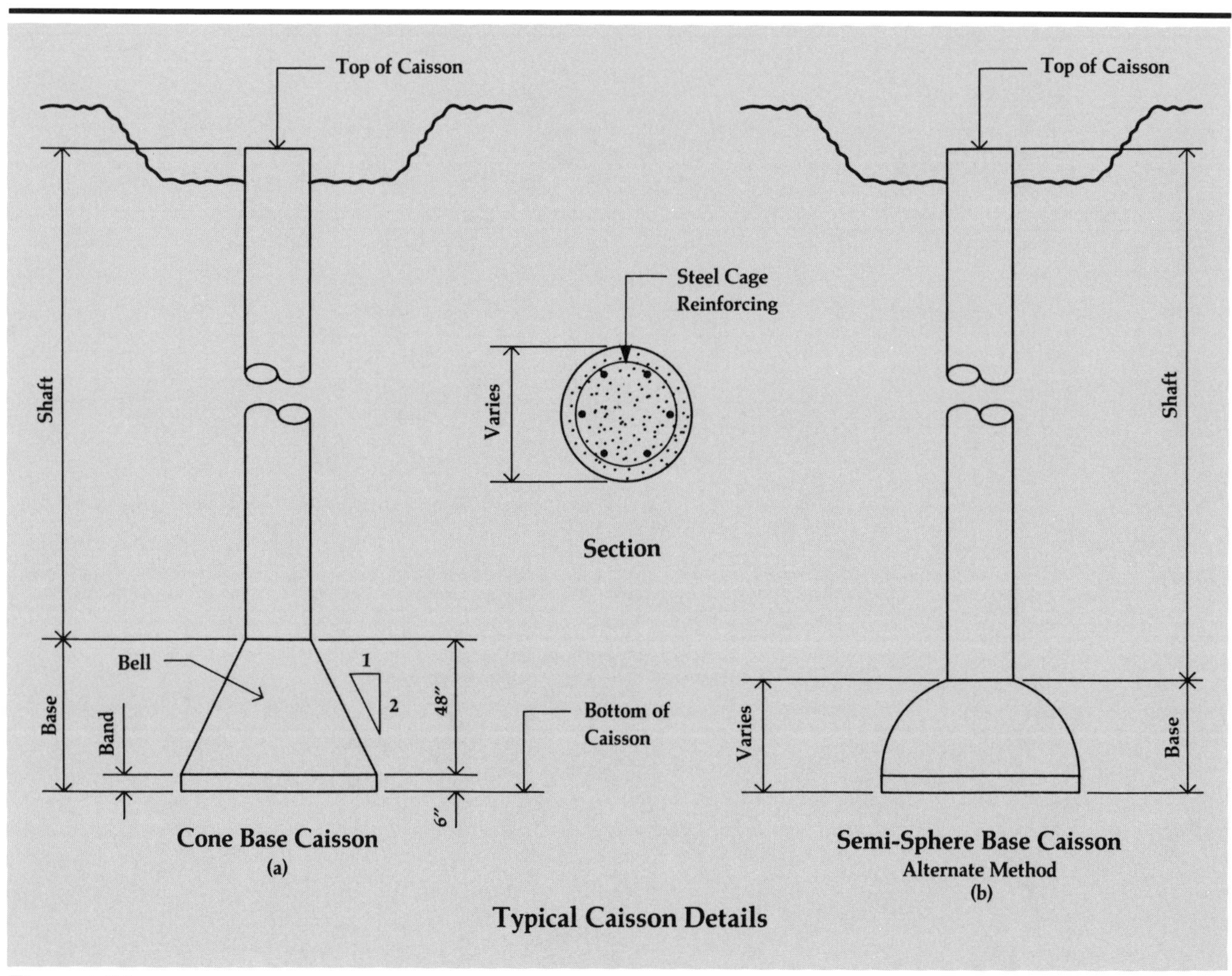

Figure 4.10

B. Or, the volume of the base can be calculated as though it were shaped like a semi-sphere (see Figure 4.10b). This method is often used because it is simpler and more realistic. The formula for the volume of a semi-spherical base is:

$$V = \frac{\pi D^3}{6} \times \frac{1}{2}$$

V = Volume of one-half of sphere

D = Diameter of base

Step 3: Add the volume of the base to the volume of the shaft for the total volume of the caisson. Again, this value can be used for the drill and disposal and concrete quantities.

Repeat this procedure for each caisson size and transfer to Quantity Sheet 4B. Total the columns and add an allowance for waste where appropriate.

Assume that the base of the caissons in our model building are cone-shaped. The calculations for each size caisson appear below.

24″ *Caissons*

Shaft: $\pi(1')^2 \times 46' = 145$ cf $\times$ 4 ea $= 580$ cf

Band: $D = 2' + 4' = 6'$

$\pi(3')^2 \times 0.5' = 14.13$ cf $\times$ 4 ea $= 56.52$ cf

Bell: $\frac{\pi(1')^2 + \pi(3')^2}{2} \times 4' = 62.8$ cf $\times$ 4 ea $= 251$ cf

Total volume: 888 cf

28″ *Caissons*

Shaft: $\pi(1.17')^2 \times 46' = 197.8$ cf $\times$ 6 ea $= 1{,}187$ cf

Band: $D = 2.33' + 4' = 6.33'$

$\pi(3.17')^2 \times 0.5' = 15.78$ cf $\times$ 6 ea $= 95$ cf

Bell: $\frac{\pi(1.17')^2 + \pi(3.17')^2}{2} \times 4' = 71.74$ cf $\times$ 6 ea $= 430$ cf

Total volume: 1,712 cf

32″ *Caissons*

Shaft: $\pi(1.33')^2 \times 46' = 255.6$ cf $\times$ 8 ea $= 2{,}045$ cf

Band: $D = 2.67' + 4' = 6.67'$

$\pi(3.33')^2 \times 0.5' = 17.42$ cf $\times$ 8 ea $= 139$ cf

Bell: $\frac{\pi(3.33')^2 + \pi(1.33')^2}{2} \times 4' \times 4' = 80.8$ cf $\times$ 8 ea $= 646$ cf

Total volume: 2,830 cf

Pile Caps

A pile cap is a concrete structural member that is placed on top of a pile or a cluster of piles. Pile caps transmit building loads to the piles rather than directly to bearing soil. Figure 4.1 shows a typical pile cap as it rests on a cluster of piles.

Means® Forms

QUANTITY SHEET

SHEET NO. QS 4B

PROJECT Admin. Bldg. | ESTIMATE NO. 1017

LOCATION Picacho, Ca. | ARCHITECT Bell & Bell | DATE March 1989

TAKE OFF BY PC | EXTENSIONS BY: ETW | CHECKED BY: NS

DESCRIPTION	NO.	DIMENSIONS ϕ	DIMENSIONS L	CONC.	UNIT	EXCAVA.	UNIT		UNIT		UNIT
Caissons											
24"	4	24"	46'								
Shaft				580	CF						
Bell				251							
Band				57							
28"	6	28"	46'								
Shaft				1187							
Bell				430							
Band				95							
32"	8	32"	46'								
Shaft				2045							
Bell				646							
Band				139							
Total				5430							
Convert to CY				201							

Figure 4.11

Takeoff Items

Pile caps are similar to spread footings, but are not always rectangular in shape. The items typically taken off for pile caps are similar to those taken off for footings. They include:

- Layout
- Structural excavation (machine and hand)
- Formwork
- Reinforcing
- Concrete
- Curing
- Backfill
- Disposal

Hand excavation plays a large role in pile cap construction because of the difficulty in moving machine excavating equipment between projecting piles. See Figure 4.12.

Takeoff Demonstration

If our model building had piles and pile caps instead of spread and strip footings, they would appear on the plans as shown in Figure 4.4. Note that there are four types of pile caps: 1-pile, 2-pile, 3-pile, and 4-pile caps. These four types should be taken off one type at a time. The dimensions of each type of pile cap are given on the plans and, for 3-pile caps, in Figure 4.13. The takeoff will be demonstrated for the 1-pile caps only. The other three types can be taken off using the same procedure. Record all quantities on Quantity Sheet 4C, Figure 4.14, located at the end of this chapter.

1-Pile Caps

Excavation: Excavate 18″ around the 1-pile cap to leave working room for forming. Machine excavate to within 6″ of the bottom. (Piles are usually cut off 6″ above the bottom grade of the pile cap after excavation is complete.)

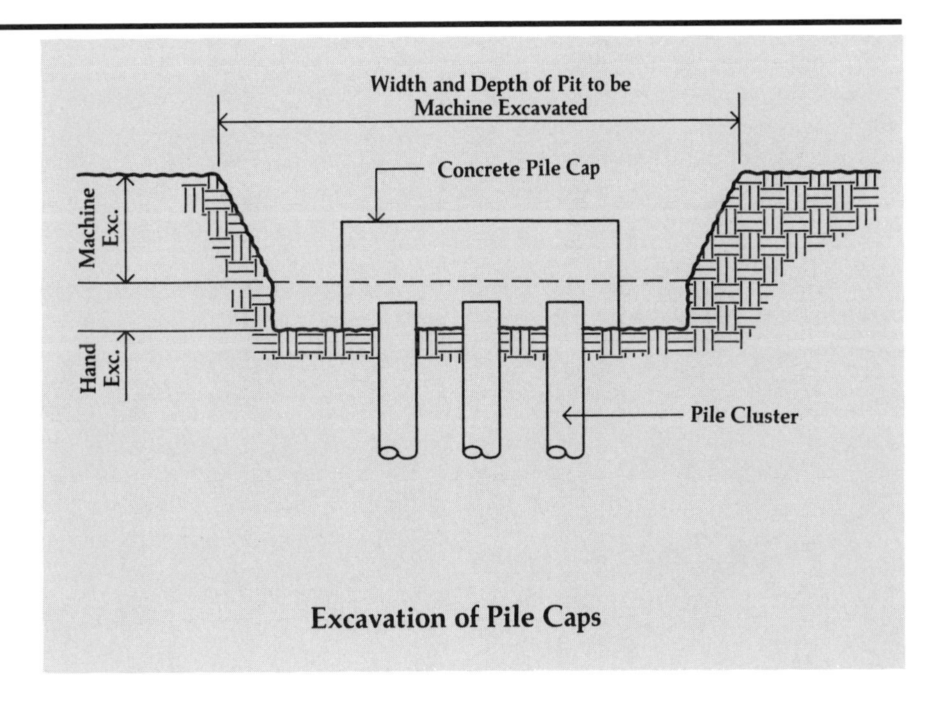

Excavation of Pile Caps

Figure 4.12

Machine excavation = 6′ × 6′ × 2′ deep × 8 ea = 576 cf
Hand excavation = 6′ × 6′ × 0.5′ deep × 8 ea = 144 cf
Total = 720 cf

Formwork: Side forms are found by multiplying the perimeter of the pile cap (4 sides × 3′) by the depth of the pile cap (1.5′) for a total of 18 square feet for each pile cap, or 144 square feet for 8 1-pile caps.

Formwork = 3′ × 4 sides × 1.5′ × 8 ea = 144 sfca

Reinforcement: Reinforcement for a 1-pile cap is found as follows:

Reinforcement = 5 ea × 2.5′ × 2 ways × 8 caps = 200 lf (#5)

Concrete: The 1-pile caps are 3′ × 3′ × 1.5′ deep, for a total of 13.5 cubic feet. Multiply this number by the number of 1-pile caps (8) for a total concrete volume of 108 cubic feet.

Concrete = 3′ × 3′ × 1.5′ × 8 ea = 108 cf

This figure is used for concrete as well as disposal quantities.

Curing: The quantity of curing necessary for the top surface area of the pile caps is found by multiplying the length × width of the pile cap × the number of caps of that type.

Curing = 3′ × 3′ × 8 caps = 72 sf

Backfill: Backfill is the total excavation less the concrete volume.

Backfill = 720 cf − 108 cf = 612 cf

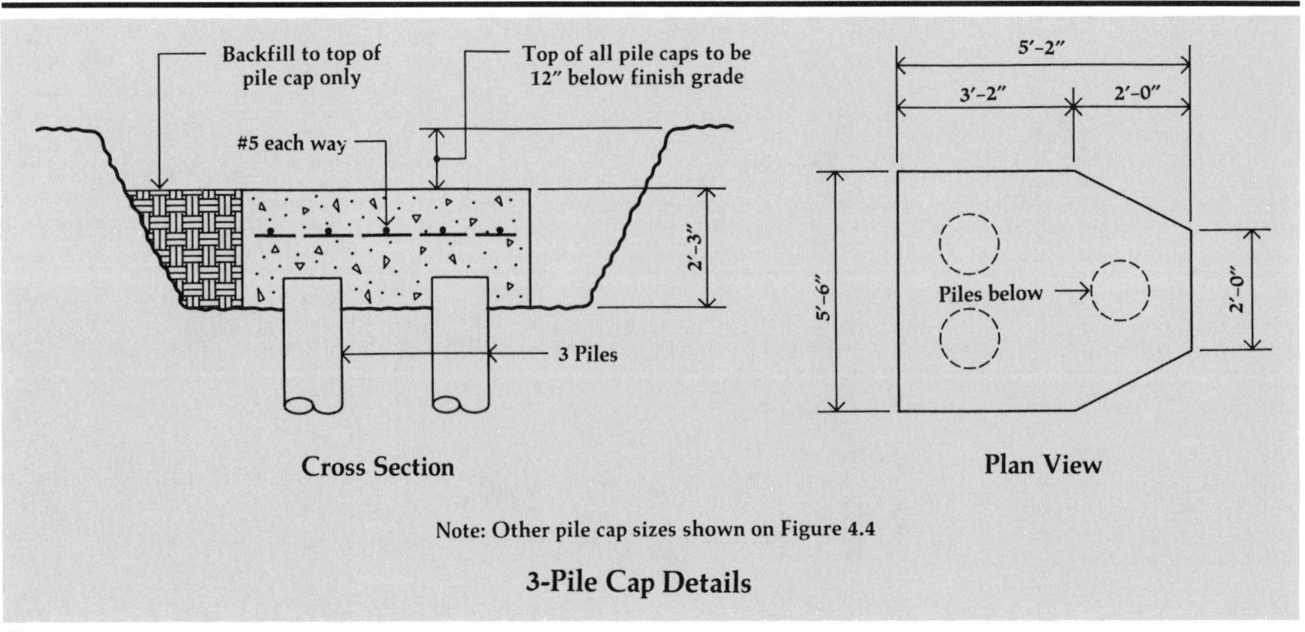

Note: Other pile cap sizes shown on Figure 4.4

3-Pile Cap Details

Figure 4.13

After allowing for an 18% compaction (612 cf × 1.18 = 722 cf), we find that there is no disposal quantity.

Take off the remaining pile caps in the same fashion. The calculations are shown below. Note that the cap for the 3-pile cluster has an irregular shape, but the others are simple rectangles. Record and extend all quantities on Quantity Sheet 4C, convert to proper units, and apply the appropriate waste factors.

2-Pile Caps

Excavation (machine): 9.5′ × 6.5′ × 3′ × 4 ea = 741 cf
(hand): 9.5′ × 6.5′ × 0.5′ × 4 ea = 124 cf

Forms: 10′ × 2.5′ × 2 × 4 ea = 200 sfca

Reinforcement: 7 ea × 6′ × 4 ea = 168 lf (# 5)
5 ea × 3′ × 4 ea = 60 lf (# 4)

Concrete: 6.5′ × 3.5′ × 2.5′ × 4 ea = 228 cf

Curing: 6.5′ × 3.5′ × 4 ea = 91 sf

Backfill: 865 cf − 228 cf = 637 cf

Disposal: 865 cf − (637 cf × 1.18) = 113 cf

3-Pile Caps

Excavation (machine): 8.5′ × 8.17′ × 2.87′ × 2 ea = 400 cf
(hand): 8.5′ × 8.17′ × 0.5′ × 2 ea = 70 cf

Forms: (5.5′ + 5.17′) × 2 × 2.25′ × 2 ea = 100 sfca
(Note: rectangular measurement is sufficient accuracy for our purposes.)

Reinforcement: 7 ea × 5′ × 2 ea = 70 lf (# 5)
7 ea × 4.7′ × 2 ea = 66 lf (# 5)

Concrete: $\left[(5.5' \times 3.17') + \left(\frac{5.5' + 2'}{2} \times 2\right)\right] \times 2.25' \times 2 \text{ ea}$
$= (17.4 \text{ sf} + 7.5 \text{ sf})^2 \times 2.25' \times 2 \text{ ea} = 116 \text{ cf}$

Curing: 24.9 sf × 2 ea = 50 sf

Backfill: 470 cf − 116 cf = 354 cf

Disposal: 470 cf − (354 cf × 1.18) = 52 cf

4-Pile Caps

Excavation (machine): 8.5′ × 8.5′ × 3′ × 4 ea = 867 cf
(hand): 8.5′ × 8.5′ × 0.5′ × 4 ea = 145 cf

Forms: 5.5′ × 4 × 2.5′ × 4 ea = 220 sfca

Reinforcement: 24 ea × 5′ = 120 lf (# 5)

Concrete: 5.5′ × 5.5′ × 2.5′ × 4 ea = 303 cf

Curing: 5.5′ × 5.5′ × 4 ea = 121 sf

Backfill: 1,012 cf − 303 cf = 709 cf

Disposal: 1,012 cf − (709 cf × 1.18) = 175 cf

This completes the takeoff of piles, caissons, and pile caps. Chapter 5 examines the takeoff procedure for foundation walls and concrete piers.

Means® Forms
QUANTITY SHEET

PROJECT Admin. Bldg.
LOCATION Picacho, Ca.
ARCHITECT Bell & Bell
TAKE OFF BY PC
EXTENSIONS BY: ETW

SHEET NO. QS 4C
ESTIMATE NO. 1017
DATE March 1989
CHECKED BY: NS

DESCRIPTION	NO.	l	w	h	MACH. EXCAVA.	UNIT	HAND EXCAVA.	UNIT	FORMS	UNIT	CONC.	UNIT	REINF.	UNIT	B'FILL	UNIT	DISPOSAL	UNIT	LAYOUT	UNIT	CURING	UNIT
Pile Caps																						
1 - Pile	8	3	3	1.5	576	CF	144	CF	144	SFCA	108	CF	200	LF	612	CF	—		8	ea.	72	SF
2 - Piles	4	6.5	3.5	2.5	741		124		200		228		228		637		113		4		91	
3 - Piles	2	5.5	5.17	2.33	400		70		100		116		136		354		52		2		50	
4 - Piles	4	5.5	5.5	2.5	867		145		220		303		120		709		175		4		121	
Total					2584	CF	483	CF	664	SFCA	755	CF	684	LF	2312	CF	340	CF	18		334	
Convert to CY					96	CY	18	CY			28	CY			86	CY	13	CY				
															+9		-9					
10% compact/18% swell															95		4					
															+17		+1					
Convert #5 Bar to LBS													713	LBS	112		5					
Waste Allowances																						
Conc 5%											1	CY										
Reinf. 18%													128	LBS								
Forms 5%									33	SFCA												
Total					96	CY	18	CY	697	SFCA	29	CY	841	LBS	112	CY	5	CY	18	ea.	334	SF

Figure 4.14

Chapter 5
Foundation Walls and Concrete Piers

Foundation Walls

Foundation walls, sometimes called *stem walls,* are that part of the building foundation which supports the exterior walls and forms a retaining structure for the portion of the building which is below grade. Foundation walls usually rest on strip footings, which were taken off in Chapter 3.

Foundation walls are generally constructed of cast-in-place (CIP) concrete or masonry block. Wall height depends on the depth of frost penetration, basement layout, or any special architectural requirements of the structure. Wall thickness is determined by code requirements, the unsupported height or length of the wall, structural load considerations, or the thickness of the wall to be supported on the upper floors. Figure 5.1 illustrates a typical CIP concrete foundation wall.

Takeoff Items

The items typically taken off for CIP concrete foundation walls include:

- Formwork
- Joints
- Steel reinforcement
- Concrete
- Point and patch (P&P)
- Dampproofing
- Rub and grind (R&G)

Keep in mind that any associated excavation and backfilling was already taken off with mass excavation and footings, and will not be discussed here.

Formwork

Formwork for CIP concrete foundation walls may be made from job-built plyform with stud framing, modular prefabricated plywood, steel-framed plywood, or prefabricated aluminum or steel. The size and characteristics of the building, as well as contractor preference, will determine which materials to use.

The quantity estimator may choose to make a separate cost item for the labor and materials required to form corners and intersections, since the cost to construct forms depends, to a great extent, on the number of corners.

Figure 5.2 illustrates formwork required for typical CIP concrete foundation walls.

Joints

Expansion and control joints are used in long walls at 30′ intervals to help relieve internal stress and control crack lines. These are usually not shown on the plans, but should be included in the quantity estimator's takeoff. List them by linear foot and wall thickness.

Steel Reinforcement

Steel reinforcement, typically a subcontracted item, may occasionally have to be taken off by the quantity estimator for cost estimating purposes. The drawings will show the sizes, number of bars, and spacings—both horizontally and vertically. The drawings will also show typical standards for hooks, bends, and laps.

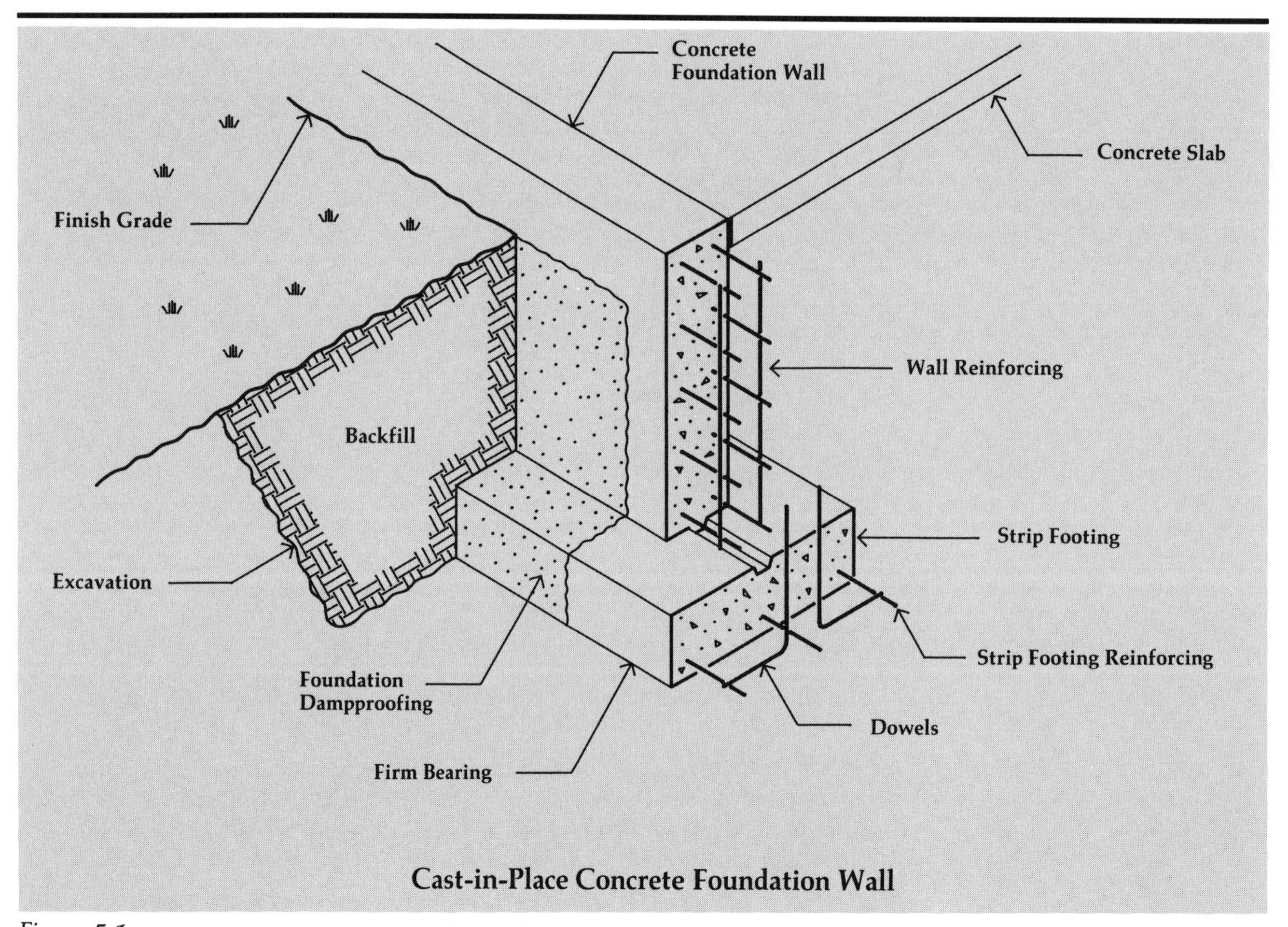

Figure 5.1

Bars are taken off by size and then converted from linear feet to pounds using a table of weights (see Chapter 12). It is not practical for the quantity estimator to take off individual hooks, bends, laps, tie wire, and supports, as a reinforcing steel detailer would do. Therefore, a percentage of weight is added based on data from previous jobs that have proved to be appropriate.

Concrete

Concrete used in the construction of foundation walls may be placed by chute, pumped into the formwork, or placed by crane and bucket. An elephant trunk or placing ports may be used for high walls to avoid dropping the concrete from great heights and to prevent the formation of cold joints. The quantity estimator should specify which method of placement will be used. This will depend on site conditions, accessibility to the wall area, and wall height. If vibration of the concrete is called for, the estimate will have to include the necessary labor and equipment rental. Concrete is listed on the quantity sheet in cubic yards.

Point and Patch (P&P)

Point and patch, a work item, is the process by which irregularities and tie rod holes in concrete surfaces are knocked off, shaved, or filled in. This is done on both sides of the foundation wall. The point and patch area is usually the same as the form area and is expressed in square feet.

Dampproofing

Dampproofing material is applied to the outside surface of the foundation wall and footing that will be covered by backfill. The quantity estimator should indicate the type of dampproofing specified and indicate the total surface area to be covered in square feet.

Figure 5.2

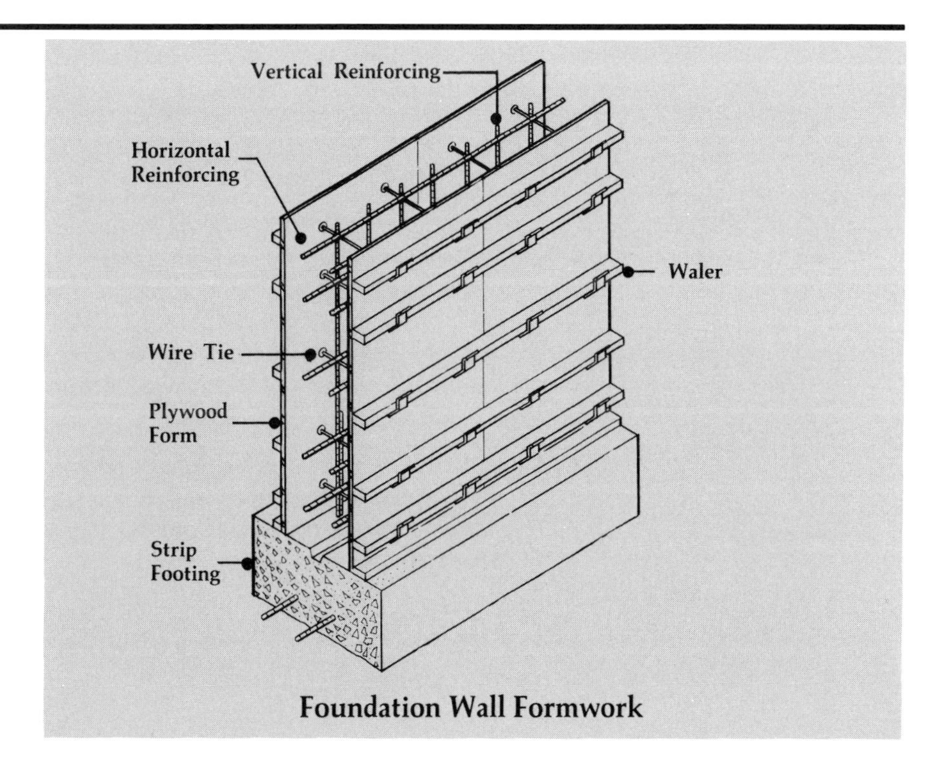

Foundation Wall Formwork

Rub and Grind (R&G)

Rub and grind, also a work item, is the fine finishing of a concrete surface using an abrasive. Rub and grind is done only to those wall surfaces that will be exposed. For foundation walls, rub and grind is performed on the interior surface area (if exposed) as well as that exterior surface area that will be exposed above ground. Rub and grind is measured in square feet.

Takeoff Demonstration

Refer to the Foundation and Footing Plan in Appendix A. Since the foundation walls rest on top of the strip footings, we can use the footing plan as our reference. The Foundation Detail sheet provides a detailed cross-section of the foundation walls. The Building Elevations in the Appendix show the elevations of both the top of footings and the top of the walls.

Assume that all surfaces will require point and patch after the forms are removed, but only those exposed to view require rub and grind.

Step 1: Exterior (Perimeter) Walls

Begin the takeoff at the northeast corner of the foundation plan and proceed in a clockwise direction. Note that this plan is aligned with the points of the compass. A column grid is superimposed on the plan for reference.

The first segment, the East Elevation, extends from point 3D to A4. The length is:

$$100' + 22' + 30' = 152 \text{ lf}$$

The width is 12" (or 1'). The depth is calculated from the top of the footing (elev 91.0') to the top of the wall (elev 95.5'), or 4.5'. The quantity of concrete is calculated by multiplying the length × width × height. The number of square feet of forms is found by multiplying length × height × 2. Point and patch quantity is the same as the form quantity. Rub and grind quantity is the same as the surface area of the exposed concrete. This is the length × approximately 1' of the interior plus approximately 1.5' on the exterior (95.5 — 94.0), 94.0 being the average finished grade outside the wall. Transfer these values to the appropriate columns on Quantity Sheet 5A (Figure 5.3), located at the end of this section.

The second segment extends from A4 to the end of the steps. The takeoff procedure is exactly the same as the first segment, except that the Average End Area formula is used for this first 10' of the South Elevation.

Step 2: Interior Walls

When takeoff has been completed for the perimeter (exterior) walls, the interior walls may be taken off. In our model, the three interior walls are the same width and height, and can be taken off as one continuous wall.

Step 3: Concluding the Takeoff

Finally, count the number of corners and intersections and note this information on Quantity Sheet 5A. When the takeoff has been completed for both exterior and interior foundation walls, review the plan to ensure that no segments have been missed. Total the columns, convert cubic feet of concrete to cubic yards, and add waste allowance as recommended in Appendix C.

Piers

A concrete pier is a short column below grade which is used to support a concentrated load. A pier is a column-like structure that rests on a spread footing and extends as high as the ground floor elevation. Figure 5.4 depicts a typical concrete pier.

Means® Forms
QUANTITY SHEET

PROJECT Admin. Bldg.
LOCATION Picacho, Ca.
TAKE OFF BY PC
ARCHITECT Bell & Bell
EXTENSIONS BY: ETW

SHEET NO. QS 5A
ESTIMATE NO. 1017
DATE March 1989
CHECKED BY: NS

DESCRIPTION	NO.	L	W	H	FORMS	REINF.	CONC.	P&P	R&G	COR/INT.	DAMP-PROOFING	EXPANSION JOINTS
Foundation Walls												
Exterior												
East Elev. (95.5-91.0)		152	1	4.5	1368 SFCA	2736 LF	684 CF	1368 SF	380 SF	5 ea.		
South Elev. $\left(\frac{4.17+7.17}{2}\right)$=		10	1	5.67	113	227	57	113	660	–		
		6	1	4.17	50	100	25	50				
		68.67	1	4.83	663	1327	332	663				
		41.33	1	5.5	455	909	227	455				
West Elev.		22	1	5.5	242	484	121	242	430	4		
		24.33	1	5.17	252	503	126	252				
		25.33	1	4.83	244	489	122	244				
		58.33	1	4.5	525	1050	262	525				
North Elev.		104	1	4.5	936	1872	468	936	260	–		
Interior Wall		151	1	4.5	1359	2718	680	1359	—	1		
Total					6207 SFCA	12415 LF	3104 CF	6207 SF	1730 SF	10 ea.	3100 SF	85 LF
Convert to CY							115 CY					
Convert #5 bar to LBS (1.043 #/LF)						12949 LBS						
Waste Allowances												
Conc. 11%							13 CY					
Reinf. 18%						2331 LBS						
Forms 5%					6517							
Total					6517 SFCA	15280 LBS	128 CY	6207 SF	1730 SF	10 ea.	3100 SF	85 LF

Note: Dampproofing = 1/2 S.F.C.A.
Expansion Joints = Average wall height = $\frac{4'9'' \times \text{linear feet of wall}}{30}$

Figure 5.3

Takeoff Items

The items typically associated with concrete piers include:

- Formwork
- Steel reinforcement
- Concrete
- Anchor bolts and base plates
- Rub and grind

Keep in mind that excavation and backfill quantities were already taken off with the footings, and need not be taken off again in this chapter.

Takeoff Demonstration

Since piers are placed on top of spread footings, we can use the Foundation and Footing Plan to take off the piers. This plan shows the location of the piers in our model administrative building.

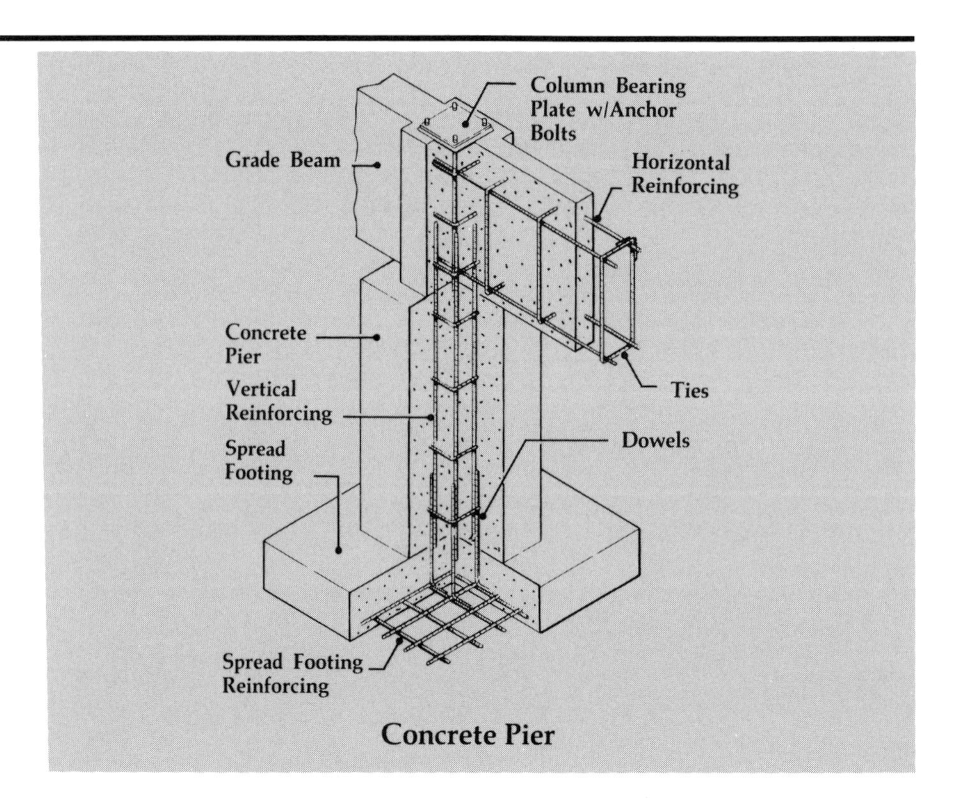

Concrete Pier

Figure 5.4

Step 1: *Formwork*

The takeoff procedure for piers is quite simple. The number of square feet of formwork is found by adding the areas of the four sides of the pier and multiplying by the number of piers. For example at footing types I and II:

$$1' \times (\text{elev } 94.17' - 91.0') \times 4 \text{ sides} \times 5 \text{ piers} = 64 \text{ sfca}$$

Transfer this value to Quantity Sheet 5B, Figure 5.5, located at the end of this chapter.

Step 2: *Concrete*

The quantity of concrete is found by calculating the total volume of the pier. The piers in this sample are 1-foot square. To find the volume of concrete, multiply the length × width × depth × the number of piers:

$$1' \times 1' \times 3.17' \times 5 \text{ ea} = 16 \text{ cf}$$

Step 3: *Anchor Bolts and Base Plates*

Our model has four 3/4″ anchor bolts and an 8″ × 8″ × 3/4″ base plate on each pier. This should be noted on the quantity sheet.

This completes the takeoff for CIP concrete foundation walls and piers. The next chapter examines the takeoff procedure for concrete slabs on grade.

Means Forms
QUANTITY SHEET

PROJECT Admin. Bldg.　　　　　SHEET NO. QS 5B
ESTIMATE NO. 1017
LOCATION Picacho, Ca.　　ARCHITECT Bell & Bell　　DATE March 1989
TAKE OFF BY KPF　　EXTENSIONS BY: KPF　　CHECKED BY: N.S.

DESCRIPTION	NO.	DIMENSIONS L	W	H	Forms	UNIT	Reinf.	UNIT	Conc.	UNIT	Anchor Bolts	UNIT	Base Plates	UNIT		UNIT
Concrete Piers																
	5	1'	1'	3.17'	64	SFCA			16	CF	20	ea.	5	ea.		
Rebar #3s, @ 6" O.C.	.375	#/LF		3'			34	Lb.								
#8s	2.67	#/LF		5'			240	Lb.								
Convert to CY									1	CY						
Waste Allowances																
Conc. 11%									—							
Reinf. 18%							50	Lb.								
Forms 5%					3	SFCA										
Total					67	SFCA	324	Lb.	1	CY	20	ea.	5	ea.		

Note: Less than 1 CY of concrete
Form & Place with wall - direct chute

Figure 5.5

Chapter 6

Concrete Floor Slabs on Grade

A concrete slab on grade is a concrete slab supported directly on a compacted granular base. The design of the slab depends on its use. That is, its thickness, strength, and the type of steel reinforcement it requires is determined by the weight of the loads that it must support.

Different sections of a building have different functions and, therefore, have different slab designs. For instance, the slabs on grade for a loading area would be different from the slabs designed for office space. The loading area would probably have a hard wearing surface topping and be able to support heavier loads. Figure 6.1 shows a typical concrete slab on grade.

Takeoff Items

The items that are taken off for concrete slabs on grade are:

- Granular base
- Grading and compaction of sub-base
- Fine grading
- Vapor barrier
- Edge forms
- Expansion joints
- Construction joints
- Welded wire fabric reinforcing
- Concrete
- Screeds
- Finish and topping
- Cure and harden
- Concrete "outs" (areas of no concrete)
- Haunches

This seems like a long list, but the quantities for all of these items are derived from just a few dimensions and simple calculations. It is important, however, that the quantity estimator does not leave any of these items out of an estimate. Even though the items above may not apply to every slab-on-grade takeoff, they do provide a good checklist.

Guidelines for Takeoff

Below are some guidelines to follow for taking off slabs on grade.

- Allow for about 25% compaction of the granular base.
- Allow 10% overlap for vapor barrier and welded wire fabric.
- Allow 5% waste for concrete.
- Make no deductions for columns or "outs" under 10 sf.
- If screeds are estimated separately from forming and placing costs, estimate 1 lf of screed per 10 sf of finish area.

Takeoff Demonstration

The following is a step-by-step demonstration of the takeoff procedure used for concrete slabs on grade. The Slab on Grade Plan in Appendix A shows the details of the concrete floor slabs in our model administrative building. The slab areas on the plan are identified by numbers inside of squares: [1].

Area [1]

Take off the slab in Area [1]. According to the slab plan, this 4" slab is placed over a 6 mil waterproof membrane that has been laid on top of a 4"-thick layer of crushed rock. The concrete slab is edged with expansion joint material and will have a cold joint running down the middle of it in each direction.

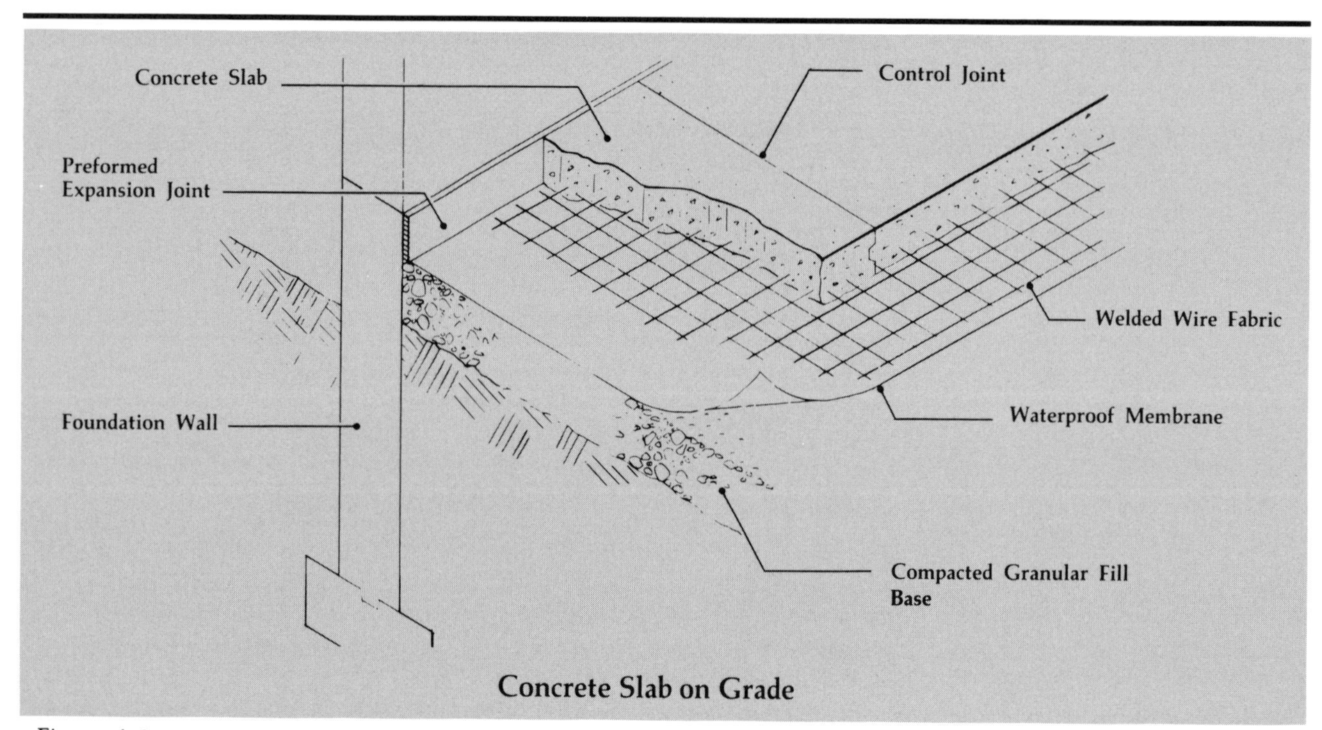

Figure 6.1

Step 1

Find the dimensions of this slab by subtracting the wall thicknesses from the outside dimensions shown on the plan. Write these dimensions on Quantity Sheet 6 in the column labeled "Dimensions." (Quantity Sheet 6 is shown in Figure 6.2, located at the end of this chapter.)

Step 2

Next, take off the fine grading of the base course that will receive the slab. This quantity is equal to the square foot area of the slab. Multiply the length of the slab in Area [1] by its width:

46′ × 44′ = 2,024 sf

This is the same quantity required for grading and compaction of the sub-base. Record these values on the quantity sheet.

Step 3

Next, determine the quantity of crushed rock base course. This is found by multiplying the area of the slab by the depth of crushed stone:

46′ × 44′ × 0.33′ = 668 cf

Step 4

Vapor barrier, finish, and cure are equal to the square foot area of the slab. They should be listed separately, however, because each has a different waste factor and a different cost.

Step 5

Next find the quantity of concrete in Area [1]. The volume of concrete is found by multiplying the length × width × depth of the slab:

46′ × 44′ × 0.33′ = 668 cf

Step 6

One cost item in all concrete slab work is the setting of screeds (pipes or other material set to grade to drag a straight edge across to control the slab thickness and obtain a level top surface). This value is found by multiplying the length of the slab by its width and dividing by 10.

Step 7

Add the number of linear feet of joints (expansion and construction joints). Notice that there are 4″ joints for 4″ slabs. The 6″ slabs of Areas [2] and [4] will require 6″ joints. Transfer these figures to the appropriate columns on Quantity Sheet 6.

This concludes the takeoff procedure for Area [1]. Remember to mark off each slab as it is taken off. Do this by lightly shading the slab area.

Area [2]

Area [2] is a reinforced 6″ slab with 6″ of base course. Although this slab is designed for heavier use, the quantities are taken off in the same manner as Area [1]. Note that the quantity of welded wire fabric required in this slab is the same as the vapor barrier, cure, and finish area.

Area [3]

Note that Area [3] is L-shaped. Always keep in mind that a slab on grade must be isolated from any foundation. The expansion joint must be figured around the perimeter of the slab as well as around each pier. For our estimate we will box out a 2′ × 2′ area around each pier requiring 8 lf of construction joint.

Area [4]

This example includes a thickened slab edge or haunch that requires excavation. The quantity estimator should take the thickened edge as 12″ wide and 6″ deep and ignore the slope around the exterior of Area [4]. Realistically speaking, the shape in the drawings is impossible to duplicate exactly in the field. Here, as in Area [3], add 8′ of expansion joint around the column.

When totalling the columns on Quantity Sheet 6, add a waste allowance to concrete, granular base, vapor barrier, and welded wire fabric. The waste allowance for the vapor barrier and the welded wire fabric is due to both cutting and to overlapping of material.

This concludes the discussion of concrete floor slabs on grade. Chapter 7 examines the takeoff procedure for cast-in-place (CIP) concrete walls.

Means® Forms
QUANTITY SHEET

PROJECT Admin. Bldg. | SHEET NO. QS 6
LOCATION Picacho, Ca. | ARCHITECT Bell & Bell | ESTIMATE NO. 1017
TAKE OFF BY PC | EXTENSIONS BY: ETW | DATE March 1989 | CHECKED BY: NS

DESCRIPTION	NO.	DIMENSIONS l	w	t	BASE COURSE	UNIT	GRADE & COMPACT SUB-BASE	UNIT	FINE GRADE	UNIT	EDGE FORMS	UNIT	VAPOR BARRIER	UNIT	CONC.	UNIT	WELDED WIRE FABRIC	UNIT	SCREEDS	UNIT	EXP. JOINTS	UNIT	CONST. JOINTS	UNIT	FINISH & CURE	UNIT	HAUNCH	UNIT
Floor Slabs on Grade																												
Area																												
1		46	44	4"	668		225		225		—		2024		668		2024		202		188	4"	90	4"	2024			
2		54	46	6"	1242		276		276		—		2484		1242		2484		248		208	6"	100	6"	2484			
3		54 124	55 28	4 4	2125		722		722		—		6500		2125		6500		650		429	4"	513	4"	6500			
4		45	56	4"	832		280		280		101		2520		832		2520		252		125	4"	101	4"	2520		101	LF
Total					4867	CF	1503	SY	1503	SY	101	LF	13528	SF	4867	CF	13528		1352	LF	742 208	4" 6"	704 100	4" 6"	13528	SF	101	LF
Convert to CY					180	CY									180	CY												
Waste Allowances																												
Conc. 6%															11	CY												
WWF 8%																	1353											
Base Course 20%					36	CY																						
Membrane 10%													1353															
Joints 10%																					74 21	4" 6"	71 10	4" 6"				
Total					216	CY	1503	SY	1503	SY	101	LF	14881	SF	191	CY	14881	SF	1352	LF	816 229	4" 6"	775 110	4" 6"	13528	SF	101	LF

Figure 6.2

Chapter 7

Concrete Walls Above Grade

Concrete walls above grade, sometimes called *curtain walls,* are non-weight-bearing walls used to enclose a structure. They can be either cast in place or precast. Although our model administrative building, shown in the plans in Appendix A, is designed with concrete block walls and brick veneer, for demonstration purposes this chapter will examine the takeoff procedure for cast-in-place walls. (See Figure 7.1.) Precast walls are examined in Chapter 13.

Takeoff Items

The following items are typically taken off for cast-in-place concrete walls above grade:

- Formwork
- Chamfer strips
- Reinforcing
- Concrete
- Surrounds
- Point and patch
- Rub and grind (for exterior walls)
- Scaffolding (for exterior walls)

CIP concrete walls above grade require all of the items found in CIP foundation walls, plus several more. Formwork needs special attention, since the concrete is often left exposed. Sharp corners or right angles of an exposed concrete wall are prone to chipping and breakage, and require chamfer strips placed inside the forms at the intersection of the forms to bevel the corners. Additionally, special form liners may be specified to obtain the desired architectural effect. These walls also typically contain more inserts and reinforcing steel and therefore require greater care when placing concrete. For these reasons, the CIP concrete walls above grade are taken off and listed separately from the CIP foundation walls.

Takeoff Demonstration

Imagine that the walls above grade in our model administrative building are constructed of CIP concrete instead of masonry. Assume that all exterior walls are 10″ thick and all interior walls are 8″ thick. Refer to the drawings in Appendix A for further information.

For walls above grade, the building elevations and cross-sections are as important as plan drawings. The drawing labeled "Wall Sections" in Appendix A shows cross-sectional views of the building and provides finish floor elevations for each wall section. Cross-sectional views of the building are seen from the north, south, east, and west. The height of the walls can be found by subtracting the bottom elevation from the top elevation. The drawing labeled "Elevations" also shows the location of window and door openings in the walls, although no dimensions are given on these views.

The quantity estimator must be careful when making deductions for wall openings. Small openings under 10 sf (for vents, ducts, and small windows) need not be deducted from the total concrete quantity. Use red pencil to list quantities that are to be deducted, to catch the eye and ensure that these items are actually deducted from the total quantity, and not added. In this book, quantities that are to be deducted will appear in boxes on the quantity sheets. Regardless of whether or not the concrete quantity is deducted, however, all openings should be taken off for forming out.

The Second Floor Plan provides the dimensions of the upper roof area and the Sections drawing shows the details of the parapet used on the roof of the building. This figure also shows a section of the CIP concrete walls when the building is two stories high, as our model administrative building is.

First Floor, Exterior Walls

Our takeoff demonstration of walls above grade begins on the first floor at the northeast corner of the building and proceeds in a clockwise direction around the perimeter of the structure.

Line 3D-3B

The first segment to be taken off is Line 3D-3B, the East Elevation.

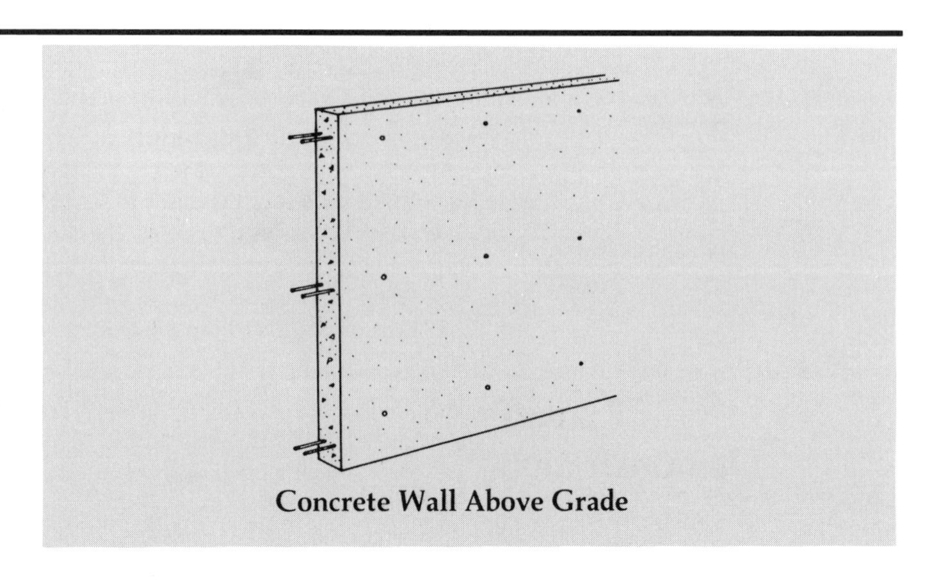

Concrete Wall Above Grade

Figure 7.1

Step 1: The East Elevation shows three door openings. Find the area of each opening (l × w) and transfer these quantities to Quantity Sheet 7 (Figure 7.2, located at the end of this chapter). Remember to place these quantities in boxes, since they represent deductions from the total concrete quantity. Do not deduct form area, as the forms go straight through with the openings "boxed out" inside the forms with the surrounds.

Step 2: Next, take off the jambs and headers (called *surrounds*) for the two large door openings by adding together 2 × height + width of each doorway. The quantity is expressed in linear feet. Chamfer strips are usually installed on the inside and outside of surrounds. Therefore, double the length of surrounds to get the quantity of chamfer. Chamfer strips are also sometimes called for on the outside vertical corner of CIP concrete walls. A strip 12′ in length would be added here.

Step 3: To calculate the quantity of formwork, multiply the length of the wall by its height × 2 (sides). The formula is:

length × width × 2 = sf of forms

Formwork should be rounded to the next whole foot.

Step 4: If called for in the specifications, the outside of this wall must receive a rub and grind finish, in addition to the basic point and patch. Find the total area of this work item by multiplying the length of the wall × its width.

We can assume that both the interior and exterior faces of all walls will receive point and patch, but at this point in the takeoff, the quantity estimator cannot be sure of the extent of the rub and grind that this wall will require. Therefore, reserve a column on Quantity Sheet 7 for that work item to be calculated in the future.

Step 5: Scaffolding will be required to erect, place, and finish concrete in walls that are 8′ or higher. The quantity of scaffolding will equal the length of the exterior face of the wall times the height of the scaffolding required. Standard tubular scaffold frames come in 5′ heights and 7′–6″ heights. Use the 7′–6″ height for this wall.

Line B3-B4

The next exterior wall segment to take off is a short section extending from B3-B4. Record these dimensions on Quantity Sheet 7. Use these dimensions to calculate the quantities of each takeoff item.

Line 4B-4A

Again, this section is shown on the East Elevation. A deduction must be made for two large windows. Do not deduct material at the corners. Use the outside length dimensions given on the drawings and do not deduct for the wall thickness, allowing the extra material in the corners to contribute toward waste.

Line A1-A4

The wall along Line A1-A4, the South Elevation, should be taken off in the same manner.

Lines 1A-1C, C1-D1, and D1-D2

The wall along Line 1A-1C is shown on the West Elevation. Line C1-D1 and D1-D2 have spandrel beams for an open, covered patio. The takeoff of these is covered in Chapter 9.

Lines C1-C2, C2-D2, and D2-D3

C1-C2 is 56′ long with two openings. C2-D2 is 45′ long with two doors. Record the dimensions and calculate the applicable quantities for each of these wall sections on Quantity Sheet 7. To close the exterior walls on the first floor, we have the 48′ section of wall from D2-D3. Record these dimensions and the calculations on the quantity sheet.

This completes the takeoff procedure for the exterior walls of the first floor. Next, take off the interior walls of this floor.

First Floor, Interior Walls

The interior walls of the first floor of our model administrative building are represented in the First Floor Plan as lines C2-C3, B2-B3, and 2B-2C. Since all interior walls are 8″ thick, they may be taken off as one line item instead of three separate items. Follow the procedure outlined above for the exterior walls.

First, list the dimensions on the quantity sheet, then calculate the forms, concrete, surrounds, and so forth. Again, record deductions, scaffolding, and, depending on finish, rub and grind.

Second Floor

The takeoff procedure for the second floor walls is the same as the first floor. Begin in the northeast corner of the building. Moving around the perimeter of the building in a clockwise direction, we can see that all the walls are the same thickness and height, including the interior wall.

We can also simplify the takeoff of scaffolding on the second floor by making one line item for the entire perimeter of this floor to the height required to construct the parapet.

Total all the columns on Quantity Sheet 7. Concrete and chamfer are the only quantities that require a waste allowance. These amounts can be found in Appendix C.

This concludes the discussion of quantity takeoff for cast-in-place concrete walls above grade. Chapter 8 examines the takeoff procedure for concrete columns.

Means® Forms
QUANTITY SHEET

PROJECT Admin Bldg.
LOCATION Picacho, Ca.
TAKE OFF BY PC
ARCHITECT Bell & Bell
EXTENSIONS BY ETW
SHEET NO. QS 7
ESTIMATE NO. 1017
DATE March 1989
CHECKED BY: NS

DESCRIPTION	NO.	DIMENSIONS l	w	h	FORM l×h×2	CONC. l×w×h	SURROUNDS	CHAMFER	P&P	R&G	SCAFFOLD
Conc. walls above grade											
First Floor (to 106.83)											
Col. Line D3 To B3		100	0.83	12.0	2400 SFCA	996 CF			2400 SF	1200 SF	750 SF
Overhead doors	2	10	0.83	9		149 CF	56 LF	112 LF	360	180	
Door 5	1	3	0.83	7		17 CF	17 LF	34 LF	42	21	
B3 to B4		22	0.83	11.33	499	207			499	249	165
Door 4	1	3.5	0.83	7		20	18	35	49	24	
B4 to A4		30	0.83	11.33	680	299			680	340	225
Window I	2	9	0.83	5.0		75	56	112	90	45	
A4 to A1		16	0.83	10.67	342	142			1982	991	945
		68.67	0.83	10.0	1374	569					
		41.33	0.83	9.33	772	320					
Window D	2	10	0.83	3		50	52	104	120	60	
Window C	1	5	0.83	3		12	16	32	30	15	
Window B	2	6	0.83	3		30	36	72	72	36	
A1 to C1		22	0.83	7.33	322	134			1552	776	638
		24.33	0.83	8.66	421	175					
		25.33	0.83	10.0	507	210					
		13.33	0.83	11.33	302	125					
Window B	2	6	0.83	3		30	36	72	72	36	
Window E	2	6	0.83	4		40	40	80	96	48	
C1 to C2		56	0.83	11.33	1269	527			1269	634	420
Window H	1	8	0.83	5		33	26	52	80	40	
Door 3	1	6.33	0.83	7		37	21	40	84	42	
C2 to D2		45	0.83	11.33	1020	423			1020	510	338
Doors 1 & 2	2	3.83	0.83	7		45	36	70	98	48	
D2 to D3		48	0.83	11.33	1088	451			1088	544	360
Window H	1	8	0.83	5		33	26	52	80	40	

Figure 7.2

Means® Forms
QUANTITY SHEET

PROJECT Admin. Bldg. SHEET NO. QS7 (con't)
ESTIMATE NO. 1017
LOCATION Picacho, Ca. ARCHITECT Bell & Bell DATE March 1989
TAKE OFF BY PC EXTENSIONS BY: ETW CHECKED BY: NS

DESCRIPTION	NO.	DIMENSIONS l	w	h	FORM l×h×2	UNIT	CONC. l×h×2	UNIT	SURROUNDS	UNIT	CHAMFER	UNIT	P&P	UNIT	R&G	UNIT	SCAFFOLD	UNIT
Interior Wall		151	0.67	12.66	3823		1281						3823				1132	
doors 6 & 7	2	3	0.67	7			29		34		68		84					
pass thru window	1	4	0.67	3			8		14		28		24					
Second Floor		296	0.83	10.67	6316		2621						6316		3158		2580	
		48	0.67	8.67	832		279						832					
window G	4	4	0.83	5			66		72		144		160					
window F	1	8	0.83	4			27		24		48		64					
door 9	1	3.5	0.83	7			20		21		42		49					
window A	4	4	0.83	3			40		56		112		96					
window H	1	8	0.83	5			32		40		80		80					
door 10	1	3	0.67	7			14		17		34		42					
door 12 & 13	2	2.5	0.67	7			23		33		66		70					
Total (both sheets)					21461	SFCA	7733	CF	746	LF	1489	LF	19519	SF	7767	SF	7553	SF
Convert to CY							286											
Waste allowances																		
Conc. 5%							14											
Forms 5%					1073				37									
Chamfer 10%											149							
Total					22534	SFCA	300	CY	783	LF	1638	LF	19519	SF	7767	SF	7553	SF

Figure 7.2 (continued)

Chapter 8
Concrete Columns

Columns are used to transmit floor and roof loads to the foundation of a structure. A variety of column shapes are found in construction, depending on architectural objectives and structural requirements. The most common are round, square, and rectangular. Figure 8.1 is a typical example of a square cast-in-place concrete column.

Takeoff Items

The following items are typically taken off for cast-in-place concrete columns:

- Formwork
- Chamfer strips
- Reinforcement
- Concrete
- Finish

CIP concrete columns lend themselves to prefabricated forms because of their uniformity in size. Prefabricated square or rectangular forms are commonly made of wood and can be adjusted in 2″ increments. Round forms are often made of aluminum and fiberglass and come in standard sizes. With proper care, prefabricated column forms can be used over again. The quantity estimator need only be concerned with the total length of the forms; the cost estimator will determine how many columns will be formed at one time to estimate the total quantity of forms required for the job.

For consistency, the designer generally uses the same size column throughout a structure, compensating for differences in load bearing requirements by using different sizes and configurations of reinforcing steel.

Takeoff Demonstration

According to the plans in Appendix A, our model administrative building has steel columns. Assume, however, that our building has been designed with cast-in-place concrete columns instead. Figure 8.2 is the Column Plan of the first floor, showing the location of each of two sizes of columns in our model administrative building. The Wall Sections plan in Appendix A gives a cross-sectional view of the building and provides the needed elevations. As the takeoff proceeds, transfer all quantities to Quantity Sheet 8 (Figure 8.4), located at the end of this chapter.

Square Columns

The following is a discussion of the takeoff procedure for square columns. Keep in mind that rectangular columns can be taken off the same way.

Type I

In Figure 8.2, we see that Type I columns are 10″ square. In Chapter 7, "Concrete Walls Above Grade," wall heights are taken from finish floor elevation to the underside of suspended slabs above. Column heights, however, should be taken from the top of the footing or pier to the underside of beams, as shown in Figure 8.3.

Assume that the roof beam is 12″ deep. The column height is:

Top of roof elevation:	106.83′
Less roof (5″ roof slab):	0.42′
Less roof beam depth:	1.00′
Less elevation at top of spread footing:	94.17′
Height of column =	11.24′

Transfer these values to the quantity sheet.

Using this information, calculate the quantity of formwork, chamfer strips, reinforcing, concrete, and finish. The formulas are provided below.

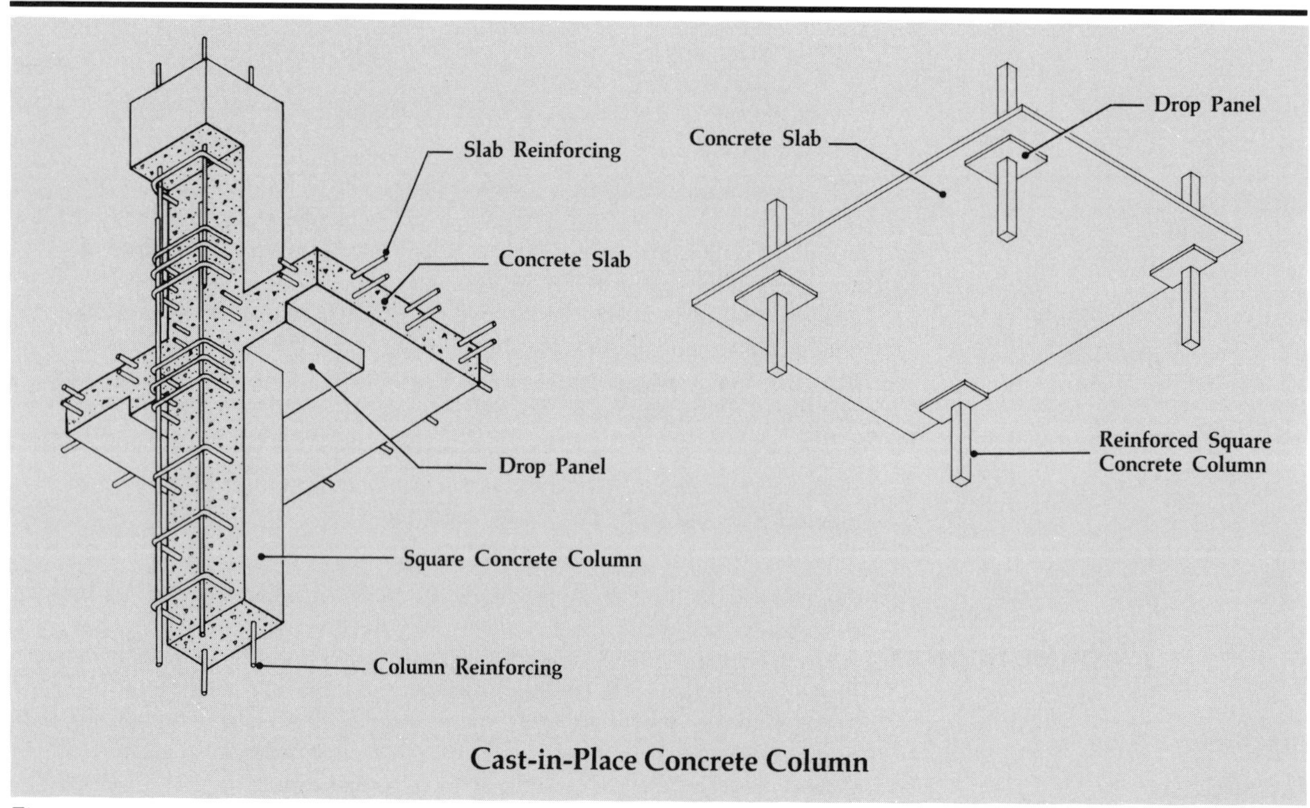

Cast-in-Place Concrete Column

Figure 8.1

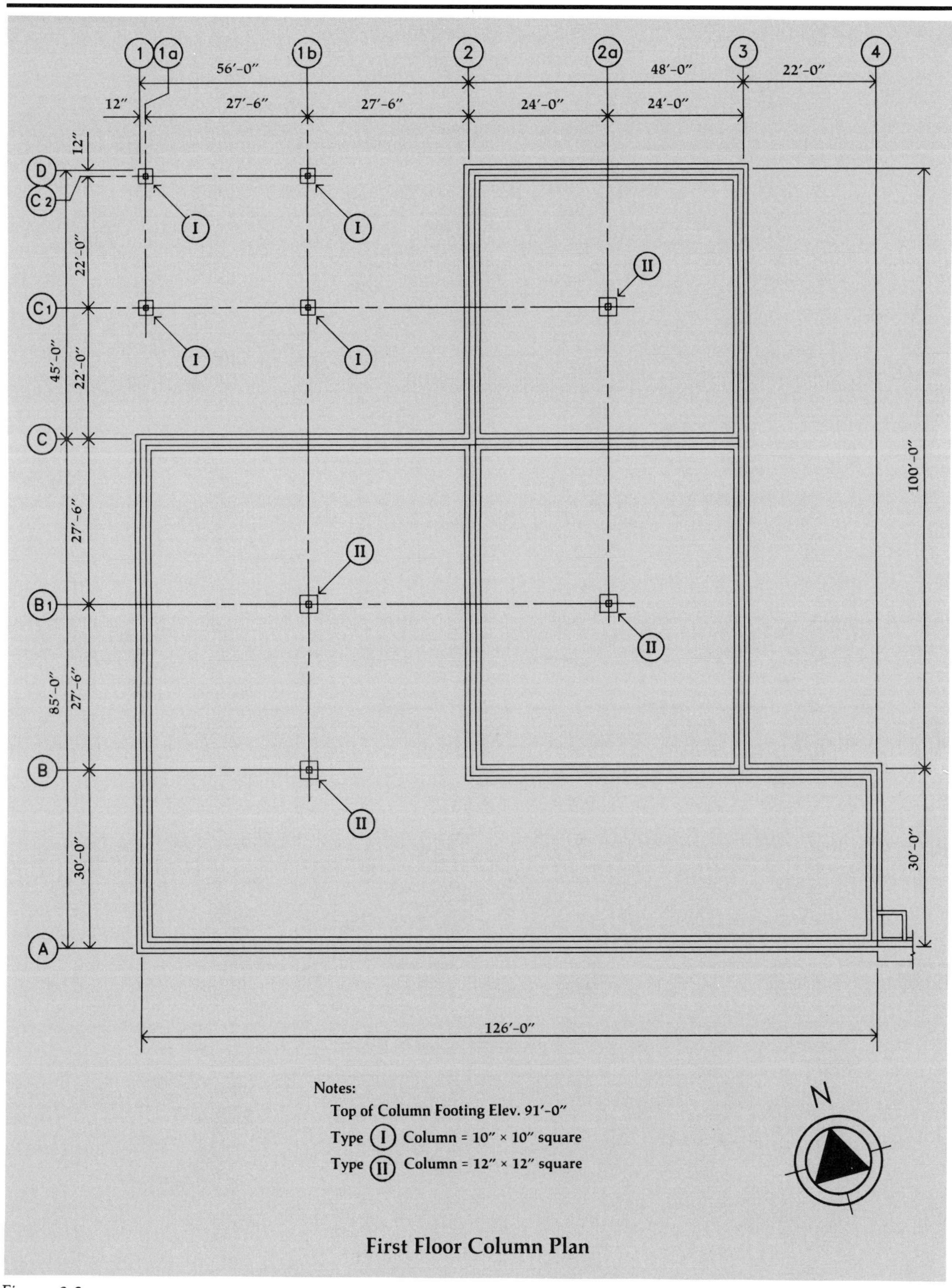

1
1a
1b
2
2a
3
4
56'-0"
48'-0"
22'-0"
12"
27'-6"
27'-6"
24'-0"
24'-0"
12"
D
C2
C1
C
B1
B
A
22'-0"
22'-0"
45'-0"
27'-6"
27'-6"
85'-0"
30'-0"
100'-0"
30'-0"
126'-0"
I
II
Notes:
Top of Column Footing Elev. 91'-0"
Type (I) Column = 10" × 10" square
Type (II) Column = 12" × 12" square
N
First Floor Column Plan

Figure 8.2

Formwork: column perimeter × height (round to next whole foot)
Chamfer strips: 4 (corners) × height
Reinforcing (longitudinal): number of bars × height
(horizontal): number of ties × perimeter
Concrete: cross-sectional area × height
Finish: same as form area

Type II

Type II columns are 12″ square. The beam depth in this area of the building is 16″. Since we did not provide piers for these columns, their height will be measured from the top of the spread footing. This is demonstrated below.

Top of roof elevation:	106.83′
Less roof slab thickness:	0.42′
Less beam depth:	1.33′
Less finish of top of spread footing:	94.17′
Height of column =	10.91′

Use these dimensions to calculate the quantity of formwork, chamfer strips, reinforcing, concrete, and finish.

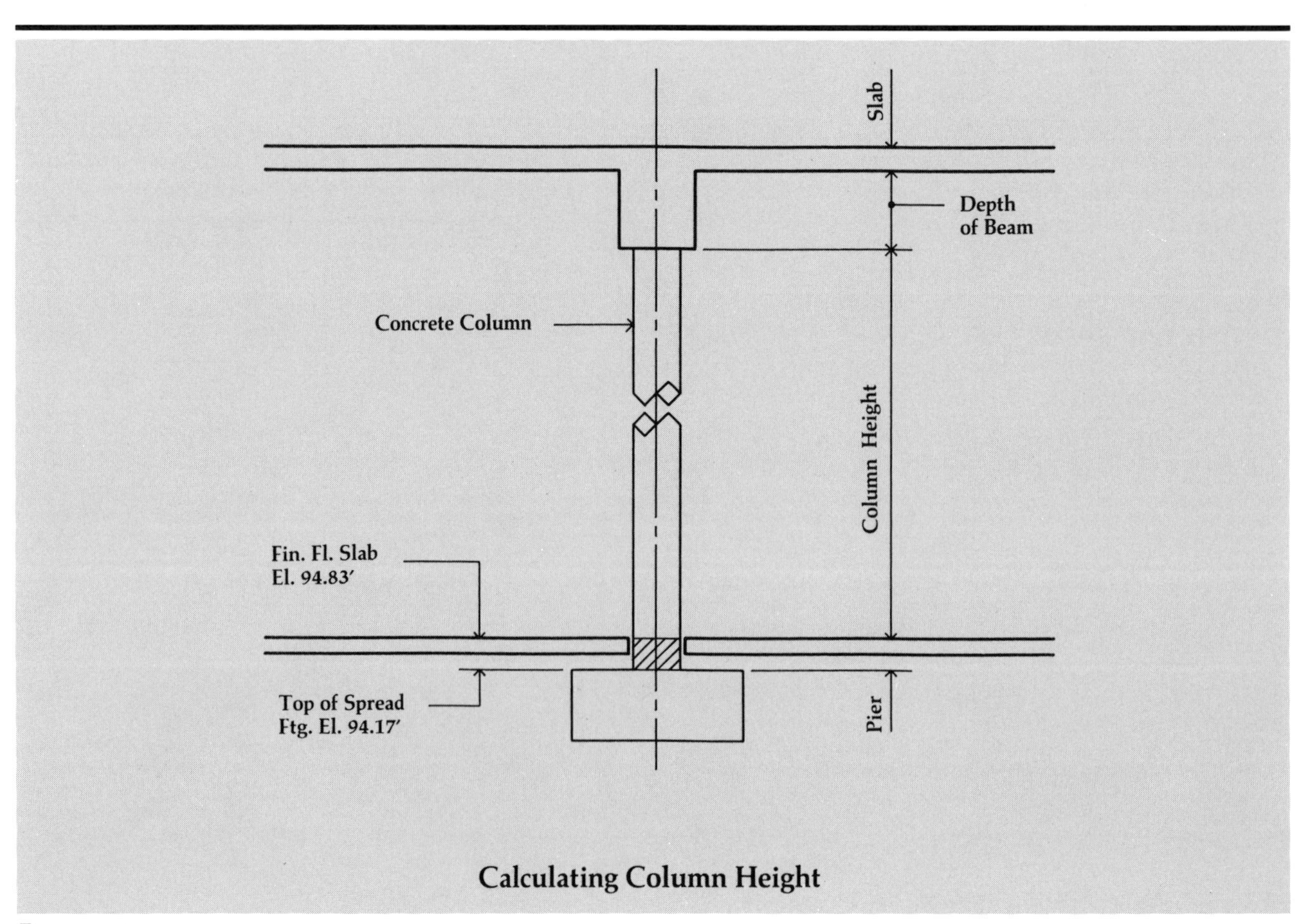

Figure 8.3

Round Columns

If these columns were round instead, with diameters equal to the sides of the square columns, they would require no chamfer strips and the forms would be circular. Circular forms are usually not job-built; they are manufactured. Therefore, they are taken off in linear feet in stock diameters and lengths. Investigation reveals that our 10" and 12" diameters are available in stock round forms, but the nearest stock length is 12', which we provide for in waste allowance.

Use the following formulas to find the quantity of each takeoff item.

> **Formwork:** column circumference × height (round to next whole foot)
> **Reinforcing (longitudinal):** number of bars × height
> **(horizontal):** number of ties × circumference
> **Concrete:** cross-sectional area × height
> **Finish:** same as form area

At the end of the takeoff, total the columns on the quantity sheet, and convert units of concrete from cubic feet to cubic yards. Convert reinforcing steel to pounds using the conversion table in Chapter 12. Add waste percentages to concrete (5%), chamfer strips (for square columns only: 10%), and reinforcing steel (10%). Add these quantities to the totals. Finally, if there is any information that the cost estimator should have regarding this structural component, the quantity estimator can simply write a note on the quantity sheet, such as "3500 psi concrete for all columns."

This concludes the discussion of CIP concrete columns. Chapter 9 examines the takeoff procedure for concrete beams.

Means Forms

QUANTITY SHEET

PROJECT Admin. Bldg. | SHEET NO. QS 8

ESTIMATE NO. 1017

LOCATION Picacho, Ca. | ARCHITECT Bell & Bell | DATE March 1989

TAKE OFF BY PC | EXTENSIONS BY: ETW | CHECKED BY: NS

DESCRIPTION	NO.	DIMENSIONS l	w	h	FORMS	UNIT	CONC.	UNIT	CHAMFER	UNIT	FINISH	UNIT	REINF #9	UNIT	REINF #4	UNIT
Concrete Columns																
Type I	4	10"	10"	11.24	150	SFCA	31	CF	180	LF	150	SF	168	LF	112	LF
Type II	4	12"	12"	10.91	175	SFCA	41	CF	175	LF	175	SF	156	LF	132	LF
Total					325	SFCA	72	CF	355	LF	325	SF	324	LF	244	LF
Convert to CY							3	CY								
Convert Reinf. to Lbs.																
#4 0.668															163	Lbs
#9 3.4													1102	Lbs.		
Waste Allowances																
Conc. 15%							—									
Reinf. 20%													220	Lbs.	33	Lbs.
Forms 5%					16											
Chamfer 10%									35							
Total					341	SFCA	3	CY	390	LF	325	SF	1322	Lbs.	196	Lbs.

Note: All concrete to be 3500 PSI

Figure 8.4

Chapter 9

Concrete Beams

Concrete Beams

A concrete beam is a structural member used to transfer loads to columns. There are several types of cast-in-place concrete beams commonly used in building construction: a beam constructed *integrally* with a floor slab, *independent beams*, *spandrel (exterior) beams*, and *bond beams*. These are illustrated in Figure 9.1.

Takeoff Items

The items typically taken off for CIP concrete beams are:

- Formwork
- Shoring
- Reinforcing
- Chamfer strips
- Concrete
- Point and patch
- Rub and grind

Integral, independent, and spandrel beams require soffit (bottom) forms and shoring to support them from below until the hardening concrete becomes self-supportive. The cost of soffit forms is considerably greater than the cost of side forms, and should be taken off separately in square feet of concrete contact area. Beam shoring is usually done with adjustable jacks and posts or timber. Shoring is taken off by the linear foot. Figure 9.2 shows beam formwork using timber shoring.

Guidelines for Takeoff

Below are some guidelines to assist the quantity estimator in taking off CIP concrete beams.

- Take off interior beams and spandrel (exterior) beams separately.
- CIP concrete beams and slabs are often placed simultaneously. Often, the beam depths given in beam schedules are "design depths," (the depth of the beam plus the concrete slab). When calculating the surface area and volume for interior beams, deduct the slab thickness. By keeping the concrete volume for the beams and slabs separate, the combined beam and slab placement cost can be figured for each floor.

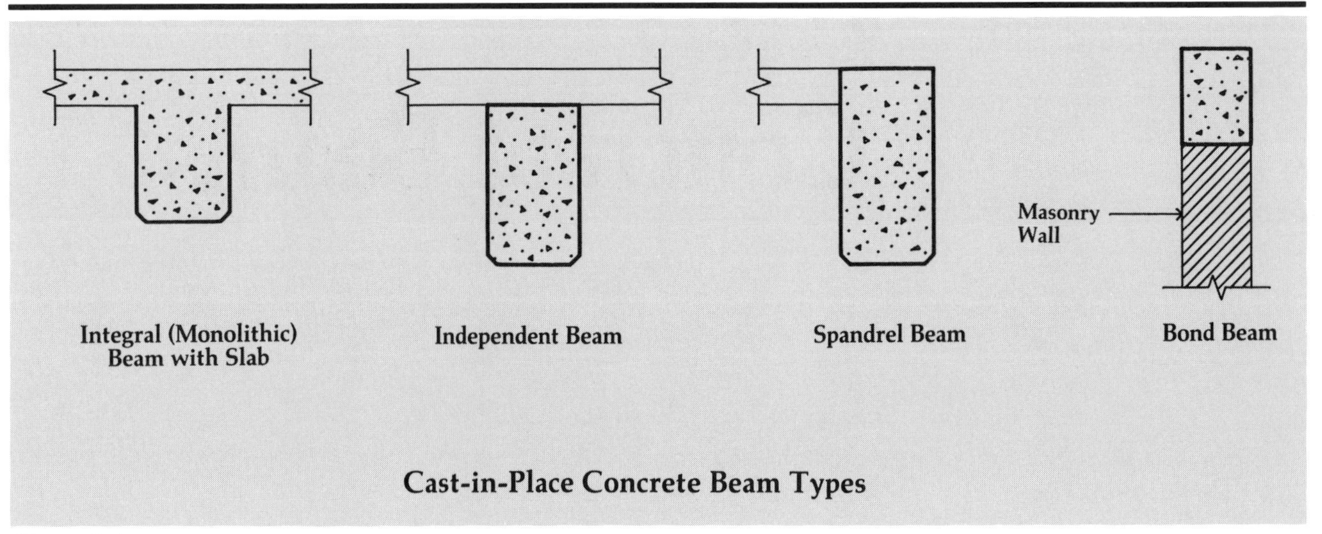

Cast-in-Place Concrete Beam Types

Figure 9.1

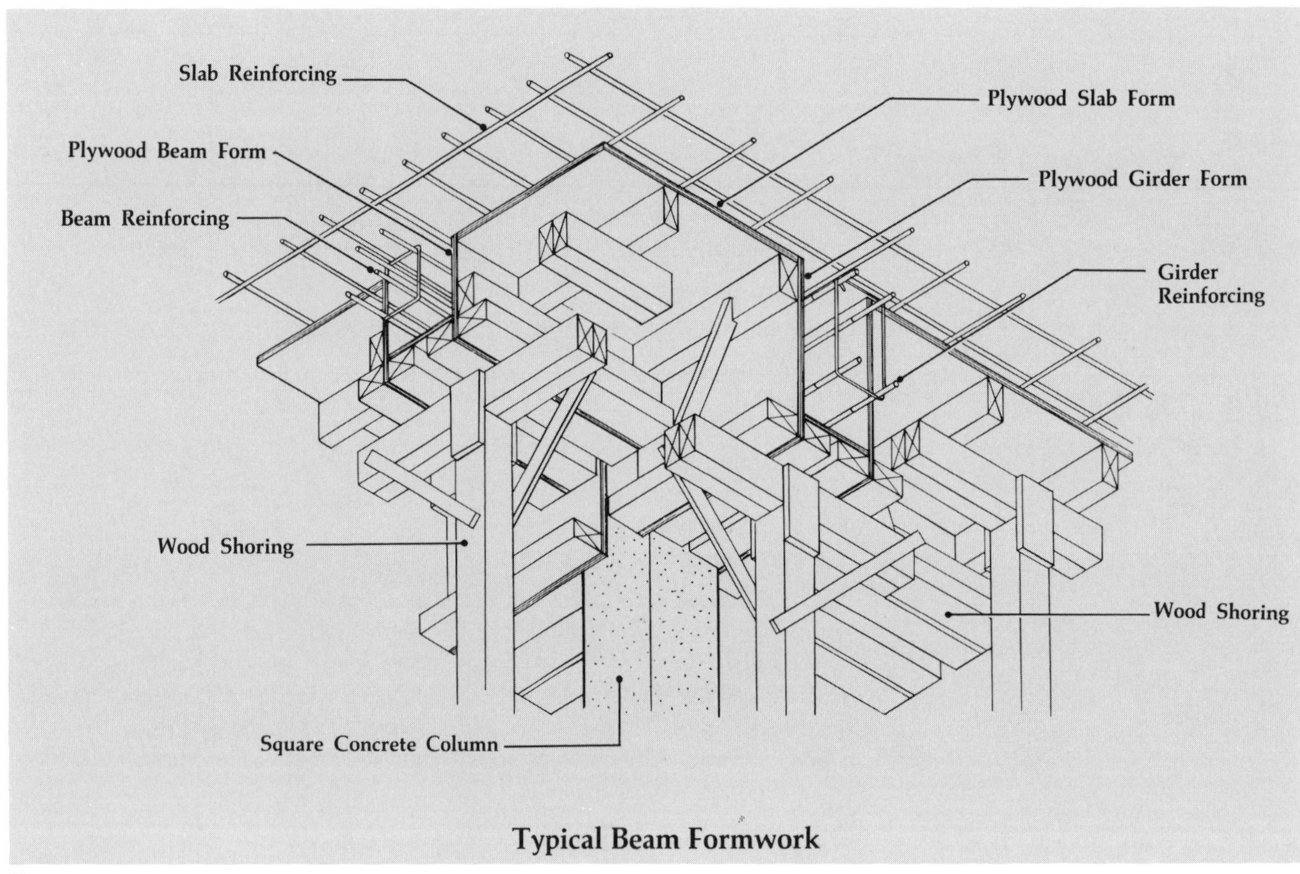

Typical Beam Formwork

Figure 9.2

- Recall that column height is figured to the underside of beams. As such, both forming and volume computations go straight through columns.
- Reinforcing steel for beams is shown either in the beam schedule on the plans or in a special reinforcing schedule. The quantity estimator lists reinforcing by size and linear foot, and converts lengths to pounds.
- When calculating concrete volume, do not deduct for columns and wall thicknesses.
- Chamfer strips are *not* used at the tops of beams.
- All formed surfaces will receive point and patch.
- Rub and grind is figured for all exposed surfaces, such as the sides and bottoms of spandrel beams, bond beams, and exposed interior beams.

Takeoff Demonstration

Although our model building does not have CIP concrete beams, in order to illustrate the takeoff procedure for this type of beam, imagine that there are a number of concrete beams running between column lines 1 and 2. These beams will be taken off and their quantities input onto Quantity Sheet 9, Figure 9.3.

Step 1: Spandrel Beams

Shoring length: D1-D2 (56′) + A1-D1 (130′) = 186 lf
Formwork (beam bottoms): l × w = 186′ × 1.33′ = 247 sfca
(side forms): l × h (outside) = 186′ × 4′ = 744 sfca
l × h (inside) = 186′ × 3.58′ = 666 sfca
Reinforcing: l × 3 (# 9) = 186′ × 3 = 558 lf (of # 9)
l × 3 (# 8) = 186′ × 3 = 558 lf (of # 8)
Chamfer strips: l × 2 = 186′ × 2 = 372 lf
Concrete: l × w × h = 186′ × 1.33′ × 3.58′ = 886 cf
Point and patch: total form area = 1,657 sf
Rub and grind: total form area = 1,657 sf

Step 2: Interior Beams (each)

Shoring length: 56 lf
Formwork (beam bottoms): l × w = 56′ × 0.67′ = 38 sfca
(side forms): l × h × 2 = 56′ × 1′ × 2 = 112 sfca
Reinforcing: l × 3 (# 7) = 56′ × 3 = 168 lf (of # 7)
l × 2 (# 6) = 56′ × 2 = 112 lf (of # 6)
Stirrups (# 3) = 57 ea × 5′ = 285 lf
Chamfer strips: l × 2 = 56′ × 2 = 112 lf
Concrete: l × w × h = 56′ × 0.67′ × 1′ = 38 cf
Point and patch: 150 sf
Rub and grind: 150 sf

Step 3: Total the Columns

Total the quantities in each column. Convert concrete volume to cubic yards; convert reinforcing steel quantity to pounds. Add a waste allowance to the concrete, chamfer, and reinforcing quantities.

Parapets

Parapets are a special type of beam that projects above the outside edge of a roof slab to act as a railing and a containment for roof covering and storm water. Unlike beams, however, parapets are not load bearing structural members.

Takeoff Items

The items typically taken off for CIP concrete parapets are:

- Forms
- Reinforcing
- Chamfer strips
- Concrete
- Point and patch
- Rub and grind

Parapets require side forms but not bottom forms, since they are built on top of the wall forms. The quantity of formwork is found by multiplying length × width × 2. Reinforcing steel is taken off in linear feet and converted to pounds. The total volume of concrete is found by multiplying length × width × depth. All formed surfaces will receive point and patch, and rub and grind will be done only to the outside faces of the parapets.

This completes the discussion of concrete beams and parapets. Chapter 10 examines the takeoff procedure for concrete elevated slabs.

Means Forms
QUANTITY SHEET

PROJECT Admin. Bldg.
LOCATION Picacho, Ca.
TAKE OFF BY PC
ARCHITECT Bell & Bell
EXTENSIONS BY ETW
SHEET NO. QS 9
ESTIMATE NO. 1017
DATE March 1989
CHECKED BY NS

DESCRIPTION	NO	DIMENSIONS l	w	h	SHORING	UNIT	BOTTOM FORM	UNIT	SIDE FORM	UNIT	CONC.	UNIT	TIES #5	UNIT	REINF. #6	UNIT	#7	UNIT	#8	UNIT	#9	UNIT	CHAMFER	UNIT	P&P	UNIT	R&G	UNIT
Conc. Beams																												
Exterior beams																												
Col. line D1-D2		56'	1.33	4.0	56	LF	75	SFCA	224		266	CF	570	LF	112	LF	168	LF					112	LF	499	SF	499	SF
				3.58					200																			
A1-D1		130	1.33	4.0	130	LF	173	SFCA	520		619	CF	1310						558	LF	558	LF	260	LF	1158	SF	1158	SF
				3.58					465																			
Interior Beams (each)		56'	0.67	1.0	56	LF	38	SFCA	112	SFCA	38	CF	285										112	LF	150	SF	150	SF
Total					242	LF	286	SFCA	1521	SFCA	923	CF	2165	LF	112	LF	168	LF	558	LF	558	LF	484	LF	1807	SF	1807	SF
Convert To CY											34	CY																
Convert LF Reinf. to LBS													2258	LBS	168	LBS	343	LBS	1490	LBS	1897	LBS						
Waste Allowances																												
Conc. 10%											3	CY																
Reinf. 20%													452		34		69		298		379							
Forms 5%							14		76																			
Chamfer 10%																							48					
Total					242	LF	300	SFCA	1597	SFCA	37	CY	2710	LBS	202	LBS	412	LBS	1788	LBS	2276	LBS	532	LF	1807	SF	1807	SF

Figure 9.3

Chapter 10

Concrete Elevated Slabs

Concrete elevated slabs are supported by columns, beams, and/or load bearing walls. There are many different types of elevated slabs. Their use depends on architectural objectives and the structural requirements (load conditions) of the building.

This chapter examines the following types of concrete elevated slabs:

- Suspended plain slabs
- Joist and pan (J&P) and waffle slabs
- Concrete topping and fill slabs

Suspended Plain Slabs

Suspended plain slabs are cast in place on slab forms or decking supported either by concrete or steel beams and joists. This is the most common type of concrete elevated slab. See Figure 10.1.

Takeoff Items

The items typically taken off for a suspended plain slab are:

- Shoring
- Slab forms
- Edge forms
- Construction joints
- Screeds
- Reinforcing
- Concrete
- Finish and cure

These items are discussed below.

Shoring

Shoring supports slab formwork from the floor below. The quantity estimator should list the total square feet and height of shoring required for each floor. The cost estimator will determine the total number of shores and support lumber required.

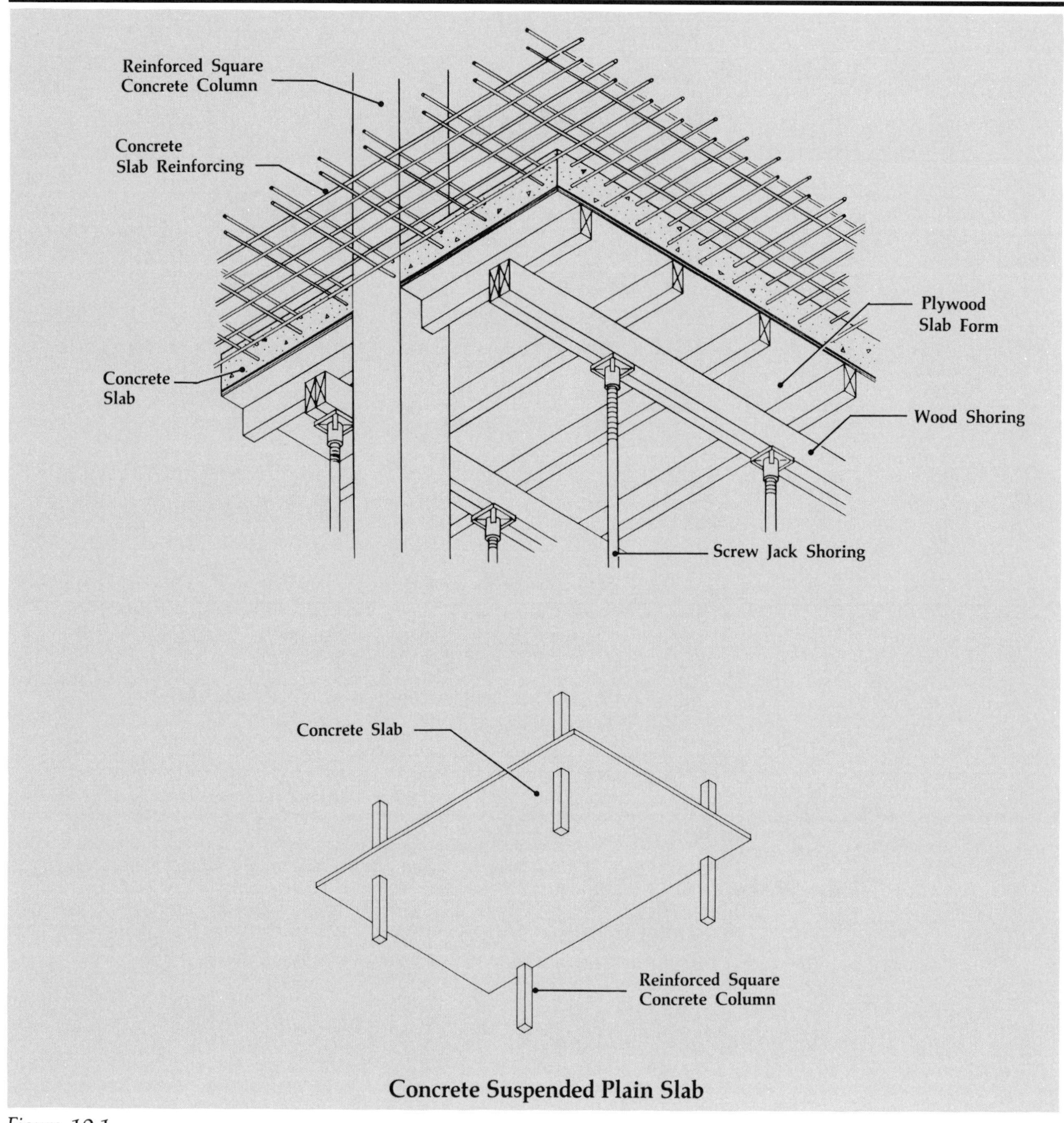

Concrete Suspended Plain Slab

Figure 10.1

Formwork

The quantity estimator should list the total area of slab forms by type for each floor. Form area is figured straight across beams and supporting walls and is therefore the same quantity as the finish area. Edge forms should be listed by linear foot for each height of form. Pay particular attention to edge forms around openings and columns. These can also contribute a significant "out" to the concrete volume and finish area.

Construction Joints

Construction joints are formed divisions between poured sections of slabs. They should be listed by the linear foot.

Screeds

Screeds may or may not be listed by the quantity estimator, depending on the cost estimator's preference. A good rule of thumb is 1 lf per 10 sf of floor.

Reinforcing

Reinforcing in concrete slabs is usually made of welded wire fabric. This quantity should be the same as the area of the slab.

Concrete

To estimate the volume of concrete in a suspended plain slab, use the same basic dimensions used to estimate slabs on grade:

length × width × thickness

Concrete should be calculated by the cubic foot for each floor and converted to cubic yards.

When calculating concrete quantities for concrete slabs on steel decking, the quantity estimator should use the full dimension of thickness from the bottom of the decking to the finished floor elevation. This will allow for the inevitable sag, or deflection, in the decking which occurs after the concrete is placed.

Finish and Cure

Finish and cure should be listed in square feet by type for each floor. Winter protection must also be considered by the cost estimator when applicable.

Takeoff Demonstration

This section demonstrates the takeoff procedure for concrete suspended plain slabs. The Second Floor Plan in Appendix A shows the dimensions of the floor slab. The Sections drawing shows the detailed cross-section of the edges of the floor slab at the wall joints. As items are taken off, transfer quantities to Quantity Sheet 10 (Figure 10.4), located at the end of this chapter. Be sure to color or shade each area after it is taken off.

The quantity calculations for each item are listed below.

Shoring: 100′ × 48′ = 4,800 sf (12.42′ high)
Slab forms: 4,800 sf
Edge forms: Edge forms are required around the perimeter of each section plus the opening at the stairs. The quantity is:

Length = 46′ + 46′ + 44′ + 44′ + 46′ + 46′ + 54′ + 54′ + 57′
= 437 lf

Construction joints: 46′ + 46′ + 44′ + 54′ = 190 lf
Screeds: 480 lf
Reinforcing: 4,800 sf
Concrete: Area × thickness = 4,800 sf × 0.31′ = 1,488 cf
Finish and cure: Area = 4,800 sf

Joist and Pan (J&P) and Waffle Slabs

An architect or engineer might design, as an alternative to the suspended plain slab, a type of elevated structural slab call a *joist and pan slab*. Joist and pan slabs are named for the prefabricated metal forms that resemble pans when turned upside down. When concrete is poured over them, *joists*, or horizontal support members, are formed between the pans. Members running perpendicular to the joists are called *bridging*. The pans are laid on top of shored formwork. Figure 10.2 shows the joist and pan system.

A variation of the joist and pan slab is the *waffle slab*. A waffle slab is a reinforced concrete slab with equally spaced ribs parallel to the sides, having a waffle-like appearance from below. Waffle slabs are usually deeper and more nearly square

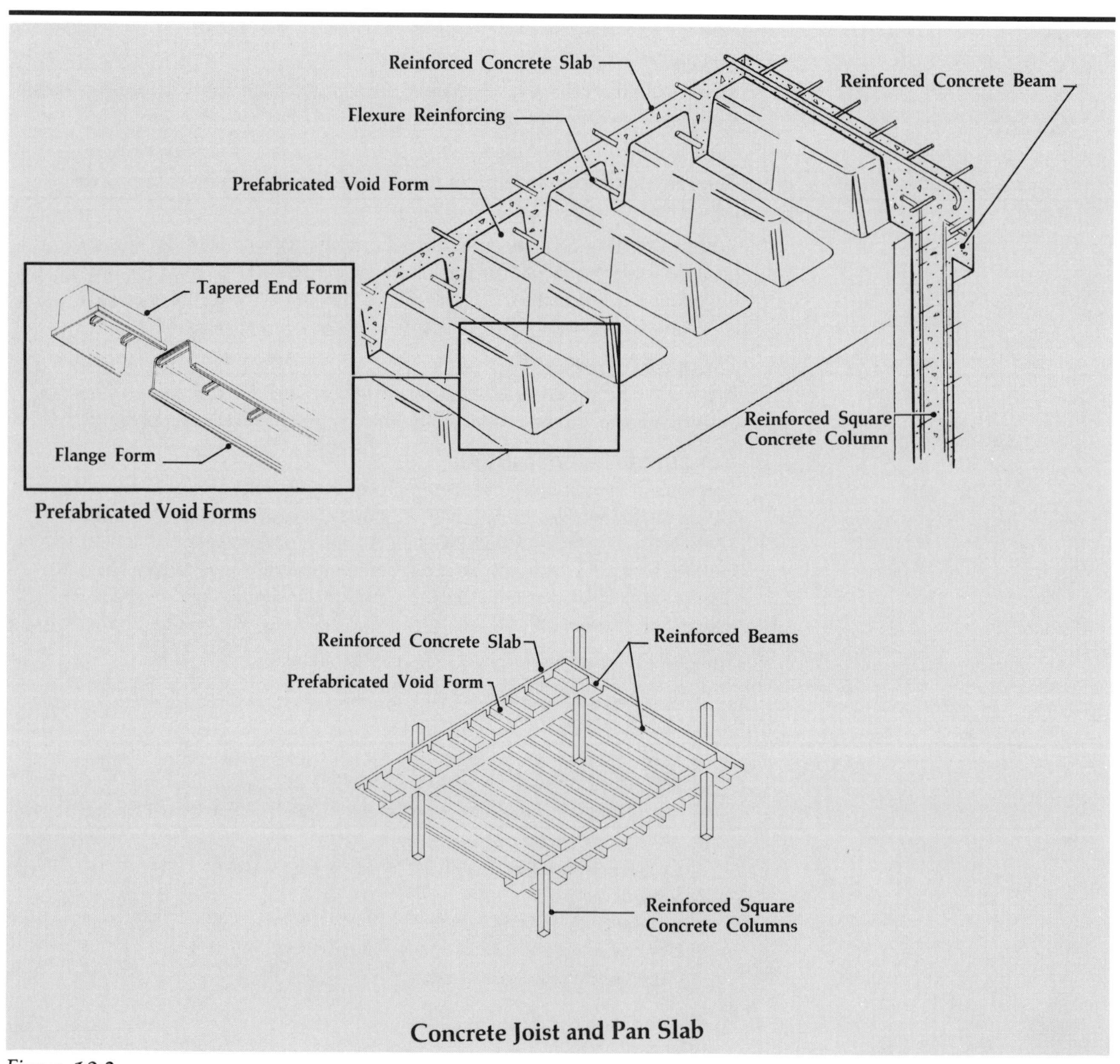

Figure 10.2

than the joist and pan slabs, and are often used for their architectural appearance, such as on an exposed ceiling. Figure 10.3 is an example of a waffle slab.

Takeoff Items

The items typically taken off for joist and pan slabs and waffle slabs are:

- Shoring
- Formwork
- Metal or fiberglass pans (for joist and pan slabs)
- Waffle forms (for waffle slabs)
- Reinforcing steel
- Screeds
- Concrete
- Finish and cure
- Point and patch (for underside of waffle slabs)
- Rub and grind (for underside of waffle slabs)

Each of these items is taken off in exactly the same way and expressed in the same units as the items taken off for suspended plain slabs. The only difference is that the underside of a waffle is typically exposed and will need cosmetic attention.

The quantity estimator lists the area of the floor to be shored and formed. The cost estimator must determine whether the domes or pans will be supported by open plank strips, or by sheeting or decking. The cost estimator will also determine how many square feet of slab will be formed at one time. The quantity estimator must then define the system and calculate the quantities.

When calculating the quantity of concrete in a system using domes or pans, figure the full depth of the slab (pan plus cover) and deduct the voids. The manufacturer provides a schedule of volumes for the voids of the various sizes of domes or pans.

Concrete Topping and Fill Slabs

Topping slabs and fill slabs are relatively thin, nonstructural slabs used for a variety of purposes including floor slabs on wood decking, the finish course on a base slab (with or without color), fill on metal stair treads, lightweight fill on a roof, fill on precast floor slabs, and topping on precast tees. Topping is a wearing surface, and concrete fill is used for leveling, insulation, and soundproofing.

Takeoff Items

The items typically taken off for topping and fill slabs are:

- Preparation of the subdeck to receive the concrete
- Edge forms (topping on precast tees)
- Concrete
- Screeds
- Finish and cure

The quantity estimator should be aware that deck preparation for precast tees is more costly than for concrete slabs because of the caulking required in the joints between tees.

Concrete volume is found by multiplying the Area × the average depth. The quantity estimator need not be concerned with concrete characteristics (such as strength, size aggregates, admixture, and so forth). His or her primary concern is finding the total quantity of concrete. Others usually determine the quality, material specifications, construction methods, reuses of materials, hoisting, placing, and cost of concrete. Still, some general contractors may instruct their quantity estimators to make a notation on the quantity sheet of the different concrete types.

Finally, the quantity estimator should list the total square feet of finishing and curing for each area of concrete topping or fill.

This concludes the discussion of concrete elevated slabs. Chapter 11 examines the takeoff procedure for concrete suspended stairs.

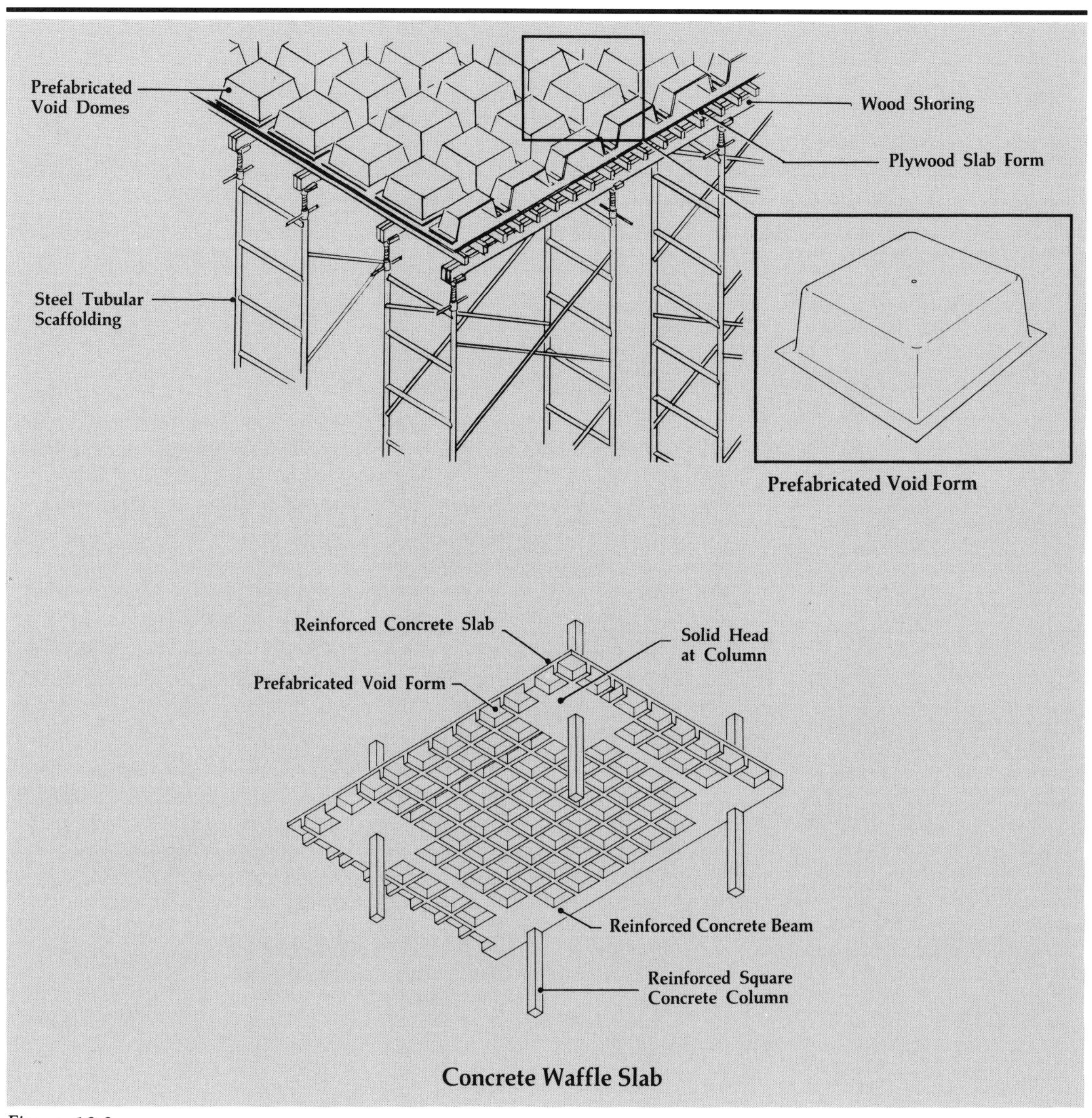
Prefabricated Void Domes
Wood Shoring
Plywood Slab Form
Steel Tubular Scaffolding
Prefabricated Void Form
Reinforced Concrete Slab
Solid Head at Column
Prefabricated Void Form
Reinforced Concrete Beam
Reinforced Square Concrete Column
Concrete Waffle Slab

Figure 10.3

Means® Forms
QUANTITY SHEET

PROJECT Admin. Bldg.
LOCATION Picacho, Ca.
TAKE OFF BY PC
ARCHITECT Bell & Bell
EXTENSIONS BY: ETW
SHEET NO. QS 10
ESTIMATE NO. 1017
DATE March 1989
CHECKED BY: NS

DESCRIPTION	NO.	DIMENSIONS l w d	Shoring	UNIT	Slab Forms	UNIT	Edge Forms	UNIT	Constr. JT.	UNIT	Screeds	UNIT	Conc.	UNIT	Reinf. WWF	UNIT	Finish & Cure	UNIT
Elevated Conc. Slab																		
2nd Floor Slab (3 3/4")		100 48 0.31	4800 9.5' HG	SF	4800		380	LF	190	LF	480	LF	1488	CF	4800	SF	4800	SF
Opening @ Stairs							57	LF					39	CF	125	SF	125	SF
Total			4800		4800		437		190		480		1449	CF	4675		4675	
Convert To Cy													54	CY				
Waste Allowances																		
Conc. 8%													4	CY				
Forms 5%					240		22											
WWF 14%															655			
Total			4800 9.5' High		5040	SF	459	LF	190	LF	480	LF	58	CY	5330	SF	4675	SF

Figure 10.4

Chapter 11
Concrete Suspended Stairs

This chapter demonstrates the takeoff procedure for cast-in-place concrete suspended stairs. Wooden stairs and steps on grade will be examined in later chapters.

Takeoff Items

The items typically taken off for concrete suspended stairs include:

- Formwork
- Reinforcing
- Concrete
- Inserts
- Finishing
- Curing

The formwork is often broken down into soffit forms, edge forms, and riser forms. Inserts include railing anchors and nosings. Additionally, the quantity estimator should note on the quantity sheet any special tread finishes, since these may represent a considerable cost.

Takeoff Demonstration

Some estimators use shortcuts for pricing out stairs, such as by linear foot of treads, slant length of stairs, or by flight. The traditional and best method is to take off and apply a cost to each of the associated items listed above. This section will demonstrate how to do this.

Figure 11.1 shows the layout and two cross-sectional views of a set of stairs. In this illustration we see that this plain suspended stairway goes from the first floor to the second floor. It makes one right-angle turn and has one landing. The stairway has 26 6-inch risers and 24 12-inch treads, and is supported along one side by a concrete wall. The other side and the underneath (the soffit) are open to view and will require finishing after the forms are removed. This is a simple stair design, but more complex and ornamental stairs would be taken off in a similar manner.

A project may have more than one stairway. If the complexity of the stairways' designs vary significantly, the stairways should be numbered (Stair # 1, Stair # 2, etc.) and taken off separately.

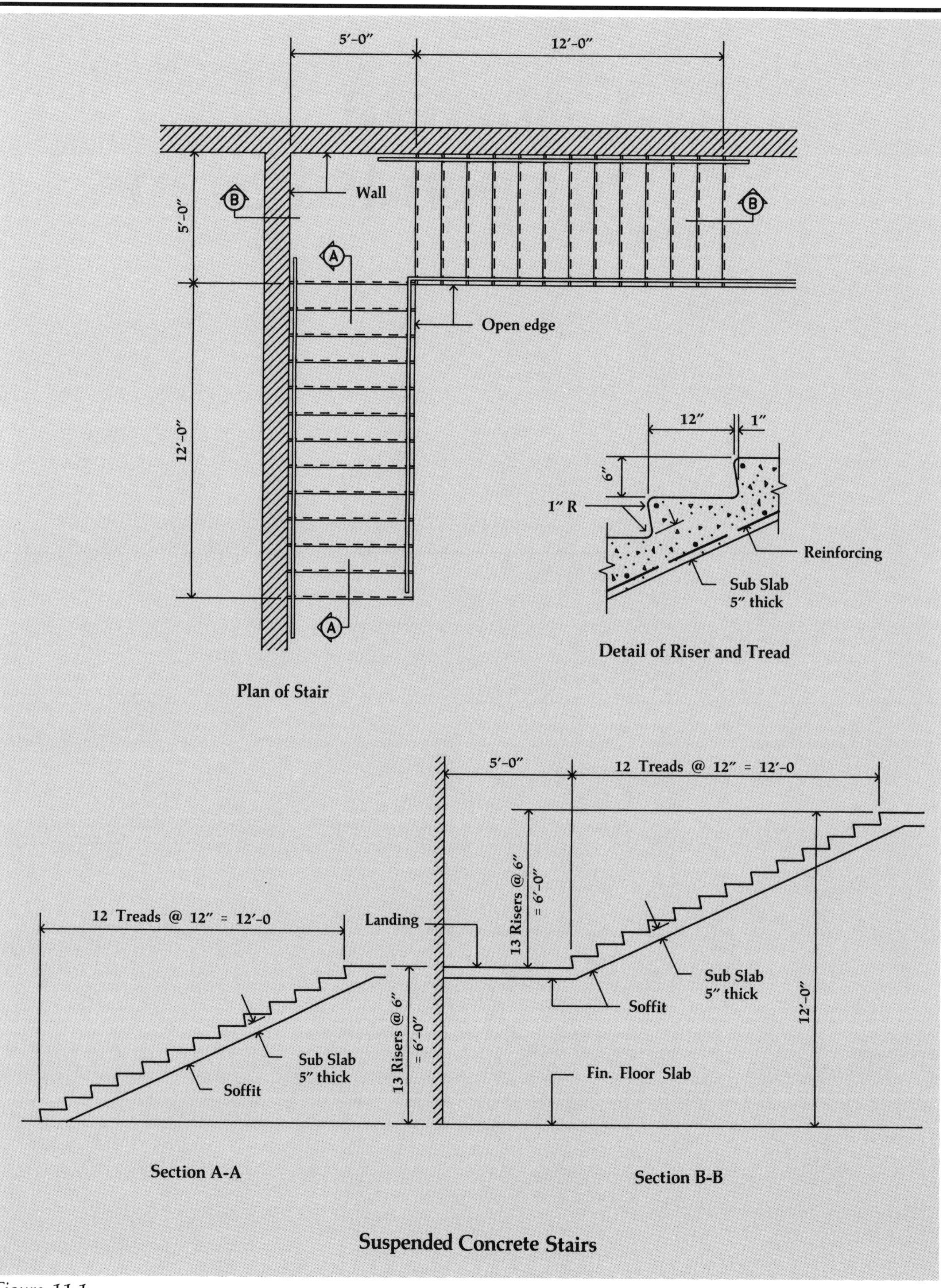

5'-0"
12'-0"
Wall
Open edge
12"
1"
6"
1" R
Reinforcing
Sub Slab
5" thick
Detail of Riser and Tread
Plan of Stair
5'-0"
12 Treads @ 12" = 12'-0
12 Treads @ 12" = 12'-0
Landing
13 Risers @ 6" = 6'-0"
13 Risers @ 6" = 6'-0"
Sub Slab
5" thick
Soffit
Sub Slab
5" thick
Soffit
12'-0"
Fin. Floor Slab
Section A-A
Section B-B
Suspended Concrete Stairs

Figure 11.1

In our example, we will designate the stairway as Stair # 1, even though it is the only stairway in the project, as a precaution, and a reminder to search for possibly "hidden" stairs. It is easy to overlook stairways on some drawings, and often a draftsman will draw one detail meant to be representative of two or more stairways.

As the takeoff proceeds, transfer all quantities to Quantity Sheet 11 (Figure 11.2) located at the end of this chapter. Be sure to shade the drawings as the items are taken off.

Step 1

In Figure 11.1, we see that the upper and lower slope portions of the soffit each have a horizontal distance of 12′, and a vertical distance of 6′. The sloped distance is:

$$\sqrt{12^2 + 6^2} = 13.42'$$

The total length of the soffit, including the landing, is:

$$13.42' + 5.0' + 13.42' = 31.84 \text{ lf}$$

Since the width is 5′, the total area of the soffit is:

$$32' \times 5.0' = 160 \text{ sf}$$

Transfer these quantities to Quantity Sheet 11.

Step 2

Next, find the quantities of each of the takeoff items. This is demonstrated below.

Formwork

The exposed side of the stairs and the treads will require forming. The quantity estimator should allow for a 12″ plank for forming this edge.

$$32' \times 1' = 32 \text{ lf}$$

The risers will also require forming:

$$26 \text{ ea} \times 5' \times 0.5' \text{ high} = 65 \text{ sf}$$

Reinforcing

Assume 160 sf of welded wire fabric, and # 5 at 6″ oc each way.

$$(32' \times 9) + (4.5 \times 64) = 576 \text{ lf}$$

Concrete

Figure the concrete by adding 1/2 the height of the treads to the height of the stair slab.

Stairs: 28′ × 5′ × (0.25′ + 0.42′	=	94 cf
Landing: 5′ × 5′ × 0.42′	=	11 cf
Total	=	105 cf

Inserts

See plans and specifications for any railing inserts or nosings.

Finishing

Because the underside of the stairs will be exposed, the soffit area must be finished. The quantity is 160 sf.

The treads will also require finishing:

$$24 \times 5' \times 1' = 120 \text{ sf}$$

The risers also need finishing:

$$26 \times 5' \times 0.5' \text{ high} = 65 \text{ sf}$$

Finish the exposed side of the stair slab plus 1/2 the height of the treads times the length:

$$(0.25' + 0.42') \times 32' = 22 \text{ sf}$$

Finish the landing:

$$5' \times 5' = 25 \text{ sf}$$

Total area to be finished:

160 sf + 130 sf + 65 sf + 22 sf + 25 sf = 402 sf

Curing

All finished areas will be sprayed with a curing compound. Use the finishing quantity for this item: 402 sf.

Step 3

Total the quantities in Quantity Sheet 11. Add an allowance for waste to the concrete quantity. Convert cubic feet of concrete to cubic yards.

This concludes the takeoff demonstration of concrete suspended stairs. Chapter 12 examines reinforcing steel in cast-in-place concrete building components.

Means® Forms
QUANTITY SHEET

PROJECT Admin. Bldg.
LOCATION Picacho, Ca.
TAKE OFF BY PC
ARCHITECT Bell & Bell
EXTENSIONS BY: ETW
SHEET NO. QS 11
ESTIMATE NO. 1017
DATE March 1989
CHECKED BY: NS

DESCRIPTION	NO.	DIMENSIONS l	DIMENSIONS w	SOFFIT FORM	EDGE FORM	RISER FORM	CONC.	WWF	FINISH	CURE	RAILINGS WALL MTD	RAILINGS POST MTD	INSERTS	REINF. #5
CIP Suspended Stairs	1	32	5	160 SF	32 LF	65 SF	105 CF	160 SF	402 SF	402 SF	27 LF	27 LF	7 ea.	
Convert to CY							4 CY							
Reinf. #s (1.043)		576												600 Lbs
Waste Allowances														
Conc. 8%							-							
Forms 5%				8	2	3								120 Lbs.
WWF 8%								13						
Reinf. 20%														
Total				168 SF	34 LF	68 SF	4 CY	173 SF	402 SF	402 SF	27 LF	27 LF	7 ea.	720 Lbs

Figure 11.2

Chapter 12

Reinforcing Steel

Reinforcing steel is used in concrete to control cracking and add tensile and compressive strength to concrete structural components. The designer specifies the size, number, and spacing of reinforcing bars or welded wire fabric. This information is either written on the plans, shown in a separate schedule, or both.

Reinforcing steel work (sometimes referred to as *rebar*) is almost always sublet to specialists who do the detailing and takeoff. However, sometimes a quantity estimator must take off reinforcing steel with sufficient accuracy for cost estimating purposes. When this is the case, the quantity estimator should take off reinforcing steel simultaneously with forms and concrete because the same measurements are used. This has been demonstrated in the preceding chapters.

Types of Reinforcing Steel

There are a number of types of reinforcing steel. The three most common types are:

- Bar stock
- Welded wire fabric
- Wire trusses and ladder strips

Bar Stock

Bar stock is measured and taken off in linear feet at each location in the building. Standard reinforcing bars range from # 3 (3/8″ diameter) to # 18 (2-1/4″ diameter). The bar number refers to the bar's diameter in eighths of an inch. The totals of the various sizes of bars are converted from linear feet to pounds by use of the factors given in the table of weights in Figure 12.1. Finally, if the quantity estimator wants to, pounds are converted to tons by dividing the total number of pounds by 2,000 (the number of pounds in a ton).

Welded Wire Fabric

Welded wire fabric (WWF) used in CIP concrete slabs is designated by spacing and wire size. For example, WWF 6 × 8 — W2 × W8 means:

WWF = Welded wire fabric
6 × 8 = Longitudinal wire spacing = 6″
Transverse wire spacing = 8″
W2 × W8 = Longitudinal wire size = W2
Transverse wire size = W8

Welded wire fabric reinforcing for concrete slabs is taken off in square feet. Common stock styles of welded wire fabric are shown in Figure 12.2.

Wire Trusses and Ladder Strips

Wire trusses and ladder strips provide horizontal reinforcement in joints in concrete block walls (see Figure 12.3). These are taken off in linear feet. The plans or specifications will note the vertical distance between joints having horizontal reinforcing.

Guidelines for Takeoff

The following is a list of guidelines for taking off reinforcing steel.

- Take off reinforcing steel simultaneously with concrete, since the same dimensions and number of units are involved. Create a separate column on the quantity sheet for each size bar or fabric for that building component.
- Check the plans and specifications for extra reinforcement required around openings.
- Do not deduct for wall or elevated slab openings that are less than 10 sf.
- Fractions of linear feet and pounds should be rounded up to the next whole foot or pound. Fractions of tons are rounded up to the next hundredth of a ton. When actual quantities or reinforcing will be reduced for window and door openings, the quantity estimator may choose to round downward.
- There is a wide range of acceptable waste percentages, depending on the building component, the type of reinforcing used in that component, the location of the reinforcing steel, overlapping requirements, the quantities of hooks and bends, and cutting. Appendix C contains a table of suggested waste allowances for reinforcing steel.

ASTM Standard Reinforcing Bars

Bar Size Designation	Area* Square Inches	Weight Pounds Per Foot	Diameter* Inches
#3	.11	.376	.375
#4	.20	.668	.500
#5	.31	1.043	.625
#6	.44	1.502	.750
#7	.60	2.044	.875
#8	.79	2.670	1.000
#9	1.00	3.400	1.128
#10	1.27	4.303	1.270
#11	1.56	5.313	1.410
#14	2.25	7.650	1.693
#18	4.00	13.600	2.257

Current ASTM Specifications cover bar sizes #14 and #18 in A615 Grade 60 and in A706 only.
*Nominal dimensions.

Figure 12.1

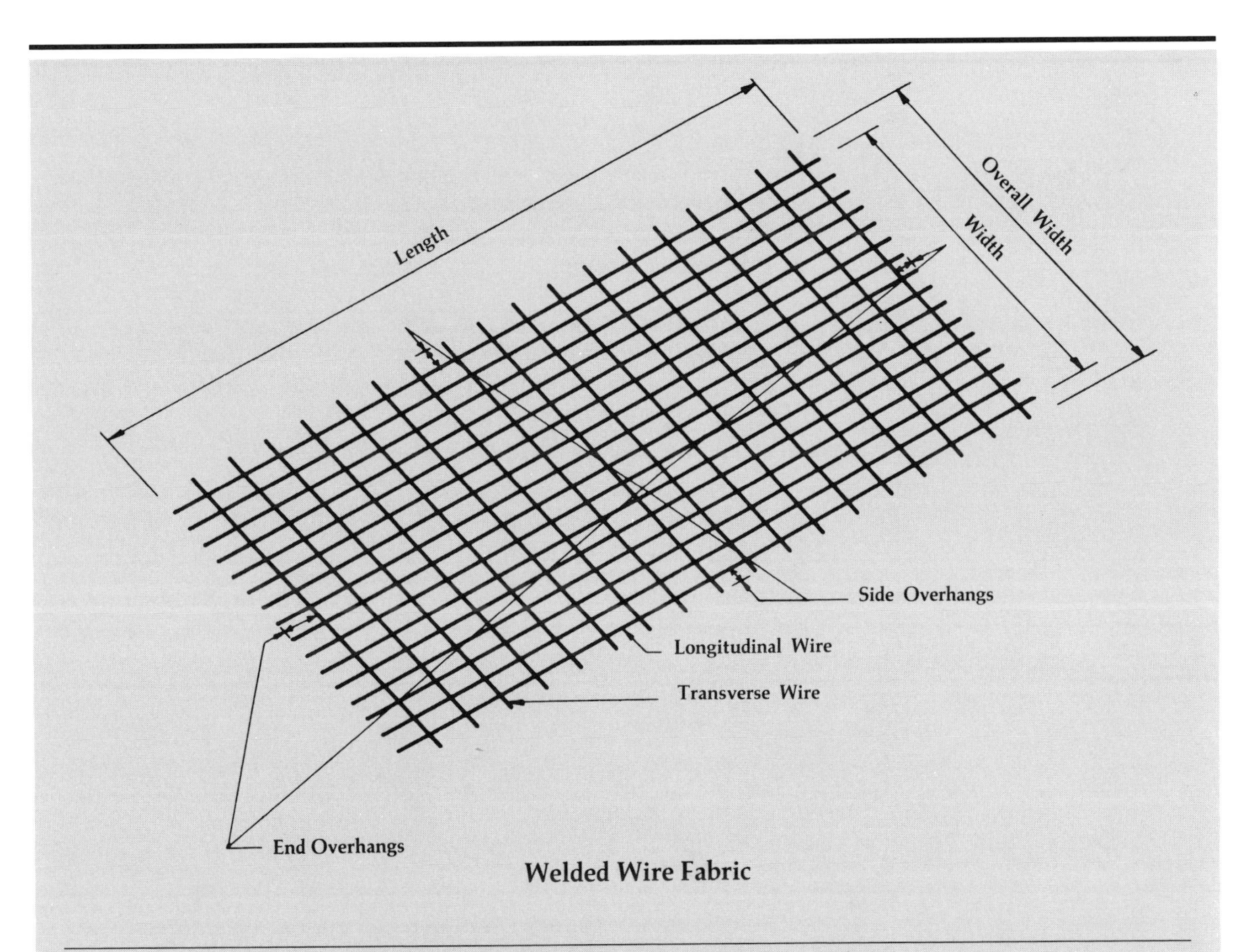

Welded Wire Fabric

Common Stock Styles of Welded Wire Fabric

	New Designation	Old Designation	Steel Area Per Foot				Approximate Weight Per 100 Sq. Ft.	
	Spacing - Cross Sectional Area	Spacing Wire Gauge	Longitudinal		Transverse			
	(IN.) - (SQ. IN. 100)	(IN.) - (AS & W)	IN.	CM	IN.	CM	LB	KG
	6 x 6 - W1.4 x W1.4	6 x 6 - 10 x 10	0.028	0.071	0.028	0.071	21	9.53
Rolls	6 x 6 - W2.0 x W2.0	6 x 6 - 8 x 8 (1)	0.040	0.102	0.040	0.102	29	13.15
Rolls	6 x 6 - W2.9 x W2.9	6 x 6 - 6 x 6	0.058	0.147	0.053	0.147	42	19.05
Rolls	6 x 6 - W4.0 x W4.0	6 x 6 - 4 x 4	0.080	0.203	0.080	0.203	58	26.31
Rolls	4 x 4 - W1.4 x W1.4	4 x 4 - 10 x 10	0.042	0.107	0.042	0.107	31	14.06
Rolls	4 x 4 - W2.0 x W2.0	4 x 4 - 8 x 8 (1)	0.060	0.152	0.060	0.152	43	19.50
Rolls	4 x 4 - W2.9 x W2.9	4 x 4 - 6 x 6	0.087	0.221	0.087	0.221	62	28.12
Rolls	4 x 4 - W4.0 x W4.0	4 x 4 - 4 x 4	0.120	0.305	0.120	0.305	85	38.56
Sheets	6 x 6 - W2.9 x W2.9	6 x 6 - 6 x 6	0.058	0.147	0.058	0.147	42	19.05
Sheets	6 x 6 - W4.0 x W4.0	6 x 6 - 4 x 4	0.080	0.203	0.080	0.203	58	26.31
Sheets	6 x 6 - W5.5 x W5.5	6 x 6 - 2 x 2 (2)	0.110	0.279	0.110	0.279	80	36.29
Sheets	6 x 6 - W4.0 x W4.0	4 x 4 - 4 x 4	0.120	0.305	0.120	0.305	85	38.56

Notes:
1. Exact W-number size for 8 gauge is W2.1
2. Exact W-number size for 2 gauge is W5.4

Figure 12.2

- Convert from linear feet to pounds, using factors from the table of weights in Figure 12.1 (pounds per linear foot). If desired, convert pounds to tons by dividing the quantity by 2,000.

Takeoff Shortcuts

When time is not available to perform a thorough takeoff, the following method may be acceptable for cost estimating purposes.

- Take off all rebar in one representative wall.
- Find the ratio of each size bar to the square foot area of the sample wall (lf/sf).
- Take off the total area of all walls of the same thickness, assuming bar sizes and spacings are the same.
- Multiply the total square feet of walls by each ratio to find the total linear feet of each size bar.

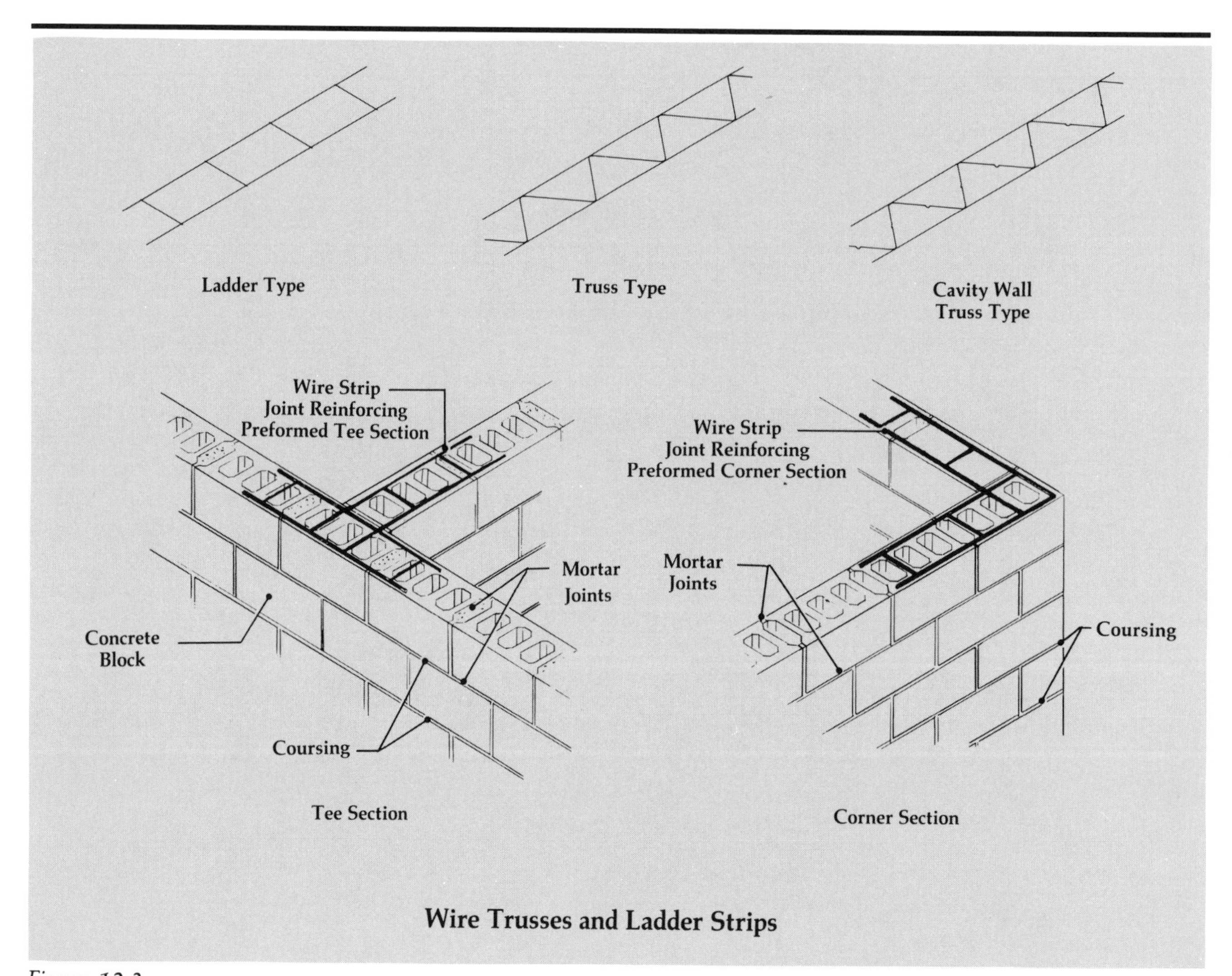

Wire Trusses and Ladder Strips

Figure 12.3

Another method for estimating a building's reinforcing steel requirements is to use predetermined proportionate quantities developed from typical designs, and apply them to each component. This method also gives the cost estimator a quick check of the quotes from reinforcing fabricators and subcontractors. Figure 12.4 is a table of these proportionate quantities.

This concludes the discussion of reinforcing steel. For a step-by-step demonstration, refer to earlier chapters on cast-in-place concrete foundation and structural components. Chapter 13 discusses the takeoff procedure for precast concrete.

Proportionate Quantities*

Type of Construction	Live Load	Span	Per S.F. of Floor Area				Per C.Y. of Concrete		
			Concrete	Forms	Reinf.	Pans	Forms	Reinf.	Pans
Flat Plate	50 psf	15 Ft.	.46 C.F.	1.06 S.F.	1.71 lb.		62 S.F.	101 lb.	
		20	.63	1.02	2.4		44	104	
		25	.79	1.02	3.03		35	104	
	100	15	.46	1.04	2.14		61	126	
		20	.71	1.02	2.72		39	104	
		25	.83	1.01	3.47		33	113	
Flat Plate (waffle construction) 20″ domes	50	20	.43	1.0	2.1	.84 S.F.	63	135	53 S.F.
		25	.52	1.0	2.9	.89	52	150	46
		30	.64	1.0	3.7	.87	42	155	37
	100	20	.51	1.0	2.3	.84	53	125	45
		25	.64	1.0	3.2	.83	42	135	35
		30	.76	1.0	4.4	.81	36	160	29
Waffle Construction 30″ domes	50	25	.69	1.06	1.83	.68	42	72	40
		30	.74	1.06	2.39	.69	39	87	39
		35	.86	1.05	2.71	.69	33	85	39
		40	.78	1.0	4.8	.68	35	165	40
Flat Slab (two way with drop panels)	50	20	.62	1.03	2.34		45	102	
		25	.77	1.03	2.99		36	105	
		30	.95	1.03	4.09		29	116	
	100	20	.64	1.03	2.83		43	119	
		25	.79	1.03	3.88		35	133	
		30	.96	1.03	4.66		29	131	
	200	20	.73	1.03	3.03		38	112	
		25	.86	1.03	4.23		32	133	
		30	1.06	1.03	5.3		26	135	
One Way Joists 20″ pans	50	15	.36	1.04	1.4	.93	78	105	70
		20	.42	1.05	1.8	.94	67	120	60
		25	.47	1.05	2.6	.94	60	150	54
	100	15	.38	1.07	1.9	.93	77	140	66
		20	.44	1.08	2.4	.94	67	150	58
		25	.52	1.07	3.5	.94	55	185	49
One Way Joists 8″ x 16″ filler blocks	50	15	.34	1.06	1.8	.81 Ea.	84	145	64 Ea.
		20	.40	1.08	2.2	.82	73	145	55
		25	.46	1.07	3.2	.83	63	190	49
	100	15	.39	1.07	1.9	.81	74	130	56
		20	.46	1.09	2.8	.82	64	160	48
		25	.53	1.10	3.6	.83	56	190	42
One Way Beam & Slab	50	15	.42	1.30	1.73		84	111	
		20	.51	1.28	2.61		68	138	
		25	.64	1.25	2.78		53	117	
	100	15	.42	1.30	1.9		84	122	
		20	.54	1.35	2.69		68	154	
		25	.69	1.37	3.93		54	154	
	200	15	.44	1.31	2.24		80	137	
		20	.58	1.40	3.30		65	163	
		25	.69	1.42	4.89		53	183	
Two Way Beam & Slab	100	15	.47	1.20	2.26		69	130	
		20	.63	1.29	3.06		55	131	
		25	.83	1.33	3.79		43	123	
	200	15	.49	1.25	2.70		41	149	
		20	.66	1.32	4.04		54	165	
		25	.88	1.32	6.08		41	187	

Figure 12.4

Proportionate Quantities (continued)*

4000 psi Concrete and 60,000 psi Reinforcing — Form and Reinforcing Quantities per C.Y.

Item	Size	Forms	Reinforcing	Minimum	Maximum
Columns (square tied)	10″ x 10″	130 S.F.C.A.	#5 to #11	220 lbs.	875 lbs.
	12″ x 12″	108	#6 to #14	200	955
	14″ x 14″	92	#7 to #14	190	900
	16″ x 16″	81	#6 to #14	187	1082
	18″ x 18″	72	#6 to #14	170	906
	20″ x 20″	65	#7 to #18	150	1080
	22″ x 22″	59	#8 to #18	153	902
	24″ x 24″	54	#8 to #18	164	884
	26″ x 26″	50	#9 to #18	169	994
	28″ x 28″	46	#9 & #18	147	864
	30″ x 30″	43	#10 to #18	146	983
	32″ x 32″	40	#10 to #18	175	866
	34″ x 34″	38	#10 to #18	157	772
	36″ x 36″	36	#10 to #18	175	852
	38″ x 38″	34	#10 to #18	158	765
	40″ x 40″	32	#10 to #18	143	692

Item	Size	Forms	Spirals	Reinforcing	Minimum	Maximum
Columns (spirally reinforced)	12″ diameter	34.5 L.F.	190 lb.	#4 to #11	165 lb.	1505 lb.
		34.5	190	#14 & #18	—	1100
	14″	25	170	#4 to #11	150	970
		25	170	#14 & #18	800	1000
	16″	19	160	#4 to #11	160	950
		19	160	#14 & #18	605	1080
	18″	15	150	#4 to #11	160	915
		15	150	#14 & #18	480	1075
	20″	12	130	#4 to #11	155	865
		12	130	#14 & #18	385	1020
	22″	10	125	#4 to #11	165	775
		10	125	#14 & #18	320	995
	24″	9	120	#4 to #11	195	800
		9	120	#14 & #18	290	1150
	26″	7.3	100	#4 to #11	200	729
		7.3	100	#14 & #18	235	1035
	28″	6.3	95	#4 to #11	175	700
		6.3	95	#14 & #18	200	1075
	30″	5.5	90	#4 to #11	180	670
		5.5	90	#14 & #18	175	1015
	32″	4.8	85	#4 to #11	185	615
		4.8	85	#14 & #18	155	955
	34″	4.3	80	#4 to #11	180	600
		4.3	80	#14 & #18	170	855
	36″	3.8	75	#4 to #11	165	570
		3.8	75	#14 & #18	155	865
	40″	3.0	70	#4 to #11	165	500
		3.0	70	#14 & #18	145	765

Figure 12.4 (*continued*)

Proportionate Quantities (continued)*

**3000 psi Concrete and 60,000 psi Reinforcing—
Form and Reinforcing Quantities per C.Y.**

Item	Type	Loading	Height	C.Y./ L.F.	Forms/ C.Y.	Reinf./ C.Y.
Retaining Walls	Cantilever	Level Backfill	4 Ft.	0.2 C.Y.	49 S.F.	35 lb.
			8	0.5	42	45
			12	0.8	35	70
			16	1.1	32	85
			20	1.6	28	105
		Highway Surcharge	4	0.3	41	35
			8	0.5	36	55
			12	0.8	33	90
			16	1.2	30	120
			20	1.7	27	155
		Railroad Surcharge	4	0.4	28	45
			8	0.8	25	65
			12	1.3	22	90
			16	1.9	20	100
			20	2.6	18	120
	Gravity, with Vertical Face	Level Backfill	4	0.4	37	None
			7	0.6	27	
			10	1.2	20	
		Sloping Surcharge	4	0.3	31	
			7	0.8	21	
			10	1.6	15	

		Live Load in Kips per Linear Foot							
		Under 1 Kip		2 to 3 Kips		4 to 5 Kips		6 to 7 Kips	
	Span	Forms	Reinf.	Forms	Reinf.	Forms	Reinf.	Forms	Reinf.
Beams	10 Ft.			90 S.F.	170#	85 S.F.	175#	75 S.F.	185#
	16	130 S.F.	165#	85	180	75	180	65	225
	20	110	170	75	185	62	200	51	200
	26	90	170	65	215	62	215	—	—
	30	85	175	60	200	—	—	—	—

Figure 12.4 (*continued*)

Proportionate Quantities (continued)*

Item	Size	Type	Forms per C.Y.	Reinforcing per C.Y.
Spread Footings	Under 1 C.Y.	1,000 psf soil	24 S.F.	44 lb.
		5,000	24	42
		10,000	24	52
	1 C.Y. to 5 C.Y.	1,000	14	49
		5,000	14	50
		10,000	14	50
	Over 5 C.Y.	1,000	9	54
		5,000	9	52
		10,000	9	56
Pile Caps (30 Ton Concrete Piles)	Under 5 C.Y.	shallow caps	20	65
		medium	20	50
		deep	20	40
	5 C.Y. to 10 C.Y.	shallow	14	55
		medium	15	45
		deep	15	40
	10 C.Y. to 20 C.Y.	shallow	11	60
		medium	11	45
		deep	12	35
	Over 20 C.Y.	shallow	9	60
		medium	9	45
		deep	10	40

Figure 12.4 (*continued*)

Proportionate Quantities (continued)*

3000 psi Concrete and 60,000 psi Reinforcing—Form and Reinforcing Quantities per C.Y.

Item	Size	Pile Spacing	50 T Pile	100 T Pile	50 T Pile	100 T Pile
Pile Caps (Steel H Piles)	Under 5 C.Y.	24″ O.C.	24 S.F.	24 S.F.	75 lb.	90 lb.
		30″	25	25	80	100
		36″	24	24	80	110
	5 C.Y. to 10 C.Y.	24″	15	15	80	110
		30″	15	15	85	110
		36″	15	15	75	90
	Over 10 C.Y.	24″	13	13	85	90
		30″	11	11	85	95
		36″	10	10	85	90

Item	Height	8″ Thick Forms	8″ Thick Reinf.	10″ Thick Forms	10″ Thick Reinf.	12″ Thick Forms	12″ Thick Reinf.	15″ Thick Forms	15″ Thick Reinf.
Basement Walls	7 Ft.	81 S.F.	44 lb.	65 S.F.	45 lb.	54 S.F.	44 lb.	41 S.F.	43 lb.
	8	↓	44	↓	45	↓	44	↓	43
	9	↓	46	↓	45	↓	44	↓	43
	10	↓	57	↓	45	↓	44	↓	43
	12	↓	83	↓	50	↓	52	↓	43
	14	↓	116	↓	65	↓	64	↓	51
	16	↓		↓	86	↓	90	↓	65
	18	↓		↓		↓	106	↓	70

*These tables show both quantities per S.F. of floor areas as well as form and reinforcing quantities per C.Y. Unusual structural requirements would increase the ratios below. High strength reinforcing would reduce the steel weights. Figures are for 3000 psi concrete and 60,000 psi reinforcing unless specified otherwise.

Figure 12.4 (*continued*)

Chapter 13
Precast Concrete

Precast concrete building components are formed, cast, and finished at a location other than their final position in the structure. Most precast concrete building components, such as beams, floor slabs, roof slabs, spandrels, and wall panels, are cast someplace other than the building site and delivered ready for erection. Some are cast on site, but not in the position in which they will appear in the building. The supplier or subcontractor bids the components either delivered to the job, or erected in place. The quantity estimator must list these on the quantity sheet by size, specification, and quantity.

An examination of the takeoff procedure for all precast concrete building components is beyond the scope of this chapter. What is important for the quantity estimator to know is that these components have similar takeoff items. The takeoff procedure for one precast component, therefore, is similar to other components. This chapter will examine the takeoff procedure for precast concrete tilt-up wall panels.

Precast Concrete Tilt-up Wall Panels

Imagine that our model administrative building will be constructed of precast tilt-up concrete wall panels. Tilt-up wall panels are usually cast horizontally on the floor slab near the location where they will be erected or tilted up. The three major stages in tilt-up precast concrete wall construction are:

- Panel construction
- Panel erection and temporary bracing
- Panel securing and finishing

The following sections examine the takeoff procedure for each of these three operations.

Panel Construction

Takeoff Items

The items taken off for panel construction are similar to those associated with ordinary concrete slab work. They include:

- Casting slab
- Edge forms
- Bond-breaking compound
- Reinforcing steel
- Lifting, bracing, and miscellaneous inserts
- Furnishing and placing concrete
- Finish and cure

The quantity estimator does not need to know the techniques of casting and erecting tilt-up wall panels, but he or she should be able to list all the takeoff items so that the cost estimator can assign a unit price to them. Figure 13.1 illustrates these items.

Takeoff Demonstration

Refer to the building elevations in Appendix A. Figure 13.2 shows tilt-up panel details. What follows is a step-by-step demonstration of the procedures used to take off tilt-up panel construction based on the information provided on these drawings. All quantities will be recorded on Quantity Sheets 13A and 13B (Figures 13.3 and 13.4), located at the end of this chapter.

Step 1: From the wall elevations we are able to calculate the width and height of each precast panel. Since the drawings do not provide the width for each individual panel, divide the total length of a wall by the number of panels to find the average width. Take the panels off in groups of similar panels, beginning with the East Elevation.

Note that the panels will overlap at the northeast corner. The 100′ wall length is therefore reduced by the 9″ wall thickness of one panel to 99.25′. The average panel width is:

$$99.25' \div 9 = 11.03'$$

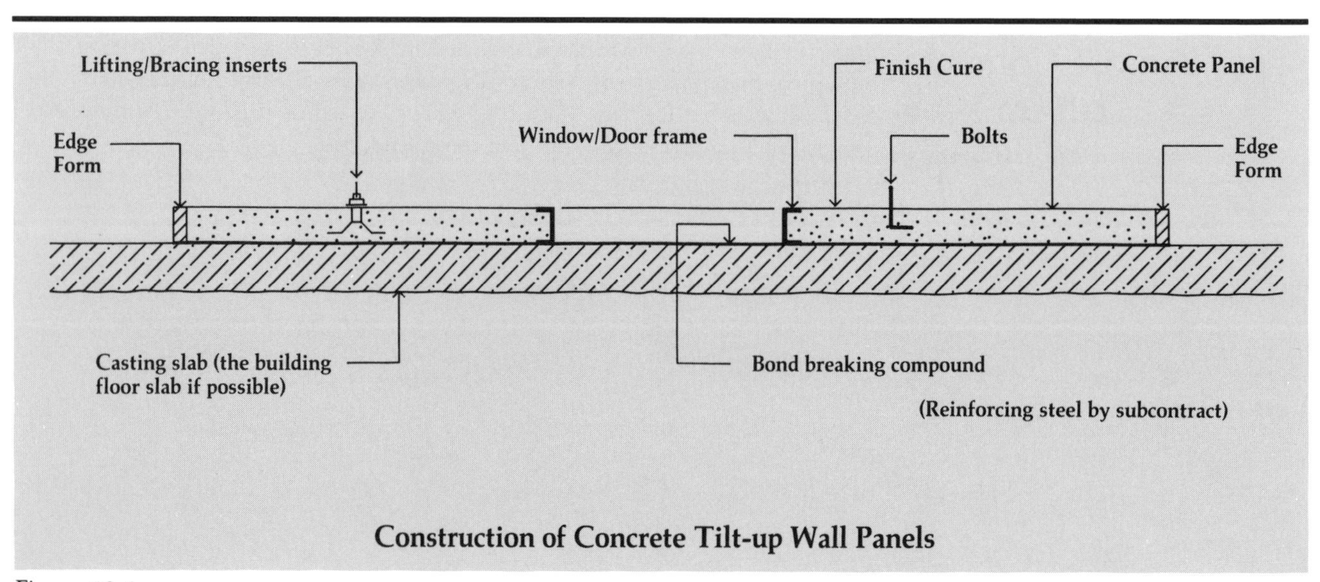

Figure 13.1

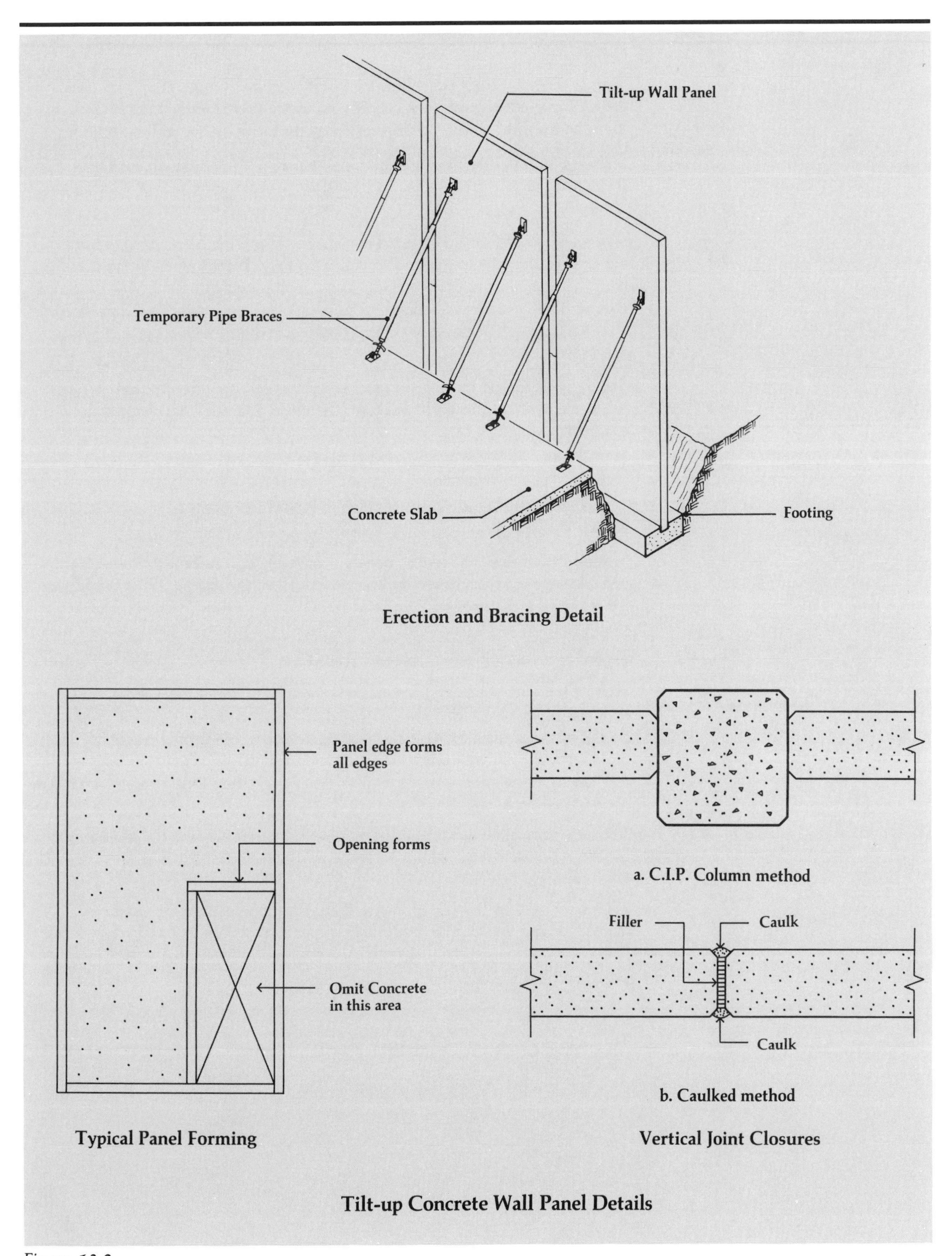
Tilt-up Wall Panel
Temporary Pipe Braces
Concrete Slab
Footing
Erection and Bracing Detail
Panel edge forms
all edges
Opening forms
Omit Concrete
in this area
a. C.I.P. Column method
Filler
Caulk
Caulk
b. Caulked method
Typical Panel Forming
Vertical Joint Closures
Tilt-up Concrete Wall Panel Details

Figure 13.2

Continue the takeoff in a clockwise direction around the building, ending with the interior walls.

Step 2: The building's floor slabs are usually cast before the tilt-up wall panels and are used as a casting slab. The quantity estimator should leave a blank space on the quantity sheet to remind the cost estimator that a casting slab is required.

Step 3: Next, calculate the quantity of edge forms around the perimeters of the panels. Record the total perimeter of the panels in linear feet on Quantity Sheet 13A.

Step 4: Bond-breaking compound is used to prevent the fresh concrete from adhering to the casting slab and to ensure an easy "break" when the slabs are lifted. The quantity of bond-breaking compound is equal to the area of the slabs with an additional amount added for waste. Do not deduct for openings. Record the total area of bond-breaking compound required for each group of panels in square feet.

Step 5: The lift and brace inserts cannot be counted until the erection requirements of the panels have been determined. Use the following rule to estimate the quantity of inserts:

Lift inserts: 1 per 50 sf; round up to the next even number; minimum of 4

Brace inserts: 2 in each low panel; 4 in each high panel

Record the total quantity for like panels on Quantity Sheet 13A.

Step 6: In our example, anchor bolts are used for the attachment of wood or metal ledgers after the panels are erected. Based on the spacing of 24" oc, divide the width of each panel by 2 and add 1:

$(12 \div 2) + 1 = 7$

Record these quantities on Quantity Sheet 13A.

Step 7: Forming is required around the perimeter of doors and windows. Deduct the areas of openings from the concrete, finishing, and curing quantities. Do not deduct from the quantity of bond-breaking compound. Although some openings are not completely enclosed within the panels and do not require forming on all four sides, calculate the quantity of forms as though they were required around the entire perimeter of the panels.

The same procedure used for the East Elevation is repeated for the takeoff of all the other elevations. Remember to shade or check off the panels as they are taken off.

After the takeoff is completed for panel construction, take off the quantities associated with the second stage of tilt-up panel construction: panel erection and temporary bracing.

Panel Erection and Temporary Bracing

Takeoff Items

The items typically associated with this second stage of precast tilt-up wall panel construction are:

- Move panels to the site or into position
- Erect, level, plumb, and brace

The quantity estimator should research the items associated with the erection and securing of the panels. Certain items cannot be reduced to quantities and must be labeled *LS* (lump sum). (See General Rule 8 in Chapter 1 for more information on lump sum quantities.)

Takeoff Demonstration

The cost of moving and/or tilting up panels is based on the number and sizes of the panels. The cost estimator will be able to determine this from the number and layout of the panels listed on the quantity sheet.

Step 1: We have already taken off the brace inserts that are embedded in the panels. The bottom of each brace is secured in the field by an insert or a field-drilled anchor during the plumbing and leveling of the panels. Count the braces that will be rented on a short-term basis. List these quantities as shown in Quantity Sheet 13A.

After taking off panel erection and bracing, take off the third stage of tilt-up panel construction: securing and finishing the panels.

Panel Securing and Finishing

There are many ways to permanently secure precast tilt-up panels once they have been erected, braced, and leveled. This can be done with wide flange steel columns, cast-in-place concrete columns or pilasters, or with wood framing members. The quantity estimator must indicate which method will be used and the quantity of materials required for that method.

Takeoff Items

Below are some of the items that are associated with securing and finishing precast wall panels:

- Caulking
- Cast-in-place columns
- Welding
- Delayed footings or slab pours
- Scaffolding
- Point and patch

Caulking is estimated for all vertical joints between panels and is recorded on the quantity sheet in linear feet.

When CIP columns are used, they are usually cast between the tilt-up panels after these have been erected. Wide flange steel columns are also used to support the tilt-up panels. Inserts in the panels are then welded or bolted to the columns.

Slab pours that are adjacent to the tilt-up panels are often left until the panels have been secured, as shown in Figure 13.2. These should be listed separately on the quantity sheet in square feet just like other slabs on grade. Scaffolding for pointing, patching, and finishing the panels should also be recorded. This quantity can be either listed in square feet or labeled *LS* (lump sum).

Takeoff Demonstration

Step 1: A variety of methods are used for anchoring and securing precast panels, depending on the individual project. Assume that in our building, wood-framed floors and roofs hold the wall panels upright permanently by means of bolted ledgers. Other metal cross and sway braces and structural beams may also provide strength and rigidity and would be part of the precast concrete takeoff.

Step 2: Figure 13.2 shows two common methods of closing the vertical gap between panels: formed and cast-in-place concrete columns, and filler and caulking. Our project uses filler and caulking. The simplest way to take off the filler is one vertical strip per panel. Then deduct a quantity for openings that displace the filler. To find the quantity of caulking, simply double the filler quantity. Had cast-in-place columns been used, they would have been taken off separately.

Step 3: Pointing and patching holes left by brace and lift inserts and any other general repairs need not be taken off again. Simply use the finish and curing quantity.

Step 4: Note the scaffolding requirement with the label *LS*.

Step 5: Total the quantities on Quantity Sheets 13A and 13B.

This concludes the takeoff demonstration of precast concrete tilt-up wall panels. Chapter 14 examines the takeoff procedure for miscellaneous concrete.

Means® Forms
QUANTITY SHEET

PROJECT Admin. Bldg. | SHEET NO. QS 13A
ESTIMATE NO. 1017
LOCATION Picacho, Ca. | ARCHITECT Bell & Bell | DATE March 1989
TAKE OFF BY PC | EXTENSIONS BY: ETW | CHECKED BY: NS

DESCRIPTION	NO	l	h	t	CASTING SLAB	EDGE FORMS	FORMS FOR OPENINGS	BOND BREAKER	LIFT INSERTS	BRACE INSERTS	SET ANCHOR BOLTS	CONC.	FINISH & CURE	REINF #4@8" E.W.
Pre-Cast Conc. Panels														
East Elevation	9	11.67	24.0	0.75		630 LF		2376 SF	48 ea.	36 ea.	63 ea.	1782 CF	2376 SF	4900 LBS.
	4	4	5	0.75			72					60	80	
	2	10	9	0.75			76					135	180	
	1	3	7	0.75			20					16	27	560
	2	14.75	13.3	0.75		112		392	8	8	18	294	392	780
	2	5	9	0.75			56					68	90	
South Elevation	1	15.0	10.7	0.75		51		160	4	2	9	120	160	320
	6	11.25	10.0	0.75		255		675	14	12	42	506	675	1350
	3	13.75	9.3	0.75		138		384	8	6	24	288	384	765
	4	12.0	13.3	0.75		202		638	14	16	28	479	638	1275
	2	10	3	0.75			52					45	60	
	1	8	4	0.75			24					24	32	
	1	5	3	0.75			16					12	15	
	1	3.5	7	0.75			21					18	25	
	2	6	3	0.75			36					27	36	335
West Elevation	2	10.5	9.3	0.75		79		195	4	4	14	146	195	390
	2	12	10.7	0.75		91		257	6	4	14	193	257	515
	2	12.5	12.0	0.75		98		300	6	8	16	225	300	600
	1	13.25	13.3	0.75		53		177	4	4	8	132	177	345
	3	15	13.3	0.75		170		598	12	12	27	449	598	1200
	9	11	13.3	0.75		437		1317	28	36	63	987	1317	2625
	2	6	3	0.75			36					27	36	
	2	6	4	0.75			40					36	48	
	4	4	3	0.75			56					36	48	
	2	3.5	7	0.75			42					37	49	365
North Elevation	5	11.0	13.3	0.75		243		731	16	20	35	549	731	1460
	2	10.5	13.3	0.75		95		279	6	8	14	209	279	560
	4	11.75	24	0.75		286		1128	24	16	28	846	1128	2260
	4	11.5	13.5	0.75		200		621	14	16	28	466	621	1245
	3	8	5	0.75			78					90	120	
	1	6	7	0.75			26					32	42	
	1	3.5	7	0.75			21					18	25	375
					LS	3140 LF	672 LF	10228 SF	216 ea.	208 ea.	431 ea.	6990 CF	9315 SF	18955 LBS
Convert to CY & Tons												259 CY		9.5 Tons
Waste Allow						157	34	1023				13		1.0
Total					LS	3297 LF	706 LF	11251 SF	216 ea.	208 ea.	431 ea.	272 CY	9315 SF	10.5 Tons

Figure 13.3

Means Forms
QUANTITY SHEET

SHEET NO. QS 15
PROJECT Admin. Bldg. — ESTIMATE NO. 1017
LOCATION Picacho, Ca. — ARCHITECT Bell & Bell — DATE March 1989
TAKE OFF BY PC — EXTENSIONS BY: ETW — CHECKED BY: NS

DESCRIPTION	NO.	DIMENSIONS			TILT UP, LABOR & EQUIP.	UNIT	BRACES	UNIT	JOINT FILLER	UNIT	CAULK	UNIT	SCAFFOLD	UNIT		UNIT
Pre-cast Conc. Panels (Cont.)																
Erecting, Securing & Finishing																
Low Panels	14				14		28		921		1842					
High Panels	45				45		90									
Total					59	ea.	118	ea.	921	LF	1842	LF				

Figure 13.4

Chapter 14
Miscellaneous Concrete

Certain nonstructural concrete building components cannot be classified under any heading other than "Miscellaneous." After the major structural elements have been taken off, such as footings, slabs, walls, columns, and beams, the quantity estimator should examine the drawings and specifications one last time for any concrete components associated with the building and its interior that have not been taken off. (Note that exterior site concrete is discussed in Chapter 15.)

Miscellaneous Concrete Building Components

The takeoff procedure for the following miscellaneous concrete building components is examined in this chapter:

- Sump pits
- Equipment and machinery bases
- Concrete cove base at walls
- Locker bases
- Fill on metal stair treads
- Cant strips

Because miscellaneous concrete building components are scattered throughout the drawings, we will not attempt to locate them on plans in Appendix A. Instead, see Quantity Sheet 14 (Figure 14.1), located at the end of this chapter, which shows how the quantities for these components are conveyed to the cost estimator.

Sump Pits

Record the volume of each sump pit and the number of each size. For a discussion of the takeoff procedure for large pits, such as catch basins and manholes, see Chapter 15, "Exterior (Site) Concrete."

Equipment and Machinery Bases

Some equipment bases are set on the grade slab while others rest on the subgrade. Equipment and machinery bases can be taken off the same way as spread footings (Chapter 3). Be sure to include any required anchor bolts and reinforcing.

Concrete Cove Base at Walls

Concrete base or *coving* at the intersection of walls and floors is often found in a "Table of Finishes," which will be discussed in Chapter 18, "Finish Carpentry." A cast-in-place concrete base is usually keyed into the floor slab. This means that the previously poured floor slab must have keyways formed to receive the base. The takeoff is simply a matter of measuring the linear feet of base. This can be done either by identifying each room, or by taking off and recording the total length for each height.

Locker Bases

Locker bases are similar to equipment bases but come in standard sizes and have a rounded edge. Locker bases are difficult to form and pour integrally with floor slabs, and are usually placed on top of the finished floor slabs. As a result, they are taken off as a separate item and listed by size and number as shown on Quantity Sheet 14.

Fill on Metal Stair Treads

Fill for the pans in metal stairs consists of a thin layer of concrete on sheet metal treads and landings. Edge forms need not be taken off, as they are a part of the prefabricated metal stair. The concrete quantity is usually expressed in square feet, which is found by multiplying the length of the slant by the width. Because of the commonly used ratios adopted by designers, this method works for high or low risers with wide or narrow treads.

Cant Strips

A cant strip is a triangular piece of concrete running continuously along the intersections between the roof and parapets or walls to prevent sharp bending of roofing material. Cant, or "C," strips can be taken off by size and expressed in linear feet.

The takeoff is not complete until the quantity estimator is sure that no components have been missed and that all of the associated items of each component, such as dovetail anchor slots, reglets, sleeves, depressed slab forms, PVC waterstops, form liners, special surface treatment, and concrete sawing, have been listed on the quantity sheet. If the quantity estimator is unsure whether or not an item should be included, he or she should always list the item, since some seemingly insignificant items can be very costly to install. The quantity estimator's goal is to take off everything that has a cost value.

Finally, total each of the columns on the quantity sheet where appropriate and round up to the nearest whole number.

This concludes the discussion of miscellaneous concrete building components. Chapter 15 examines the takeoff procedure for exterior (site) concrete and paving.

Means® Forms

QUANTITY SHEET

SHEET NO. QS 14

PROJECT Admin. Bldg. ESTIMATE NO. 1017

LOCATION Picacho, Ca. ARCHITECT Bell & Bell DATE March 1989

TAKE OFF BY PC EXTENSIONS BY: ETW CHECKED BY: NS

DESCRIPTION	NO.	DIMENSIONS l	w	d		UNIT		UNIT		UNIT		UNIT
Sump Pits	1	3^{5}	3^{0}	2^{5}	1							
	1	4^{0}	5^{0}	4^{5}	1							
					2	ea.						
Equipment Bases							ANCHOR BOLTS		EXP. JOINT			
	1	5^{0}	4^{0}	0^{75}	20		4		18			
	2	3^{5}	3^{5}	0^{67}	25		8		28			
	1	7^{34}	4^{5}	0^{83}	33		6		24			
					78	SF	18	ea.	70	LF		
Concrete Cove					4" High		6" High					
					110	LF	45	LF				
Locker Bases	4	8^{0}	2^{0}	0^{50}	32	LF						
Fill on metal stairs	12	5^{0}	1^{5}	0^{17}	90	SF						
Cant strip		6"x6"			330	LF						

Figure 14.1

Chapter 15

Exterior (Site) Concrete and Paving

After the structural and interior concrete building components have been taken off, the quantity estimator should take off those concrete components that are outside and separate from the building. These are referred to as *exterior* or *site concrete*. (This chapter will also discuss asphalt pavement.)

Exterior Components

Some of the exterior components that a quantity estimator may need to take off are precast parking (wheel) bumpers, flag pole bases, driveways, post bases, patching over ditches, splash blocks, yard walls, and slabs and footings for sheds.

The following exterior components will be examined in this chapter:

- Steps on grade
- Stoops and aprons (at doorways)
- Retaining wall
- Plain curbs
- Planter curbs
- Catch basins
- Sidewalks
- Asphalt pavement

The Site Plan in Appendix A shows the location of each of these components. The quantities are recorded (and some of them broken down into associated items) on Quantity Sheet 15 (Figure 15.1), located at the end of this chapter.

Steps on Grade

Projects that contain a few small steps on grade will not produce significant quantities of items such as formwork, concrete, and finishing. For these projects, the quantity estimator may prefer to calculate the linear feet of tread. Four steps that are 5′ wide would be taken off as 20 lf of tread (4 steps x 5′). If the project has many sets of steps, however, the quantity estimator should follow the takeoff procedure for concrete suspended stairs in Chapter 11.

Stoops and Aprons

Stoops and aprons are concrete slabs at building entrances. They sometimes have short cutoff walls around the outside perimeter. Takeoff items include excavation, base material, forms, expansion joints, reinforcing, concrete, and curing.

Retaining Wall

Retaining walls contain the same associated items and are taken off the same way as building foundations. The retaining wall for our model building is shown east of the building. Assume that the excavation is neat to the bottom of the footing at elev 90.0′.

Curbs and Catch Basins

As a rule, the components for plain curbs, planter curbs, and catch basins need not be itemized. Curbs, however, are broken down into *straight* and *radius* sections. They are easily priced out by the linear foot or unit.

Sidewalks

Sidewalks come in a variety of sizes, shapes, and finishes. All of the items associated with their construction must be taken off except when unit price sub bids are expected. Then the quantity estimator can take off the sidewalks in square feet.

Asphalt Pavement

Asphalt pavement is specified by material and thickness of each course. Typical items taken off for asphalt pavement are fine grade, base course, binder course, and wearing course. All items are taken off by the square foot and converted to square yards. Convert the base, binder, and wearing course quantities to tons. Unit weights will vary depending on the aggregate used.

Takeoff Demonstration

This section provides the calculations for taking off the concrete building components described above. Refer to the drawings in Appendix A for the location and details of these components.

Step 1: Steps on Grade

At the south end of the paved area there are steps on grade that extend to the top of the retaining wall. The quantity estimator can take these off in total linear feet:

6 treads × 5′ = 30 lf of tread

Step 2: Stoops

Concrete stoops are shown at the two entrances on the east side of the building. Each stoop is 8′ × 4′.

Hand excavation: (8′ × 4′ × 0.5′) × 2 = 32 cf
Base material: 32 cf
Formwork: 16′ × 0.5′ × 2 = 16 sfca
Reinforcing: [(8 × 7.5′) + (16 × 3.5′)] × 2 = 232 lf (# 5 bars at 6″ each way)
Expansion joints: 20 lf
Concrete: (8′ × 4′ × 0.5′) × 2 = 32 cf
Curing: 32 sf × 2 = 64 sf

Step 3: Aprons

The concrete apron at the two automotive doors is 30′ × 4′.

Hand excavation: 30′ × 4′ × 0.5′ = 60 cf
Base material: 60 cf
Formwork: (30′ + 8′) × 0.5′ = 19 sfca
Reinforcing: (60 × 3.5′) + (8 × 29.5′) = 446 lf (# 5 bars at 6″ each way)
Expansion joint: 30 lf
Concrete: 30′ × 4′ × 0.5′ = 60 cf
Curing: 30′ × 4′ = 120 sf

Step 4: Retaining Wall

Machine excavation: 4′ × 8′ × 165′ = 5,280 cf
Formwork (footings): 165′ × 1′ × 2 = 330 sfca

$$\textbf{(walls):}\ 165' \times \frac{4.5' + 6.5'}{2} \times 2 = 1{,}815 \text{ sfca}$$

Reinforcing: 164 × 6.75′ = 1,107 lf (# 7 hook bars)
164 × 3.5′ = 574 lf (# 7 straight bars)
11 × 164′ = 1,804 lf (# 5 horizontal bars, 30′ long; add 15′ for lapping for a total of 1,819 lf
Concrete: 165′ × [(1′ × 4′) + (1′ × 5.5′)] = 1,568 cf
Rub and grind: 165′ × 3′ = 495 sf

Step 5: Plain Curbs

Plain concrete curbs are shown along the east side of the paved area and part of the west side. Scale the concrete curbs for dimensions.

Straight curbs: 330 lf
Radius curbs: 70 lf

Step 6: Planter Curbs

Planter curbs are located in the center of the parking area.

Straight curbs: 126 lf
Radius curbs: 32 lf

Step 7: Catch Basins

There are three catch basins shown on the plan. Record this number on the quantity sheet.

Step 8: Sidewalks

A 5′ wide sidewalk runs along the west side of the parking lot for 110′, and along the west side of the building for 108′. The total quantity is:

(110′ + 108′) × 5′ = 1,090 sf

An 8′ wide sidewalk runs across the front of the building and into the entrance. The total quantity is:

120′ × 8′ = 960 sf

Step 9: Asphalt Pavement

The area to be paved is 14,500 sf, or 1,610 sy. A quick estimate of paving tonnage is 110 lbs/sy/inch.

Fine grade: 1,610 sy
4″ Gravel base: 14,500 sf × 0.333′ = 4,830 cf, or 179 cy
2″ Binder course: 14,500 sf × 0.17′ = 2,465 cf, or 91 cy
1″ Wearing course: 14,500 sf × 0.08′ = 1,160 cf, or 43 cy

This concludes the takeoff of exterior (site) concrete and pavement. Chapter 16 examines the takeoff procedure for masonry.

Means® Forms
QUANTITY SHEET

PROJECT Admin. Bldg. — SHEET NO. QS 15

LOCATION Picacho, Ca. — ARCHITECT Bell & Bell — ESTIMATE NO. 1017

TAKE OFF BY PC — EXTENSIONS BY: ETW — DATE March 1989

CHECKED BY: NS

DESCRIPTION	NO.	DIMENSIONS l w d		HAND EXCAVA	BASE MAT'L	FORMS	REINF.	CONC.	EXP. JOINTS	CURE & FINISH	R&G	EXCAV. @ RET. WALL	CHAMFER STRIP	
Site Conc. & Paving														
Steps on grade-6 treads x 5'w	1	5'	30 LF											
Stoops	2	8' 4' 0.5'		32 CF	32 CF	16 SFCA	232 LF #5	32 CF	20 LF	64 SF				
Apron	1	30' 4' 0.5'		60 CF	60 CF	19 SFCA	446 LF #5	60 CF	30 LF	120 SF				
Retaining Wall - Footing		165' 4' 1'					900 LF #7	660				5280 CF		
Wall		165' 1' 5.5'				1815 SFCA	4100 #5	908			495		330	
Total				92 CF	92 CF	1850 SFCA	4780 LF #5 900 LF #7	1660 CF	50 LF	184 SF	495 SF	5280 CF	330	
Convert to CY & Reinf. to LBS				4 CY	4 CY		4985 LBS #5 1840 LBS #7	61 CY				196 CY		
Waste Allowances														
Conc. 10%				–				6						
Forms 5%						95								
Reinf. 18%							685 #7							
Total				4 CY	4 CY	1945 SFCA	7510 LBS #	67 CY	50 LF	184 SF	495 SF	196 CY	330	
Plain Curbs - straight		330 LF												
radius		70 LF												
Planter Curbs - straight		126 LF												
radius		32 LF												
Catch Basins		3 ea.												
Sidewalk 5' wide		218' 5'	1090 SF											
8' wide		120' 8'	960 SF											
Asphalt Paving		14,500 SF												
Fine grade			1610 SY											
4" Gravel base		0.33	4830 CF =	179 CY										
2" Binder Course		0.17	2465 CF =	177 TONS										
1" Wearing Course		0.08	1160 CF =	89 TONS										

Figure 15.1

Chapter 16
Masonry

Masonry is a term used to describe construction of exterior or interior walls using relatively small and uniformly shaped modular units of mineral composition such as concrete block, clay brick, or stone. Masonry may be used instead of cast-in-place (CIP) or precast concrete for structural load bearing walls (reinforced or unreinforced), or it may be used as a veneer. This chapter discusses the takeoff procedure for concrete block construction with brick veneer.

Concrete Block Construction with Brick Veneer

Concrete Block

Concrete blocks come in a variety of materials, weights, sizes, shapes, colors, and surface textures. Concrete block is a structural material that is often used instead of CIP concrete walls or columns because (1) it is faster to install, (2) it has a pleasing architectural appearance, (3) it provides insulation, and (4) in many cases it is less costly than conventional concrete construction. Figure 16.1 shows the components of concrete block construction.

Takeoff Items

The items typically taken off for concrete block construction include:

- Type, weight, and size of concrete block
- Waterproofing
- Stucco cover
- Type and size of joints
- Openings (for doors and windows)
- Lintels
- Pilasters
- Weld plates
- Expansion joints
- Reinforcing
- Grouting
- Insulation

Brick Veneer

Brick veneer is a type of wall facing made of clay bricks laid against a structural wall but not structurally bonded to the wall and bearing no load other than its own weight. It is used for decorative purposes and provides a measure of insulation to the building.

Takeoff Items

The items typically taken off for brick veneer include:

- Type and size of brick
- Type of bond
- Type of mortar and joints
- Cap brick
- Chimneys
- Dovetail anchor slots

Some of these items are simply noted on the quantity sheet. For example, the quantity estimator will note the type of brick and mortar on the quantity sheet for the cost estimator to use in his or her pricing. Figure 16.2 illustrates concrete block construction with brick veneer.

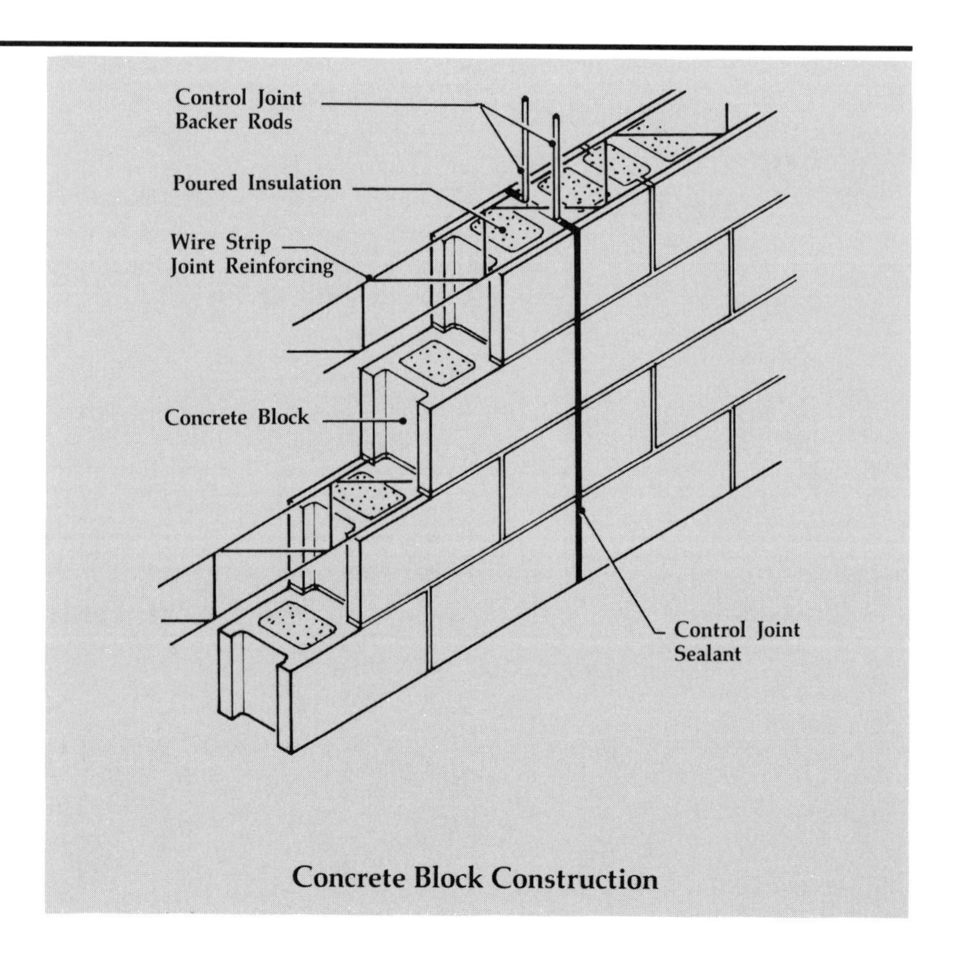

Figure 16.1

Guidelines for Takeoff

The following guidelines are suggested for taking off concrete block and brick veneer.

- The quantity estimator's objective is to take off only those items that fall within the scope of a masonry contractor's work, so that a cost estimate can be made that closely approximates a masonry sub bid.
- In some regions, masonry contractors take off the placement of reinforcing steel only (not the furnishing). In other regions, masonry sub bids include both the furnishing and placing of joint reinforcing. The cost estimator should be aware of this and compile his or her estimate accordingly. See Chapter 12 for more information on reinforcing steel.
- The quantity estimator need not calculate the number of each type of block or brick, or the number of cubic yards of mortar materials, since that is the masonry subcontractor's responsibility.
- For the general contractor's purposes, concrete block and clay brick are taken off in square feet of face surface, with quantities separated into categories according to type, size, wall thickness, and surface finish. Take off the quantity for shoring of openings. Subtract the areas of all openings. Items such as cap blocks, cap bricks, lintel beams, and pilasters are taken off in linear feet. Fractions are rounded up to the next whole square or linear foot.
- Take off exterior walls first, beginning with the northeast corner of the building, and proceed in a clockwise direction. Take off one type of wall at a time.
- Take off pilasters and chimneys.
- Take off inserts that the masonry contractor must grout into the block or brickwork, whether or not he or she furnishes the material.
- Note the quantity of scaffolding required.

Figure 16.2

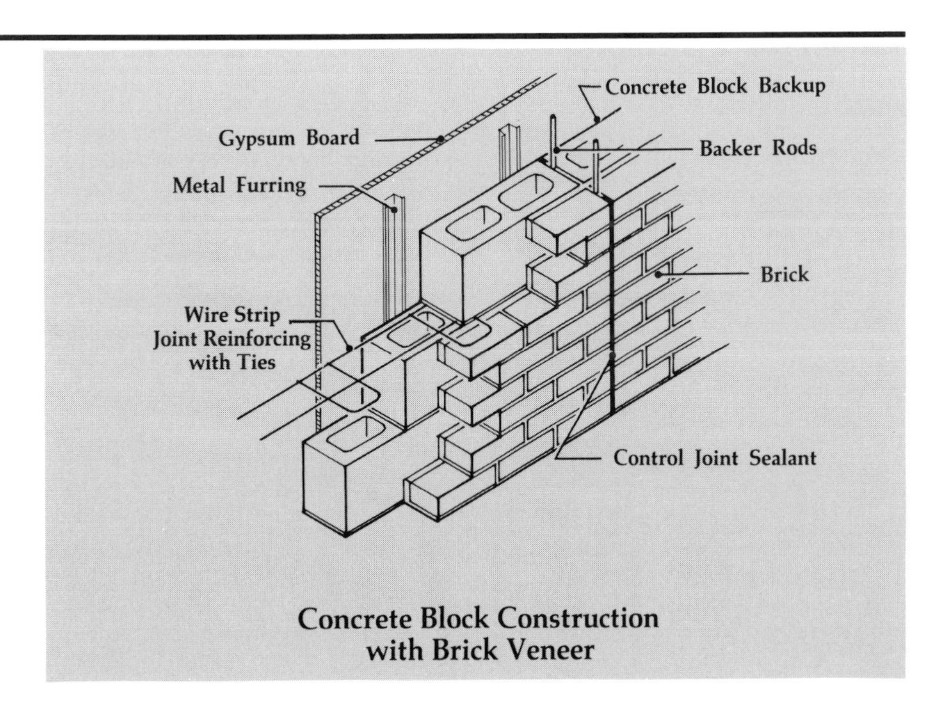

Concrete Block Construction with Brick Veneer

Takeoff Demonstration

Refer to the floor plans, exterior elevations, and wall sections in Appendix A for the details of the masonry construction in our model administrative building. Record all quantities on Quantity Sheet 16 (Figure 16.3), located at the end of this chapter.

In this project example, ignore the finishing of all interior faces of walls, since they will be covered with gypsum board (an exception is the interior face of the parapet wall, which will have concave joints to reduce the effects of weather).

A cost item (column on the quantity sheet) should be reserved for the blocking out of door and window openings and the shoring up of lintels. These structures are temporary, and are removed after lintels become strong enough to support the overhead loads. A convenient unit of measurement for blocking and shoring is square feet (the areas of openings). This is a repeat of the quantities taken off for deduction from the overall wall areas and is recorded on the quantity sheet.

Lintels are an additional cost item. They may be designed of steel, precast concrete, CIP concrete, or special block units filled with reinforcing steel and cement mortar grout. Our model building has lintels fabricated from steel angles. These will be taken off in Chapter 19. When concrete or masonry lintels are used, the different designs and sizes of lintels that are detailed in the drawings should be separated for cost estimating purposes. The quantity, in linear feet, is found in the process of measuring openings for deductive areas and for blocking and shoring.

Truss-type concrete block joint reinforcing will be provided once every 6 brick courses, or once every 16″ of wall height.

Expansion joints are placed in walls at intervals and locations where cracking is most likely to occur. In our example, a continuous vertical grouted masonry joint will be raked out on the exterior wall face and filled with flexible caulking material. Horizontal reinforcing steel runs unbroken through the joints. Assume a joint every 30 linear feet of wall.

Take off the 12″-thick walls (8″ concrete block with brick veneer) beginning with the East Elevation and proceeding around the building in a clockwise direction.

East Elevation

Step 1: 8″ Block Wall and Brick Veneer

The East Elevation is in two segments: 3D-3B (100′ long) and 4B-4A (30′ long).

100′ × 24′ (height) = 2,400 sf
30′ × 13.33′ (height) = 400 sf

Step 2: Openings

For the East Elevation, deduct the openings for 6 windows and 3 doors, including the two large doors, and list quantities for blocking and shoring. These quantities are recorded on Quantity Sheet 16 (notes at the bottom of Quantity Sheet 16 clarify and give additional information regarding the column headings). Notice that deductions are enclosed in blocks to differentiate them from additions.

Step 3: Joint Reinforcing

The total quantity of joint reinforcing is found as follows:

$$\frac{24}{1.33} \times 100' = 1{,}800 \text{ lf}$$

$$\frac{13.33}{1.33} \times 30' = 300 \text{ lf}$$

South Elevation

The South Elevation is 126′ long. Deduct the 12″ thickness of the section previously taken off for a net length of 125′. The distances to each of the foundation wall steps is shown on the Foundation and Footing Plan.

Step 1: 8″ Block Wall and Brick Veneer

First Floor: (16′ − 1′) = 15.00′ × 10.66′ (height) = 160 sf
68.67′ × 10.00′ = 687 sf
41.33′ × 9.33′ = 386 sf
Total Length = 125.00′ Total Area = 1,233 sf

Second Floor: 48′ × 13.33′ (height) = 640 sf

Step 2: Openings

Deduct for windows and doors on the first and second floors.

Step 3: Joint Reinforcing

$\frac{10.66}{1.33} \times 125' = 1{,}000$ lf

$\frac{13.33}{1.33} \times 48' = 480$ lf

West Elevation

Step 1: 8″ Block Walls and Brick Veneer

First Floor: (22′ − 1′) = 21.00′ × 9.33′ (height) = 196 sf
24.33′ × 10.66′ = 260 sf
25.33′ × 12.00′ = 304 sf
13.33′ × 13.33′ = 178 sf
45.00′ × 13.33′ = 600 sf
Total Length = 129.00′ Total Area = 1,538 sf

Second Floor: 100′ × 13.33′ (height) = 1,333 sf

Step 2: Openings

Deduct for 4 windows and 2 doors on the first floor and 4 windows on the second floor.

Step 3: Joint Reinforcing

$\frac{13.33}{1.33} \times 129' = 1{,}290$ lf

$\frac{13.33}{1.33} \times 100' = 1{,}000$ lf

North Elevation

Step 1: 8″ Block Walls and Brick Veneer

First Floor: 55′ × 13.33′ (height) = 733 sf
21′ × 13.33′ = 280 sf
Total Length = 76′
47′ × 24.00′ (height) = 1,128 sf
Total Area = 2,141 sf

Second Floor: 46′ × 13.33′ (height) = 613 sf

Step 2: Openings

Deduct for 3 windows and 2 doors.

Step 3: Joint Reinforcing

The total amount of joint reinforcing is calculated below.

$$\frac{13.33}{1.33} \times 76' = 760 \text{ lf}$$

$$\frac{24}{1.33} \times 47' = 846 \text{ lf}$$

$$\frac{13.33}{1.33} \times 46' = 460 \text{ lf}$$

Interior Walls

Step 1: 12" Block Wall

The interior walls have flush tooled joints on both sides.
The total area of the interior walls is found as follows:

C2-C3:	46′ × 12′	=	552 sf
B2-B3:	54′ × 12′	=	648 sf
C2-B2:	46′ × 12′	=	552 sf
Total Length =	146′	Total Area =	1,752 sf

Step 2: Openings

Deduct for 2 doors and a pass-through window.

This concludes the takeoff for masonry. It is common practice among most masonry subcontractors not to add a waste allowance to the quantity totals. Turn now to Chapter 17, a discussion of the takeoff procedure for rough carpentry.

Means® Forms
QUANTITY SHEET

PROJECT Admin. Bldg.
LOCATION Picacho, Ca. ARCHITECT Bell & Bell
TAKE OFF BY PC EXTENSIONS BY: ETW

SHEET NO. QS 16
ESTIMATE NO. 1017
DATE March 1989
CHECKED BY: NS

DESCRIPTION	NO.	DIMENSIONS w	DIMENSIONS h	8" Conc. Block	UNIT	12" Conc. Block	UNIT	Brick	UNIT	Joint Reinf.	UNIT	Expan Joints	UNIT	Blocking & Shoring	UNIT
Masonry															
East Elev.		100	24'	2400				2400		1800	LF				
		30	13.3	400				400		300	LF	58	LF		
window G	4	4	5	80				80						80	
door 5	1	3	7	21				21						21	
overhead door	2	10	9	180				180						180	
window I	2	9	5	90				90						90	
South Elev.		15	10.7	160				160							
		68.7	10	687				687							
		41.3	9.3	386				386		1000					
		48	13.3	640				640		480		44	LF		
window D	2	10	3	60				60						60	
window F	1	8	4	32				32						32	
door 9	1	3.5	7	25				25						25	
window C	1	5	3	15				15						15	
window B	2	6	3	36				36						36	
West Elev.		21	9.3	196				196							
		24.3	10.7	260				260							
		25.3	12.0	304				304							
		13.3	13.3	178				178							
		45	13.3	600				600		1290					
		100	13.3	1333				1333		1000		58	LF		
window B	2	6	3	36				36						36	
window E	2	6	4	48				48						48	
window A	4	4	3	48				48						48	
doors 1 & 2	2	3.5	7	49				49						49	
North Elev.		55	13.3	733				733							
		21	13.3	280				280		760					
		47	24	1128				1128		846					
		46	13.3	613				613		460		44	LF		
window H	3	8	5	120				120						120	
door 3	1	6	7	42				42						42	
door 4	1	3.5	7	25				25						25	
Interior Walls		46	12			552									
		54	12			648									
		46	12			552				1314					
doors 6 & 7	2	3.5	7			49								49	
pass-thru window	1	4	3			12								12	
Total				9391	SF	1703	LF	9391	SF	9250	LF	204	LF	968	SF

Figure 16.3

Chapter 17

Rough Carpentry

Even in a fireproof building made of concrete or steel, there are miscellaneous wood items to take off. Buildings can be constructed with concrete or masonry and have wood-framed roofs and interior partitions. Some buildings may be made entirely of wood.

Because of the detail involved in taking off rough carpentry in a building this size, this chapter will not demonstrate the takeoff procedure. Once the quantity estimator studies the framing details, the takeoff is simply a matter of counting units and checking them off on the plans. Instead, this chapter will discuss briefly the two major categories of rough carpentry construction and suggest guidelines for their takeoff. These two categories are:

- Lumber
- Rough hardware

Lumber

Chapter 1 stated that a quantity estimate is generally not intended for the direct ordering of materials and does not need to be overly precise. For rough carpentry, however, quantities should be estimated as accurately as possible so that the cost estimator can obtain firm quotations from lumber dealers.

This can be done only by listing the length, cross-sectional dimensions, species, and grade of every piece of lumber required for the project. With very little modification, a thorough quantity estimate can serve as a "lumber list," or as the basis for ordering the material, should a superintendent choose to use it.

A complete and accurate quantity estimate can also be used as a checklist by the project superintendent for separating lumber into piles for the different uses, such as roof framing and ceiling framing.

Takeoff Items

The following building components are constructed of lumber and are taken off in sequence by the quantity estimator (see Figure 17.1):

- Sills, posts, and girders
- Floor and ceiling (platform) framing
- Roof framing
- Exterior wall framing (including door and window framing)
- Subflooring and sheathing
- Interior partitions

Sills, Posts, and Girders

These are taken off by size and quantity. Simply count the number of sills, posts, and girders on the plans, making a separate column on the quantity sheet for each size. Total the columns and convert quantities to Thousand Board Feet (MBF).

Floor and Ceiling (Platform) Framing

These items are indicated on the plans by size and spacing. Be sure to add for double joists under partitions, headers around openings, laps at bearings, ledgers, blocking, and bridging. List each item by size and quantity. Total the columns and convert to MBF.

Roof Framing

Roof framing, shown in Figure 17.2, is similar to floor framing in that the total quantity of each stock size is listed on the quantity sheet and converted to MBF. If the roof is pitched, the rafters must be measured along the slope, not the horizontal distance. Special attention must be given to overhangs, soffit framing, knee braces, collar ties, and ridge poles. If wood roof trusses or glue-laminated beams are used, the quantity estimator need only give the span, load, pitch, and number required. The cost estimator can then get a price from the manufacturer.

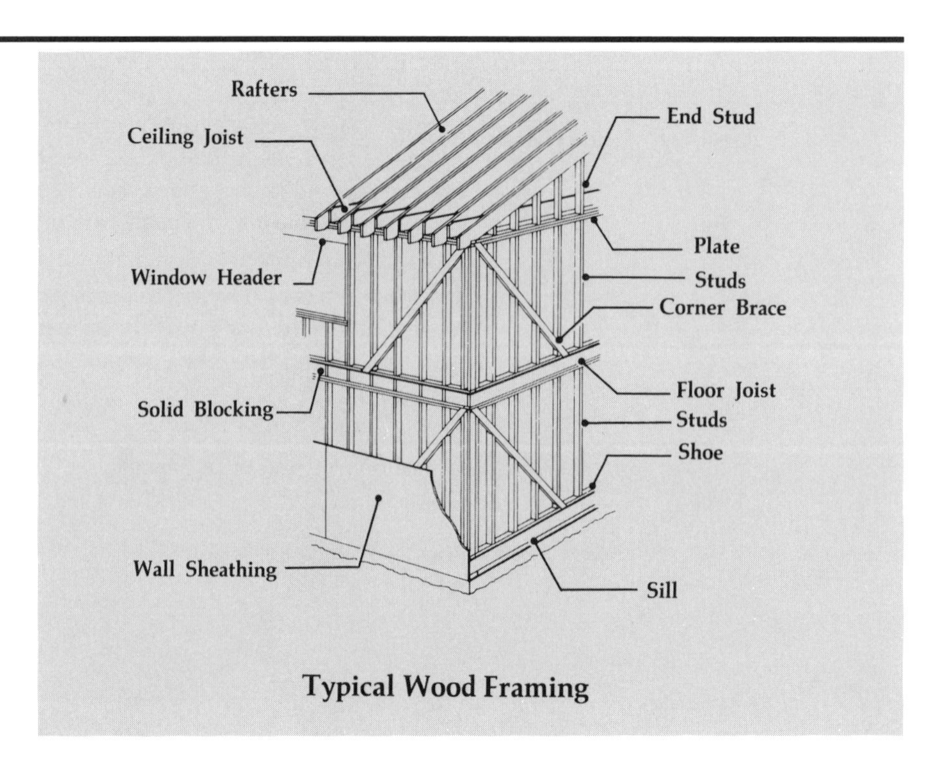

Figure 17.1

Wall Framing

This item is shown on the plans by stud size and spacing. Added to this are the sole, plate, corners, headers, and wall intersections.

Do not forget to take off bridging, blocking, fire stops, and bracing. Haulages should be recorded in standard lengths. Again, total the lengths and convert to MBF.

Subflooring and Sheathing

These are usually made of plywood or manufactured pressed wood of different thicknesses in standard 4′ × 8′ and 4′ × 10′ sheets. These are sold by the square foot rather than by MBF, and should be added up this way on the quantity sheet. Sometimes square edge or tongue and groove boards are specified. If so, they are usually nailed diagonally, with 20% added for waste.

Interior Partitions

Interior partitions, like exterior wall framing, include studs, soles, plates, headers, corners, and wall intersections. This is where the quantity estimator should also include door frames, furring, blocking, grounds, and wood basement stairs. Partitions and blocking quantities should be converted to MBF, door frames and stairs by number of units, and furring and grounds by linear foot.

Guidelines for Takeoff

The following is a list of guidelines for taking off lumber.

- Take off exterior and floor framing first, then interior framing. If masonry and concrete have already been taken off, the building perimeter and floor areas will be known.
- Separate the specified grades of material and make note of each item on the quantity sheet.

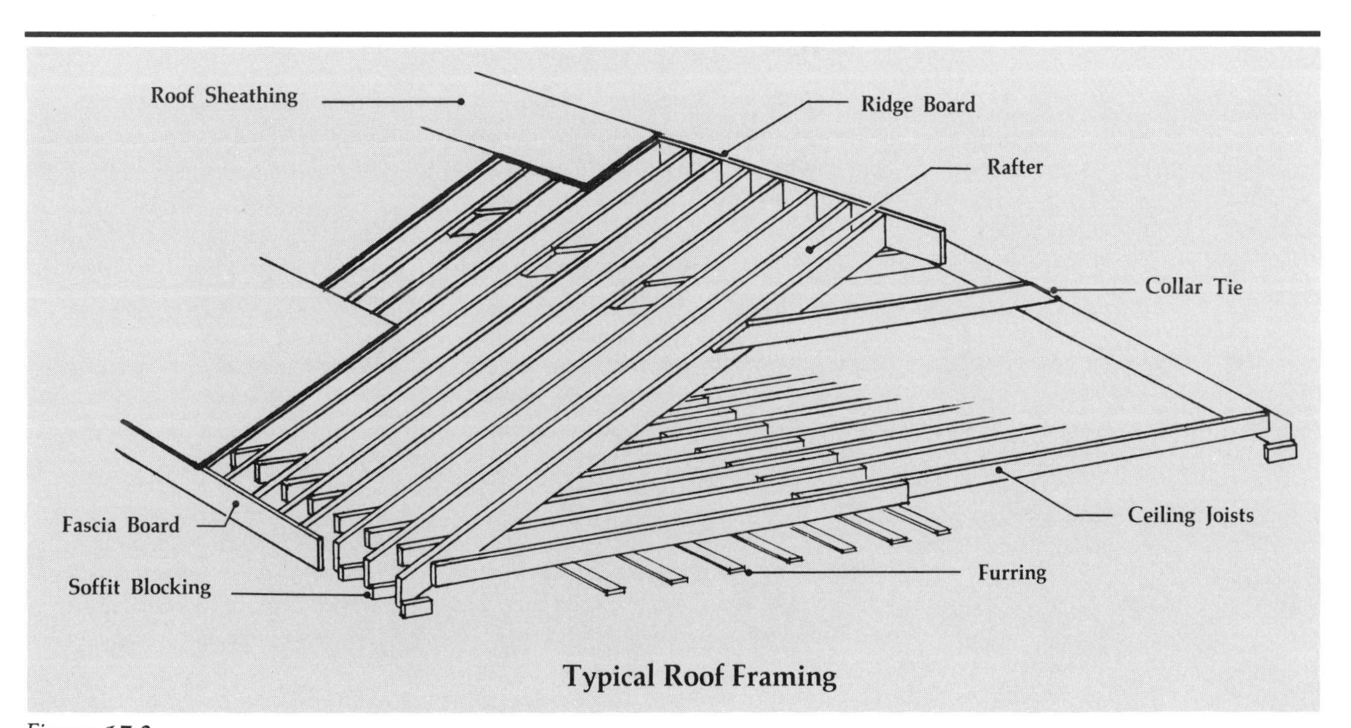

Typical Roof Framing

Figure 17.2

- Group all members by size. Use a systematic method to check off on the plans. Transfer all quantities to the quantity sheet.
- List boards, planks, and timbers by the board foot (bf). Lengths over 8′ are increased to the nearest even number of feet.
- When wood trusses are used instead of conventional roof framing, list the quantity, span, pitch, load, and any other pertinent information that the manufacturer will need.
- Prefabricated walls, particularly in residential units, are commonly used in certain parts of the country. A quantity estimate for these is not necessary, as the manufacturer quotes these complete.
- The conversion of stock sizes of lumber to board feet is simple:

  One board foot = 1′ × 1′ × 1″, or 144 cubic inches

  These conversions are determined from the *nominal* sizes, not the *dressed* (finished) sizes.
- An alternative method of taking off rough carpentry is to use the Tables of Proportionate Quantities shown in Appendix D. These should be used with discretion. Any unique building features should be taken into consideration.

Determining Waste Allowance

Determining the proper waste allowance for lumber is more complex than for concrete and earthwork, and is subject to change by those who will have direct control over the work. The following factors must be considered:

1. The amount of detail shown on the drawings, and the amount of guesswork required of the quantity estimator
2. The possibility of error on the part of the quantity estimator, particularly errors of omission
3. The possibility of bent, broken, knotty, or split or damaged lumber
4. The unanticipated need for extra material for miscellaneous purposes
5. Misuse of lumber, such as using framing lumber for concrete formwork or shoring
6. The possibility of theft or vandalism. This can vary greatly depending on the security of the work site which, unfortunately, is difficult for a quantity estimator to predict
7. The precision of the takeoff

The quantity of waste that a quantity estimator allows is determined by experience on similar projects. The quantity estimator might expect, based on past experience, a percentage of waste in the 4% to 10% range. The following is a waste projection based on the seven factors listed above.

1. Quality of drawings	0.75%
2. Quantity estimator's error	1.00
3. Faulty material	1.00
4. Accidental damage	1.50
5. Miscellaneous need	2.00
6. Loss through misuse	1.25
7. Theft or vandalism	1.50
Total =	9.00
8. Imprecision in the takeoff (deduct)	− 2.00
	7.00%

The quantity estimator should check to see if the projected waste percentage is in line with the actual waste experienced in completed buildings of comparable size and complexity. Figure 17.3, Quantity Sheet 17A, shows the takeoff for lumber.

Means® Forms
QUANTITY SHEET

PROJECT Admin. Bldg.	SHEET NO. QS 17A (PG. 1 of 4)
ESTIMATE NO. 1017
LOCATION Picacho, Ca.	ARCHITECT Bell & Bell	DATE March 1989
TAKE OFF BY PC	EXTENSIONS BY: DR	CHECKED BY: CV

DESCRIPTION	NO.	DIMENSIONS	THICKNESS	SPECIES	GRADE	QUANT	UNIT
Plywood							
Roof Sheathing - high roof		48^{0} x 100^{0}	5/8"	DF	X-CD	4800	SF
low roof		58^{25} x 134^{67}	"	"	" "	7845	
						12645	
waste allowance	3%					379	
						13024	
adjust to 4'x 8' (407 sheets)				→	→	13024	SF
Floor Sheathing		48^{0} x 100^{0}	3/4"	DF	INT-BC	4800	SF
deduct stairwell		→				105	
						4695	
waste allowance	3%					141	
						4836	
adjust to 4'x 8' (152 sheets)				→	→	4864	SF
Lounge Deck Sheathing		71^{0} x 31^{0}	3/4"	DF	X-BC	2201	SF
waste allowance	3%					66	
						2267	
adjust to 4'x 8' (71 sheets)				→	→	2272	SF
Soffit Roof Overhang		247^{0} x 2^{0}	3/8"	DF	X-AB	494	SF
waste allowance	3%					15	
						509	
adjust to 4'x 8' (16 sheets)				→	→	512	SF
Wall Sheathing							
line 3, d-b		100^{0} x 24^{0}	5/8"	DF	X-CD	2400	SF
	4	4^{0} x 5^{0}	"	"	" "	80	
	1	8^{0} x 10^{0}	"	"	" "	80	
	2	10^{0} x 10^{0}	"	"	" "	200	
b, 3-4		22^{5} x 12^{0}	"	"	" "	270	
4, b-a		30^{67} x 12^{0}	"	"	" "	368	
	2	9^{0} x 5^{0}	"	"	" "	90	
a, 4-1		127^{0} x 12^{0}	"	"	" "	1524	
	2	10^{0} x 5^{0}	"	"	" "	100	
	1	6^{0} x 7^{0}	"	"	" "	42	
		56^{0} x 5/2	"	"	" "	140	
1, a-c		80^{67} x 12^{0}	"	"	" "	968	
	3	6^{0} x 5^{0}	"	"	" "	90	
d, 1-2		56^{0} x 5/2	"	"	" "	140	
d, 2-3		48^{67} x 24^{0}	"	"	" "	1168	
	2	8^{0} x 5^{0}	"	"	" "	80	
CARRY FORWARD						6,216	SF

Figure 17.3

Means® Forms

QUANTITY SHEET

SHEET NO. QS 17A (PG. 2 of 4)

PROJECT Admin. Bldg. — ESTIMATE NO. 1017

LOCATION Picacho, Ca. — ARCHITECT Bell & Bell — DATE March 1989

TAKE OFF BY PC — EXTENSIONS BY: DR — CHECKED BY: CV

DESCRIPTION	NO.	DIMENSIONS			THICKNESS	UNIT	SPECIES	UNIT	GRADE	UNIT	QUANT	UNIT
Plywood Wall Sheathing Forwarded											6216	SF
2, b-d		100^{0}	x	24^{0}	5/8"		DF		X-CD		2400	
	2	3^{0}	x	7^{0}	"		"		" "		42	
	4	4^{0}	x	3^{0}	"		"		" "		48	
b, 2-3		48^{5}	x	24^{0}	"		"		" "		1164	
	3	3^{0}	x	7^{0}	"		"		" "		63	
	1	8^{0}	x	4^{0}	"		"		" "		32	
											9595	
waste allowance	5%										480	
											10075	
adjust to 4'x8' (315 sheets)											10080	SF
Glue-Laminated Beams					NUMBER EACH		SIZE		LENGTH		WT. EACH BEAM LBS	
low roof					1		8"x30"		50'-6"		3383	
" "					7		8"x24"		56'-6"		3028	
lounge deck					4		10"x30"		30'-8"		2546	
2nd floor					4		10"x30"		48'-6"		4025	
Stair												
stringers	8	2x14		14			DF		struc		262	BF
beams	5	4x6		6			"		struc		60	
posts	4	4x4		6			"		struc		32	
joist	5	2x6		6			"		const		30	
brace	8	2x4		8			"		const		43	
sleeper	5	2x4		6			"		const PT		20	
blocking	4	2x6		6			"		const		24	
Total											471	BF
plywood treads	21	1^{0}	x	5^{0}	3/4		DF		Int. BC		105	SF
landing	1	5^{0}	x	5^{0}	"		"		" "		25	
											130	
Waste allowance	20%										26	
											156	
adjust to 4'x8' (5 sheets)											160	SF
plywood risers	23	5^{0}	x	0^{5}	1/2"		DF		Int. BC		58	SF
adjust to 4'x8' (2 sheets)											64	SF

Figure 17.3 *(continued)*

Means® Forms
QUANTITY SHEET

SHEET NO. QS 17A (PG. 3 of 4)

PROJECT Admin. Bldg. ESTIMATE NO. 1017

LOCATION Picacho, Ca. ARCHITECT Bell & Bell DATE March 1989

TAKE OFF BY PC EXTENSIONS BY: DR CHECKED BY: CV

DESCRIPTION	NO.	DIMENSIONS		Species	Grade	Features	Board Feet
Rough Carpentry							
Roof Framing							
parapets	Ran	2x4	1790	DF	con/std		1199
joists	153	2x6	18	DF	const		2754
blocking	Ran	2x6	600	DF	con/std		600
" under ply edges	Ran	2x4	600	DF	con/std		400
beams	8	4x8	26	DF	struc.	Premium	555
facia	13	2x10	20	RW	con/ht	RS	434
rafters	201	2x8	20	DF	const		5360
blocking	Ran	2x8	528	DF	con/std		704
" under ply edges	Ran	2x4	1040	DF	con/std		697
beams	14	4x6	20	DF	struc		560
"	7	4x8	20	DF	struc		374
posts	8	4x4	6	DF	struc		64
braces	48	2x4	12	DF	con/std		386
Roof-Lounge Deck							
joists	100	2x10	20	DF	#1		3340
blocking	Ran	2x10	224	DF	con/std		374
" under ply edges	Ran	2x4	580	DF	con/std		389
handrailing - sill	11	2x4	12	RW	con/ht	RS	88
post	21	4x4	8	RW	con/ht	RS	225
rails	33	2x3	12	RW	con/ht	RS	198
cap	11	2x6	12	RW	con/ht	RS	132
facia	Ran	1x12	126	RW	con/ht	RS	126
Ceiling Framing							
2nd Floor - beams	8	4x6	26	DF	struc	Premium	416
joists	231	2x4	16	DF	const		2476
blocking	Ran	2x4	600	DF	con/std		400
ribbons	Ran	1x4	300	DF	con/std		100
1st Floor - joists	367	2x4	18	DF	const		4426
blocking	Ran	2x4	924	DF	con/std		619
ribbons	Ran	1x4	128	DF	con/std		43
Walls 2nd Floor							
Exter - posts	5	4x4	18	DF	struc		120
sills	Ran	2x4	300	DF	con/std		200
blocking	Ran	2x4	300	DF	con/std		200
studs	253	2x4	10	DF	const		1695
plates	Ran	2x4	600	DF	con/std		400
bracing	Ran	2x4	112	DF	con/std		75
low wall	Ran	2x4	216	DF	const		144
Lintels	1	4x10	16	DF	const		53
CARRY FORWARD							30326

Figure 17.3 (*continued*)

Means® Forms
QUANTITY SHEET

SHEET NO. QS 17A (PG.4 of 4)
PROJECT Admin. Bldg. ESTIMATE NO. 1017
LOCATION Picacho, Ca. ARCHITECT Bell & Bell DATE March 1989
TAKE OFF BY PC EXTENSIONS BY: DR CHECKED BY: CV

DESCRIPTION	NO.	DIMENSIONS			Species	UNIT	Grade	UNIT	Features	UNIT	Board Feet	UNIT
CARRIED FORWARD											30326	
lintels	3	4x8	12		DF		const.				96	
"	1	4x6	6		DF		const.				12	
inter-sills	Ran	2x4	50		DF		con/std.				34	
blocking	Ran	2x4	50		DF		con/std.				34	
studs	40	2x4	10		DF		const.				268	
plates	Ran	2x4	100		DF		con/std.				67	
1st Floor												
exter-posts	12	6x8	10		DF		struc.				480	
"	16	6x10	10		DF		struc.				800	
sills	Ran	2x4	320		DF		const.		PT		214	
"	Ran	2x6	300		DF		const.		PT		300	
blocking	Ran	2x4	320		DF		con/std.				214	
"	Ran	2x6	300		DF		con/std.				300	
studs	268	2x4	12		DF		const.				2144	
"	168	2x6	12		DF		const.				2016	
plates	Ran	2x4	640		DF		con/std.				429	
"	Ran	2x6	200		DF		con/std.				200	
braces	8	2x4	16		DF		con/std.				86	
"	8	2x6	16		DF		con/std.				128	
lintels	3	4x10	12		DF		const.				120	
"	1	4x12	20		DF		const.				80	
"	1	4x12	18		DF		const.				72	
"	1	6x10	16		DF		const.				80	
"	2	6x12	10		DF		const.				120	
"	1	6x6	16		DF		const.				48	
inter-sills	Ran	2x6	150		DF		const.		PT		150	
blocking	Ran	2x6	150		DF		con/std.				150	
studs	120	2x6	12		DF		const.				1440	
plates	Ran	2x6	300		DF		con/std.				300	
2nd Floor Framing												
joists	228	2x10	18		DF		#1				6840	
blocking	Ran	2x10	450		DF		con/std.				750	
" under ply edges	Ran	2x4	625		DF		con/std.				419	
											48717	
Waste Allowance											3410	
Gross Quantity											52127	

Figure 17.3 (continued)

Rough Hardware

Rough hardware refers to all of the manufactured items in rough carpentry work that are used to fasten together wood members. This section will examine the rough hardware items that are part of the general contractor's rough carpentry work.

Takeoff Items

The items taken off for rough hardware are:

- Nails
- Bolts
- Joist hangers

Nails

Nails are made from steel, aluminum, or other metals and come in a wide variety of shapes and sizes. Nails are driven into wood to make permanent connections. The term *penny* (d) is used to refer to the size of the nail. The most common nail sizes used in rough carpentry range from 6d to 20d.

Nails are not always itemized by the quantity estimator. Some quantity estimators merely make the notation "nails, *LS*", leaving the breakdown of size and quantity to the cost estimator or superintendent. Quantity estimators should take off only the most common sizes and not be concerned with galvanized, nongalvanized, common, box, or finish. Figure 17.4 shows some representative weights and number of nails per pound for different sizes of the most commonly used nails. Figure 17.5 shows some representative quantities of nails used in different types of framing.

The information given on nails, and the lumber and plywood lists previously taken off, produce the quantities of nails shown in Quantity Sheet 17B, Figure 17.7, located at the end of this chapter.

Bolts

Bolts are used to secure wood structural members where the dimensions of the members are too large to use nails. Bolts have a solid head at one end and are threaded at the other. They come in a variety of shapes, sizes, and materials. The four major types of bolts are:

- Anchor bolts (anchor wood to concrete)
- Machine bolts (connect wood to wood)
- Carriage bolts (connect wood to steel)
- Lag bolts (like machine bolts, but the threaded ends are tapered to screw into holes drilled in wood)

Nails, Number per Pound	
6d	160
8d	90
10d	60
16d	40
20d	30

Figure 17.4

Experienced quantity estimators take off bolts and other rough hardware with the lumber and plywood, rather than returning later for a separate takeoff. In this book, however, the takeoff demonstration is shown independently.

Quantity Sheet 17B shows anchor bolts in two locations only: (1) wall sills anchored to floor slabs or footings, and (2) ledger boards anchored to concrete or concrete block walls. Other projects may contain anchor bolts in other locations, such as steel column base plates connected to piers or footings.

Pay attention to the type of washers that are specified, such as malleable iron, square cut, and so forth. The cost of washers can vary greatly, and the type of washer is very important from the structural engineer's point of view.

The length of anchor bolts excludes the 90-degree return. Bolt information includes the length and diameter, and the kind of metal, if specified (steel, galvanized, nickel, etc.). Machine bolt lengths are measured from the thread end to the bottom of the head. Information given on drawings is often limited to the distance of embedment into walls or floors, leaving the quantity estimator to decide the actual length of the bolt.

Drawings should show the sizes and locations of all bolts. If the drawings are not this detailed, the quantity estimator should note on the quantity sheet, "Misc. bolts, LS" to call the cost estimator's attention to this fact.

Joist Hangers

Joist hangers are manufactured from sheet or plate metal in a variety of shapes and sizes to support the ends of joists. (See Figure 17.6.) Joist hangers should be taken off only when clearly detailed or specified. A quantity estimator is not required to "design" any part of a project. A quantity estimator may notice places on the drawings where joist hangers could be used, but are not called for. He or she should make a note for the cost estimator or superintendent if a large number of joist hangers are involved.

Nails, Quantity for Various Uses

Use	Lumber Dimensions	Pounds per MBF
Roof framing	2 x 6	15
	2 x 8	18
Floor framing	2 x 10	22
Ceiling framing	2 x 4	12
Wall framing	2 x 4	15
	2 x 6	18
Sheathing	—	20
Misc. blocking	—	25

Figure 17.5

There are a number of other hardware items, such as straps, angles, post caps, and "T" connectors, that may be used in construction. The quantity estimator should take off all hardware that is called out on the plans and specifications, or that he or she can reasonably anticipate. A few pieces of overlooked hardware may not have an effect on the cost estimate of a large project, but a large number of important hardware items can add up to a significant cost item. Ideally, the takeoff (excluding nails) should be thorough and specific enough to send to hardware suppliers for price quotations should the estimator wish to do so. Figure 17.7, Quantity Sheet 17B, shows the takeoff for carpentry hardware.

This concludes the discussion of rough carpentry takeoff. Chapter 18 examines the takeoff procedure for finish carpentry.

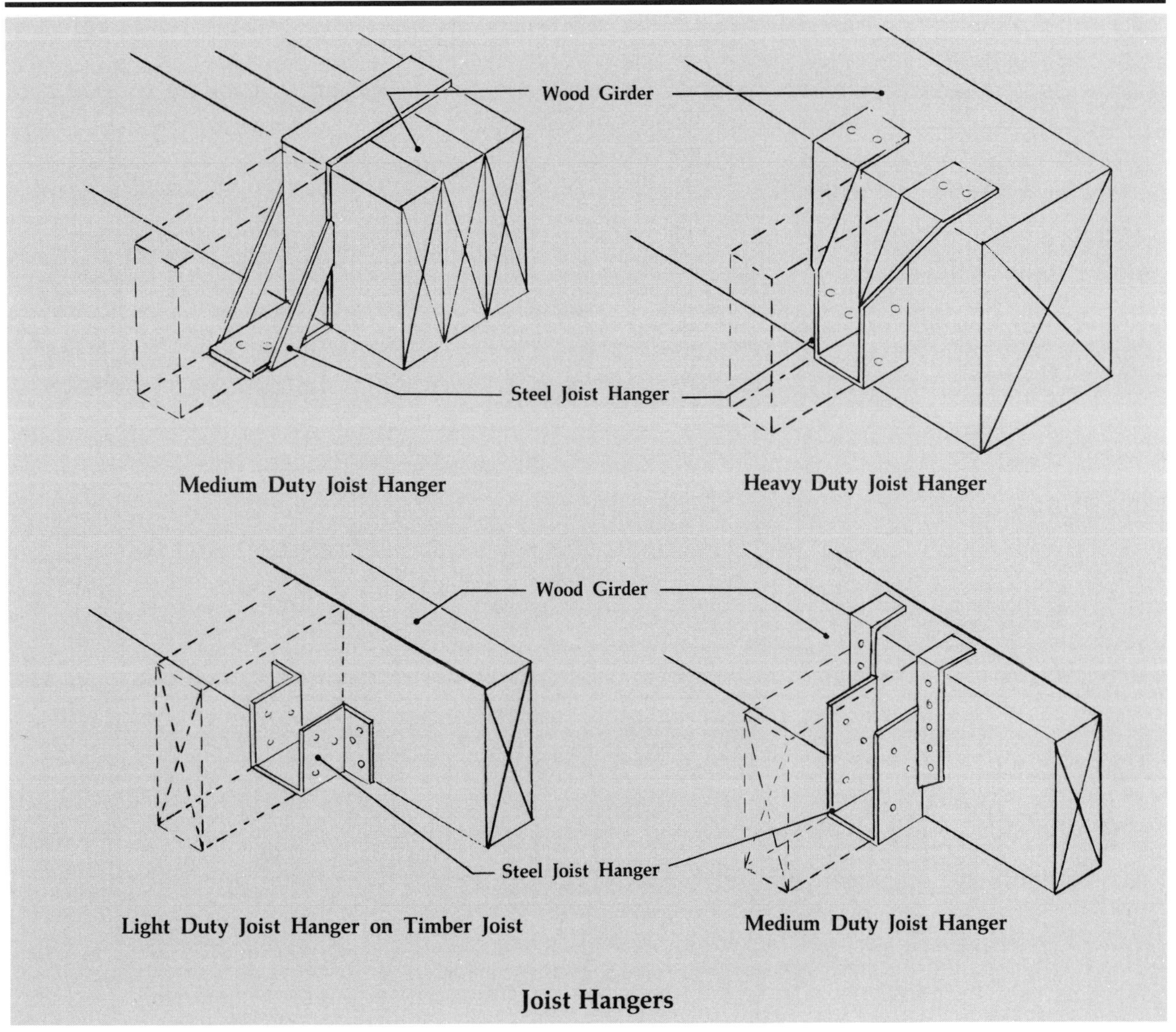

Figure 17.6

Means® Forms

QUANTITY SHEET

SHEET NO. QS 17B

PROJECT Admin. Bldg. ESTIMATE NO. 1017

LOCATION Picacho, Ca. ARCHITECT Bell & Bell DATE March 1989

TAKE OFF BY PC EXTENSIONS BY: DR CHECKED BY: CV

DESCRIPTION	NO.	DIMENSIONS			
Rough Hardware					
Nails - Roof Framing			MBF	UNIT	LBS
		2 x 4	1.6	13	21
		2 x 6	3.4	15	51
		2 x 8	6.1	18	110
beams		4 x 8	1.1	10	11
floor framing		2 x 10	11.3	22	249
ceiling framing		2 x 4	3.4	12	41
wall framing		2 x 4	6.3	15	95
		2 x 6	2.9	18	52
sheathing plywood			30.8	20	616
misc. blocking			12.5	25	313
					1559
waste allowance 20%					312
Total nails of all kinds →					1871 LBS
Anchor Bolts (AB's)		SIZE	WASHER		NUMBER
wall sill bolt		5/8" x 8"	square cut		363 ea.
ledger bolt		3/4" x 6"	Malleable		180 ea.
Machine Bolts					
		1/2" x 6"	Malleable		210 ea.
		5/8" x 8"	"		72 ea.
		5/8" x 10"	"		115 ea.
		3/4" x 12"	"		27 ea.
Lag Bolts		1/4" x 6"	stamped		45 ea.
		3/8" x 8"	"		52 ea.
Misc. Bolts					LS
Joist Hangers	For	2" x 8"			67 ea.
	For	2" x 4"			1196 ea.
Alternate Angle Clips					(1196 ea.)
Joist Bridging		2 x 6 joists			150 ea.
		2 x 8 joists			200 ea.
		2 x 10 joists			320 ea.

Figure 17.7

Chapter 18

Finish Carpentry

Finish carpentry is carpentry work that is exposed to view and which therefore requires the use of quality materials and skillful installation. Rough carpentry, on the other hand, is for structural purposes and is usually hidden beneath finish exteriors so that it cannot be seen.

The purpose of the finish carpentry takeoff is to (1) construct a checklist to analyze millwork sub-bids or quotations, and (2) provide a basis for estimating the cost of installation labor and special materials that are not supplied by subcontractors.

Finish Carpentry Categories

Finish carpentry work can be categorized according to the sources from which the required materials will be purchased. Categorizing in this way enables the cost estimator to place his or her orders more efficiently. These categories are as follows:

- Millwork
- Nonmillwork
- Rough hardware (for finish carpentry)
- Miscellaneous items installed by finish carpenters
- Cabinets and casework

Each of these categories is discussed below.

Millwork

Millwork is a term for certain finish carpentry materials that require special shaping or fabricating by a mill, such as doors, windows, cabinets, moldings, and shelving.

Nonmillwork

Nonmillwork is a term for finish carpentry materials that are of stock manufacture (they do not have to be modified in the mill or cabinet shop), such as standard sawn and dressed trim, lumber, and hardwood paneling.

Rough Hardware

Rough hardware for finish carpentry includes nails, bolts, screws, and angles used to fasten wood members together. These items are not ordinarily exposed to view.

Miscellaneous Items

Miscellaneous finish carpentry items are not made of wood but are customarily installed by finish carpenters. These items include metal doors and frames, finish hardware, and building specialties.

Cabinets and Casework

Cabinets and casework are constructed in cabinet shops by subcontractors. Included in this category are counters, base cabinets, wall cabinets, and shelving units.

The quantity estimator should be familiar with the general contractor's sources for the various finish carpentry materials, since this information could affect the method and degree of detail of the takeoff. The quantity estimator must know who will supply the materials and who will install them before he or she can perform a proper takeoff. Figure 18.1 is a table that a quantity estimator might create which shows who supplies each finish carpentry item, and the reason for taking off that item (i.e., whether the general contractor will purchase and install them, or whether they will be supplied by a subcontractor and installed by the general contractor).

Note that in Figure 18.1, many of the items are obtained from the millwork supplier, although in commercial and industrial construction, suppliers rarely install materials (with the exception of unusual casework). Millwork and finish carpentry materials are almost always installed by the general contractor's employees. The main purpose of the takeoff, therefore, is to provide the information required to make a *labor cost* estimate. Incidental to that may be some minor materials not furnished by the millwork supplier, such as stripping, backing, blocking, and bracing, which are not practical to itemize, and for which the quantity estimator or cost estimator can only make an allowance.

Categorizing Finish Carpentry Work

Finish Carpentry Item	Furnished By	Purpose of Take Off
Doors & frames	Door supplier	Estimation of installation labor
Windows & frames	Window supplier	" "
Finish hardware	Hardware supplier	" "
Wood moldings & trim	Millwork supplier	" "
Paneling, hardwood, etc.	Millwork supplier	" "
Stair treads, risers, rails	Millwork supplier	" "
Shelving	Millwork supplier	" "
Miscellaneous millwork	Millwork supplier	" "
Cabinets & casework	Millwork supplier	" "
Rough hardware	General Contractor	To purchase & install

Figure 18.1

Millwork bids vary in the items they include and propose to furnish. The ideal millwork bid will include "everything" delivered to the job site, and leave very little material for the quantity estimator to take off for separate purchasing. A quantity estimator must anticipate the materials that will be furnished to the job site by the millwork supplier and the materials that must be purchased additionally. This distinction is necessary for a proper takeoff.

Takeoff Items

Unfortunately, categorizing finish carpentry by source is not practical for takeoff purposes; it is not very useful when trying to assess how much material will be needed on the project and which materials will be provided by subcontractors. For scheduling and installation purposes, and for ease in takeoff, finish carpentry is generally categorized in groups of similar items. The finish carpentry items that will be taken off our model administrative building are:

- Doors
- Door frames
- Door hardware (requiring special labor)
- Windows
- Window frames
- Exterior trim
- Interior trim
- Stairs
- Rough hardware
- Cabinets and shelving

Each of these items is examined below.

Doors and Door Frames

Doors are often presented in a door schedule. A door schedule provides more detailed information than the floor plans. The door and door frames are taken off by cross-reference between the floor plans and a door schedule. The plans show locations of the doors, and the schedule shows sizes and other necessary information. The doors in our present project are summarized in the schedule in Figure 18.2. As the doors are taken off, they should be checked off or shaded on both the drawings and door schedule.

Since the purpose of the takeoff is to estimate labor costs, it is not necessary to determine the size of the door frames unless they are exceptionally large. However, we do need to distinguish between exterior and interior frames because of the differing labor costs. For now, postpone the takeoff of casings, as they are installed as a separate item.

Metal Doors

Commercial- or industrial-quality metal doors are not usually available from general building material or lumber suppliers. They are normally quoted in a lump sum bid by metal door manufacturers. Therefore, the quantity estimator's main concern is installation labor. The sizes of doors should be noted, since size affects labor costs.

Door No.	Type	Material	Size			Hardware						Remarks
			Th	W	H	Lock set	Auto closure	Threshold	Kick plate	Push plate	Panic hdwe.	
①	A	Metal	$1\frac{3}{4}$	3′-6″	7′-0″	×	×	×			×	
②	A	Metal	$1\frac{3}{4}$	3′-6″	7′-0″	×	×	×			×	Type
(Pr.) ③	A	Metal	$1\frac{3}{4}$	3′-0″	7′-0″	×	×	×			×	A
④	D	Metal	$1\frac{3}{4}$	3′-6″	7′-0″	×	×	×			×	
⑤	B	Metal	$1\frac{3}{4}$	3′-0″	7′-0″	×	×	×			×	
⑥	C	Metal	$1\frac{3}{4}$	3′-0″	7′-0″	×	×	×	×	×		B
⑦	C	Metal	$1\frac{3}{4}$	3′-0″	7′-0″	×	×	×	×	×		
⑧	D	Metal	$1\frac{3}{8}$	3′-0″	7′-0″	×			×			
⑨	D	Metal	$1\frac{3}{4}$	3′-6″	7′-0″	×	×	×			×	C
⑩	B	Metal	$1\frac{3}{4}$	3′-0″	7′-0″		×					
⑪	B	Metal	$1\frac{3}{4}$	3′-0″	7′-0″		×					
⑫	D	Metal	$1\frac{3}{8}$	2′-6″	7′-0″		×	×	×	×		D
⑬	D	Metal	$1\frac{3}{8}$	2′-6″	7′-0″		×	×	×	×		

Figure 18.2

Metal Door Frames

The size of the metal door frames is not important, unless they are exceptionally large. The labor cost to install metal door frames is not significantly affected by the size of the frames. Thus, the quantity estimator need only count the number of frames. However, if frame sizes exceed 5′ wide and 7′ high, the sizes should be noted on the quantity sheet.

Door Hardware

Door hardware is furnished by hardware suppliers who perform their own takeoffs. Therefore, the quantity estimator's takeoff is installation-oriented. In a typical project, the following hardware is taken off by the general contractor's quantity estimator:

- Door hardware (that may occur on some, but not all, doors)
- Cabinet hardware (installation is included in the installation cost of cabinets, and is discussed in detail in a later section)
- Miscellaneous hardware (such as shelf standards)

In our present project, the door hardware to be taken off consists of:

- Automatic closers
- Thresholds
- Kick plates
- Push plates
- Panic hardware

Automatic closers fasten to the doors and door frames and, by means of springs or hydraulic-powered arms, maintain the doors in a closed position.

Thresholds are specially shaped plates secured to the floor beneath doors to close the gap and seal out the weather.

Kick plates and *push plates* are metal plates attached to the doors to protect them from damage.

Panic hardware is an assembly mounted to the door which allows it to be opened easily in case of emergency simply by applying pressure to a horizontal bar.

Not all finish hardware needs to be itemized for installation cost. For example, door hinges and locksets are included in the cost to install doors and therefore need not be taken off. Only those units of hardware that require separate pricing for installation must be taken off. See Quantity Sheet 18A, Figure 18.5.

Windows

Our project contains nine different types or sizes of windows, labeled A through I. They will arrive at the job site complete with glass and hardware, ready to be installed. Take off the windows by type and number of each size.

Window Frames

Window frames are taken off by type and number of each size. Trim is taken off separately. See the window schedule in Figure 18.3, and Quantity Sheet 18B, Figure 18.6.

Exterior Trim

Exterior trim consists of casings for doors and windows. These are easily taken off from the given door and window sizes.

The finish schedule, shown in Figure 18.4, is very important to the quantity estimator because it summarizes for each room all of the finishes required for floors, walls, and ceilings. Not everything on the finish schedule applies to finish carpentry. The quantity estimator must select and check off only those items on the schedule that belong to the category of finish carpentry. He or she may refer to the finish schedule in the future as the takeoff of other trades proceeds.

In finish carpentry, it is important to distinguish between hardwood and softwood. Hardwood costs more to install than softwood because it takes longer to saw, fit, nail, and so forth. But there is no need to make the fine distinction between species such as oak, walnut, or birch. When no mention of the kind of wood is made, the wood is assumed to be softwood.

Window Schedule

Window Type	Material	W	H	Remarks
A	Alum	4′-0″	3′-0″	
B	Alum	6′-0″	3′-0″	
C	Alum	5′-0″	3′-0″	
D	Alum	10′-0″	3′-0″	w/6″ × 4″ × $\frac{1}{4}$″ tubing mullion
E	Alum	6′-0″	4′-0″	
F	Alum	8′-0″	4′-0″	
G	Alum	4′-0″	5′-0″	
H	Alum	8′-0″	5′-0″	
I	Alum	9′-0″	5′-0″	w/6″ × 4″ × $\frac{1}{4}$″ tubing mullion

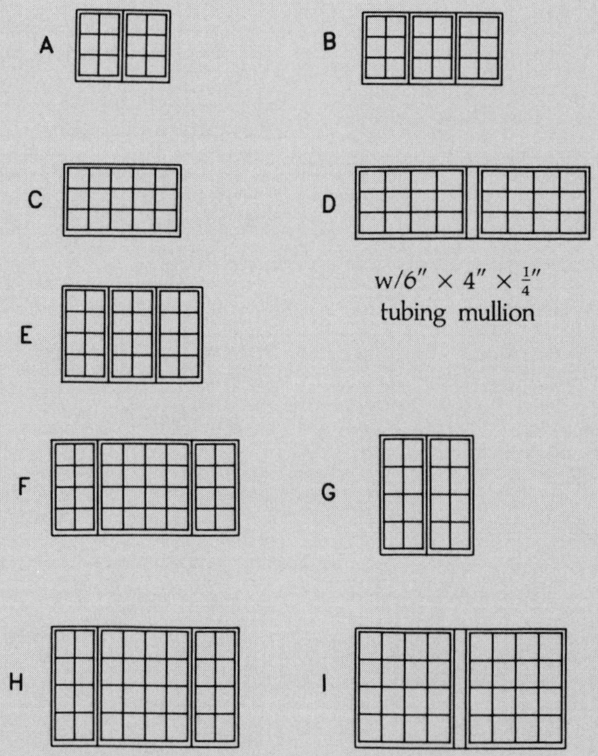

Figure 18.3

Finish Schedule

Room No.	Description	Floors			Walls				Ceiling	Base			
		Exposed concrete	Ceramic tile	Carpet	Gyp. board	Wood paneling	Ceramic tile 4″-0″ high	Painted block	Acoustic tile	Ceramic tile	Wood	Vinyl cove	Ceiling height
101	Lobby			×	×	×			×		×	×	9′-6″
102	General offices			×	×				×			×	9′-6″
103	Public utilities			×	×				×			×	9′-6″
104	Automotive	×			×			×	×			×	10′-4½″
105	Storage	×			×							×	10′-0″
106	Plumbing & electric	×			×				×			×	10′-0″
201	Conference			×	×	×			×		×	×	8′-0″
202	Engineering			×	×				×			×	8′-0″
203	Women's restroom		×	×			×		×	×			8′-0″
204	Men's restroom		×	×			×		×	×			8′-0″

Figure 18.4

The floor plans in Appendix A show a number of walls that are to be covered with wood paneling applied over gypsum board. We can take the wall lengths from the floor plans, but the heights are given on the wall elevations. Refer to the door and window schedules for the areas to be deducted for openings in the paneling. When all of the wall paneling is taken off, add a waste allowance and then adjust for full-sized sheets.

Interior Trim

Interior trim consists of door and window casings, ceiling molding, and baseboard molding. We will postpone items associated with the stairs to be taken off together under miscellaneous finish carpentry work.

The door and window casings are taken off easily based on the information provided in the door and window schedules (Figures 18.2 and 18.3). For baseboard quantities, refer to the finish schedule in Figure 18.4.

It is advisable to add an amount to all net quantities for cutting and waste, keeping in mind that one of the purposes of the finish carpentry takeoff is to check against millwork quotations. All of the interior and exterior trim quantities in our takeoff include a 10% waste allowance.

Stairs

Wood stair finish work consists of treads, risers, stringers, handrails, wall caps, and molding. Note that if wood stairs are used, the treads, handrail, and cap would be hardwood. In addition, take off the railing brackets, counting one near each end of each section of railing, and at approximately 4′ oc.

For demonstration purposes (not shown on the quantity sheet), imagine that we have a 5′ wide stairway with finished wood treads and risers. Although the top tread will be part of the second floor, we will include them in our count. The handrail is two sloped sections of 14′ each, and 2 horizontal sections of 5′ each, for a total of 38 lf. The stringers on both sides of the sloped sections total 56 lf. The cap continues on the wall around the stairwell at the second floor. The length of molding under the cap is twice the length of the cap.

Rough Hardware

Rough hardware, such as nails and screws, cannot be itemized, but the quantity estimator should remind the estimator to include a cost allowance. We do this by using the symbol "LS", denoting a lump sum amount.

Cabinets and Shelving

For convenience, cabinets can be classified as follows:

- Wall cabinets that stand on the floor and are 4′ or higher
- Overhead (OH) wall cabinets that are fastened to the wall with no support underneath
- Base wall cabinets that stand on the floor against the wall and are less than 4′ high
- Island floor cabinets that stand free from walls on at least three sides
- Island overhead cabinets are similar to island base cabinets, except that they do not touch the floor, and are usually supported from the ceiling or by posts

Shelving can be classified as follows:

- Adjustable shelves
- Stationary shelves

Like other finish carpentry items, cabinets and shelves come to the job site ready for installation by the general contractor's employees. Consequently, the quantity estimator is labor-oriented in his or her approach to the takeoff. The quantity estimator does not need to be concerned with the many details and parts that are involved with cabinet construction, only with the units in bulk—overall length, height, and depth—as this is the essential information that the cost estimator needs. See Quantity Sheet 18C (Figure 18.7), located at the end of this chapter.

As a rule, cabinets and shelves are taken off as follows:

- Base cabinets are taken off in linear feet, with the depth, type of wood, and type of top noted.
- Wall cabinets are taken off in square feet of front face, with the depth noted.
- Overhead wall cabinets are taken off in square feet of front face surface, with the depth and type of wood noted.
- Shelving generally follows the rules for cabinets. Fixed wall type shelves are measured by the square foot of front face surface, and the depth is noted. A simple sketch will show the number of shelves and vertical dividers. Single shelves are taken off in linear feet, and the depth noted.

The height and depth dimensions are usually given on the drawings, but the length dimensions are often not given because the cabinets are expected to fill the available space, depending on field measurements. For the takeoff, the quantity estimator often scales for length. Since lengths cannot be scaled accurately, they should be shown in even foot lengths (rounded upward).

The following is a list of additional guidelines for taking off cabinets and shelving.

- The quantity estimator should follow the order of interior elevations given on the drawings (A, B, C, and so forth) and proceed from room to room. This method simplifies the checking process and could possibly serve as a guide to the project superintendent when scheduling fabrication and delivery to the job site.
- Cabinets are assumed to be softwood, unless hardwood is noted.
- Cabinets are assumed to be "standard" quality unless terms such as "custom" or "premium" are applied. The term "premium" implies a high quality in cabinet work and, consequently, more time, care, and cost in the installation. Natural finish, as compared to paint grade, is another distinction a quantity estimator should note on the takeoff, as installation for natural finish cabinets is more expensive than for paint grade.
- Do not itemize ordinary hardware as the cost of these items is included in the cost of installing the cabinets. Any additional hardware that will affect the cost of installation should be noted.
- When writing down the dimensions on the quantity sheet, state them in the following order: length, height, depth.
- Unlike footings and other building components, which are taken off in decimal feet, cabinet dimensions are written down on the quantity sheet in feet and inches (that is, 12'-6', not 12.5').
- Check off or shade the plans as the cabinets are taken off to avoid omitting or doubling quantities. This should not be done until the individual cabinet is actually taken off.
- On the quantity sheet, only hardwood paneling requires totaling, since it is taken off in square feet. The other items, such as doors, windows, and trim, are taken off individually and require no totaling.

This concludes the discussion of finish carpentry. The next chapter examines the takeoff procedure for structural steel.

Means® Forms

QUANTITY SHEET

SHEET NO. QS 18A

PROJECT Admin. Bldg. | ESTIMATE NO. 1017

LOCATION Picacho, Ca. | ARCHITECT Bell & Bell | DATE March 1989

TAKE OFF BY PC | EXTENSIONS BY: ETW | CHECKED BY: NS

DESCRIPTION	DOOR TYPE	DIMENSIONS w	h	t		UNIT		UNIT		UNIT		UNIT
Metal Doors												
Slab door	D	2⁶	7⁰	1 3/8	2	ea.						
1 hr rated		3⁰	7⁰	1 3/8	1	ea.						
		3⁶	7⁰	1 3/4	2	ea.						
8"x 20" glazed wire glass	C	3⁰	7⁰	1 3/4	2	ea.						
Half glazed wire glass	B	3⁰	7⁰	1 3/4	3	ea.						
Paneled	A											
single		3⁶	7⁰	1 3/4	2	ea.						
pair		3⁰	7⁰	1 3/4	1	ea.						
Metal Door Frames												
	D	2⁶	7⁰	1 3/8	2	ea.						
	D	3⁰	7⁰	1 3/8	1	ea.						
	B & C	3⁰	7⁰	1 3/4	5	ea.						
	A & D	3⁶	7⁰	1 3/4	4	ea.						
	A	6⁰	7⁰	1 3/4	1	ea.						
Door Hardware												
Lock set					9	ea.						
Auto closure					12	ea.						
Threshold					10	ea.						
Kick Plate					5	ea.						
Push Plate					4	ea.						
Panic Hardware					6	ea.						

Figure 18.5

Means® Forms

QUANTITY SHEET

SHEET NO. QS 18B

PROJECT Admin. Bldg. — ESTIMATE NO. 1017

LOCATION Picacho, Ca. — ARCHITECT Bell & Bell — DATE March 1989

TAKE OFF BY PC — EXTENSIONS BY: ETW — CHECKED BY: NS

DESCRIPTION	WINDOW TYPE	DIMENSIONS w	DIMENSIONS h		UNIT		UNIT		UNIT		UNIT
Windows (Alum.)											
Fixed, 12 Panes	A	4⁰	3⁰	4	ea.						
" 18 "	B	6⁰	3⁰	4	ea.						
" 15 "	C	5⁰	3⁰	1	ea.						
" 24 "	D	10⁰	3⁰	2	ea.						
" 24 "	E	6⁰	4⁰	2	ea.						
" 32 "	F	8⁰	4⁰	1	ea.						
" 16 "	G	4⁰	5⁰	4	ea.						
" 32 "	H	8⁰	5⁰	3	ea.						
" 32 "	I	9⁰	5⁰	2	ea.						
Window Frames (Alum.)	A	4⁰	3⁰	4	ea.						
	B	6⁰	3⁰	4	ea.						
	C	5⁰	3⁰	1	ea.						
	D	10⁰	3⁰	2	ea.						
	E	6⁰	4⁰	2	ea.						
	F	8⁰	4⁰	1	ea.						
	G	4⁰	5⁰	4	ea.						
	H	8⁰	5⁰	3	ea.						
	I	9⁰	5⁰	2	ea.						

Figure 18.6

Means® Forms

QUANTITY SHEET

SHEET NO. QS 18C

PROJECT Admin. Bldg.　　ESTIMATE NO. 1017

LOCATION Picacho, Bldg.　　ARCHITECT Bell & Bell　　DATE March 1989

TAKE OFF BY PC　　EXTENSIONS BY: ETW　　CHECKED BY: NS

DESCRIPTION	NO.	DIMENSIONS w	DIMENSIONS h		QTY	UNIT		UNIT		UNIT		UNIT
Finish Carpentry (Misc.)												
Hardwood Paneling 1/4" Thk.												
Room 201		48	8		384	SF						
Room 101		55	9⁶		523	SF						
window H	1	8	5		40							
Total					867	SF						
waste allowances 8%					936	SF						
Interior Trim												
door casing		3/4" x 2 1/2"			248	LF						
window casing		3/4" x 1 5/8"			355	LF						
window stool		7/8" x 2 1/2"			157	LF						
window apron		3/4" x 2 1/2"			157	LF						
baseboard @ wood paneling		3/4" x 3 1/2"			113	LF						
Pass Thru Window Frame with Counter		4⁰	3⁰		1	ea.						
Rough Hardware						LS						
Cabinets & Shelves												
Room 103												
Birch wall shelving unit 20⁰ x 8⁰ x 1²					160	SF						
Room 104												
Base wall cab lam plastic top Drawers, Doors, Shelves 3⁰ x 2⁶					30	LF						
Overhead Shelving Unit 3⁰ x 1²					40	LF						
Room 202												
wall-hung plan table birch 3⁰ deep					40	LF						

Figure 18.7

Chapter 19
Structural Steel

Structural steel refers to the steel load bearing members that contribute to the "structure" of the building, such as columns, beams, braces, and their connecting plates. Structural steel work is almost always sublet to specialists who fabricate the material components in their steel shops, transport them to job sites, and erect them in place. Figure 19.1 shows the components in a typical structural steel assembly.

A general contractor's quantity estimator takes off steel when (1) the project's steel requirements are too small to interest subcontractors, (2) there is not enough time to obtain a sub bid, (3) a noncompetitive sub bid is expected, or (4) the cost estimate is intended to be preliminary.

Takeoff Items

The items typically taken off for structural steel include:

- The number of each type and size steel beams
- The number of each type and size steel columns
- Column anchor bolts and base plates
- Beam seats
- Beam connecting plates
- Lintels
- Mullions

Manufactured steel shapes that come in stock sizes are taken off in linear feet first, then converted to pounds according to the manufacturer's tables of properties. After the total number of linear feet has been determined, convert pounds to tons. All fractional measurements should be rounded to the next whole foot or pound.

Lintels and mullions may be taken off with structural steel or miscellaneous metal. Usually if they are shown on the structural drawings, they are taken off with structural steel. If they are shown on the architectural drawings, they are taken off with miscellaneous metal.

Incidental and associated steel items, such as base plates, beam seats, and connecting base plates, may be taken off by counting the number of units.

Takeoff Demonstration

This section demonstrates the takeoff procedure for the structural steel components in our model administrative building. Refer to the Second Floor and Low Roof Framing Plan and the High Roof Framing Plan in Appendix A. Notice that the floor plan has an extended grid system that coincides with the lines of the beams and columns, making possible the identification and back-checking of each item in the takeoff. Transfer all quantities to Quantity Sheets 19A (Figure 19.2) and 19B (Figure 19.3), located at the end of this chapter.

Start the takeoff at the high roof and work down to the first floor. Take off each floor in a clockwise direction. Notice that beams are spliced over columns. Therefore, each row of beams is composed of two individual beams. Take them off in their true individual lengths.

Second Floor Beams and Columns

Step 1: Line $C_1$2-$C_1$3

There are 2 beams 18″ deep and weighing 50 pounds per linear foot. The length of each beam is 24 feet. The quantity is:

$2 \times 24' = 48$ lf

The height of the column over which the two beams are spliced is:

$9.42' - 1.5'$ (room height − depth of beam) $= 7.92'$ (round to 8′)

This column weighs 33 pounds per linear foot.

Step 2: Line $B_1$2-$B_1$3

The two beams on the second floor, represented by line $B_1$2-$B_1$3, have the same length as in Step 1: 24 lf. The column is also the same as that in Step 1.

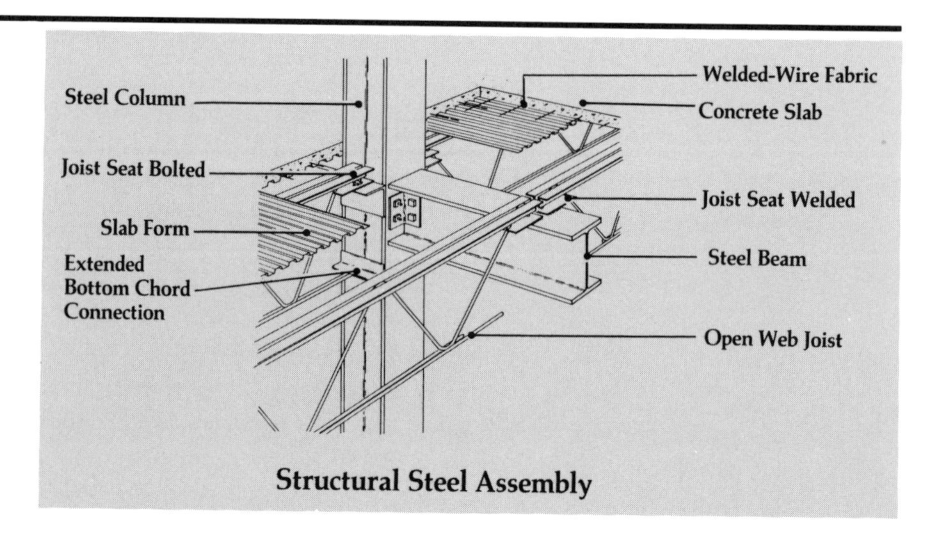

Structural Steel Assembly

Figure 19.1

First Floor Beams and Columns

Step 1: Line $C_1 2$-$C_1 3$

Moving down to the first floor, take off the steel along line $C_1 2$-$C_1 3$, then proceed in a clockwise direction. The length of each beam is 24'. These beams are 21" deep, and weigh 73 pounds per linear foot. The column height, which continues through to the second floor, is:

107.5 (elev second floor slab) — 94.17 (top of concrete pier) = 13.33 lf (round to 14')

The column weighs 45 pounds per linear foot.

In addition, there is also steel framing at the stairwell:

(W12 × 19) Length = 22' + 7' + 10.16' + 12.33' = 51.5'

Step 2: Line $B_1 2$-$B_1 3$

Beams and columns on line $B_1 2$-$B_1 3$ are the same as those in Step 1.

Step 3: Line $B_1 1$-$B_1 2$

On line $B_1 1$-$B_1 2$, the beams are 18" deep and weigh 50 pounds. Each beam is 28 lf. The column is 12' and weighs 31 pounds per linear foot.

Step 4: Line $C_1 1$-$C_1 2$

On line $C_1 1$-$C_1 2$, the beam is 28 lf and weighs 50 pounds per linear foot. The column is a 6" diameter pipe, whose height is the same as in Step 3: 12'. This column weighs 18.97 pounds per linear foot.

Step 5: Line $D_1 1$-$D_1 2$

The beam represented by line $D_1 1$-$D_1 2$ weighs 60 pounds per linear foot. The length of this beam is the same as that in Step 4. The column is also the same as in Step 4.

Lintels and Mullions

Next, take off the lintels and mullions. Start with the East Elevation and proceed in a clockwise direction. All lintels for our building are the same: three angles, 5" × 3-1/2" × 3/8', weighing 31 pounds per linear foot. The only exception is at the overhead doors, where the lintels will be three angles, 6" × 3-1/2" × 3/8', weighing 35 pounds per linear foot. Specifications require lintels to extend at least 6" into the block walls on each side of openings. Therefore, each lintel will be 1 foot longer than the width of openings.

The mullion is a piece of rectangular tubing, 6" × 4" × 1/4", weighing 15.6 pounds per linear foot. Transfer all quantities to Quantity Sheet 19B (Figure 19.3), located at the end of this chapter.

Step 1: East Elevation

East Elevation windows labeled "G", in the second floor, have a combined lintel length of:

4' + 1' = 5 lf

Door number 5 has a lintel length of:

5' + 1' = 6 lf

The two overhead doors each have lintel lengths of:

10' + 1' = 11 lf

Windows labeled "I" have a continuous lintel over both windows, and one vertical mullion. The Window Schedule in Figure 18.3 shows these windows to be 9′ wide. The total length of lintel, including 4″ over the mullion, is:

> 2.67′ between windows + (2 × 0.5′) + (2 × 9′) + (2 × 0.33) = 22.33 lf (round to 23′)

Window height in Figure 18.3 is 5′. Therefore, mullion height is 5 lf.

Step 2: South Elevation

Moving to the South Elevation, we find the Window D lintel to be:

> 2.67′ + 10′ + 10′ + 1′ + 0.67′ = 24.34 lf (round to 25′)

The mullion is 3′ high.

Window F on the second floor has a lintel length of:

> 8′ + 1′ = 9 lf

Door 9 has a lintel length of:

> 3.5′ + 1′ = 4.5 lf (round to 5′)

Window C has a lintel length of:

> 5′ + 1′ = 6 lf

Windows labeled "B" have a lintel length of:

> 2.67′ + 6′ + 6′ + 1′ = 15.67 lf (round to 16′)

Step 3: West Elevation

Windows B will be similar to those in the South Elevation: 16 lf.

Windows labeled "E" on the West Elevation have a combined lintel length of:

> 6′ + 1′ = 7 lf

Windows labeled "A", second floor, have a combined lintel length of:

> 4′ + 1′ = 5 lf

Doors 1 and 2 have a combined lintel length of:

> 3.5′ + 1′ = 4.5′ (round to 5)

Step 4: North Elevation

Windows labeled "H" on the North Elevation have a combined lintel length of:

> 8′ + 1′ = 9 lf

Door 3 has a lintel length of:

> 6′ + 1′ = 7 lf

Door 4 has a lintel length of:

> 3.5′ + 1′ = 4.5′ (round to 5 lf)

Concluding the Takeoff

Total the columns on Quantity Sheets 19A and 19B, and express in linear feet. Multiply by the given weights per linear foot to obtain total pounds. Convert pounds to tons. It is not feasible for a quantity estimator to add waste allowance to structural steel in the way that it is added to lumber, plywood, and gypsum board.

This concludes the takeoff demonstration for structural steel. Chapter 20 examines the takeoff procedure for open-web steel joists and metal decking.

Figure 19.2

Means® Forms
QUANTITY SHEET

SHEET NO. QS 19A
ESTIMATE NO. 1017

PROJECT Admin. Bldg.
LOCATION Picacho, Ca. ARCHITECT Bell & Bell DATE March 1989
TAKE OFF BY PC EXTENSIONS BY: ETW CHECKED BY: NS

DESCRIPTION		NO.	DIMENSIONS ℓ	LBS	UNIT	UNIT	UNIT	UNIT	UNIT	UNIT
Structural Steel										
2nd Floor										
C,2 - C,3	W18 x 50	2	24	2400						
	W10 x 33	1	8	264						
B,2 - B,3	W18 x 50	2	24	2400						
	W10 x 33	1	8	264						
1st Floor										
C,2 - C,3	W21 x 73	2	24	3504						
	W10 x 45	1	14	630						
@ stairs	W12 x 19	1	52	988						
	4"Ø x 10.79	1	9	97						
B,2 - B,3	W21 x 73	2	24	3504						
	W10 x 45	1	14	630						
B1 - B2	W18 x 50	2	28	2800						
	W8 x 31	1	12	372						
B,1 - B,2	W18 x 50	2	28	2800						
	W8 x 31	1	12	372						
C,1 - C,2	W18 x 50	2	28	2800						
	6"Ø x 18.97	1	12	228						
D1 - D2	W18 x 60	2	28	3360						
	6"Ø x 18.97	1	12	228						
C1 - C,1	W18 x 60	1	22	1320						
	6"Ø x 18.97	1	12	228						
C,1 - D1	W18 x 60	1	22	1320						
	6"Ø x 18.97	1	12	228						
				30737	LBS = 15.37 TONS					

Means® Forms
QUANTITY SHEET

PROJECT Admin. Bldg.
LOCATION Picacho, Ca.
TAKE OFF BY PC
ARCHITECT Bell & Bell
EXTENSIONS BY: ETW
SHEET NO. QS 19B
ESTIMATE NO. 1017
DATE March 1989
CHECKED BY: NS

DESCRIPTION	NO.	DIMENSIONS ℓ	wt.		UNIT	UNIT	UNIT	UNIT	UNIT	UNIT
Lintels & Mullions										
East Elevation										
window 'G'	4	5	31#	620						
Door 5	1	6	31	186						
Overhead Doors	2	11	35	770						
window I	1	23	31	713						
Mullion	1	5	16	80						
South Elevation										
window D	1	25	31	775						
Mullion	1	3	16	48						
window F	1	9	31	279						
Door 9	1	5	31	155						
window C	1	6	31	186						
window B	1	16	31	496						
West Elevation										
window B	1	16	31							
window E	2	7	31	434						
window A	4	5	31	620						
Doors 1&2	2	5	31	310						
North Elevation										
window H	3	9	31	837						
Door 3	1	7	31	217						
Door 4	1	5	31	155						
				6881	LBS = 3.44 Tons					

Figure 19.3

Chapter 20

Open-Web Steel Joists and Metal Decking

Open-web steel joists are relatively lightweight steel trusses used for direct support of floors and roof decks. Metal decking or slab forms can be secured directly on top of the joists and used as a form for concrete floors, roof slabs, or for other roofing materials. Wood decks can also be applied directly to joists with nailers.

Takeoff Items

The items typically taken off for open-web steel joists and metal decking are:

- Open-web joists (length, spacing, and size of each)
- End welds
- Horizontal bridging
- Decking or slab form

Figure 20.1 illustrates these items, which will be discussed in more detail in the guidelines below.

Guidelines for Takeoff

The following guidelines should be used when taking off open-web joists and metal deck construction.

- Study the drawings and specifications to identify the size and spacing of the joists, the method of end attachment, and the different types of decking.
- Open-web joists are taken off by size (length and depth). The total quantity is then converted to tons so that the erection cost can be determined by the cost estimator.
- Welding is required where joist ends meet steel beams. Take off the number of end welds and weld plates (if any). Bearing plates are often used where joist ends rest on masonry walls. The quantity estimator need not itemize the number of bearing plates to be grouted on masonry walls. Grouting work will be done by the masonry subcontractor.
- Horizontal bridging refers to the steel rods that pass through the open webs of joists horizontally and at right angles. They are installed laterally to stiffen the joists and distribute the load. Take off bridging in linear feet.

- Metal decking or slab form may be secured to the joists either by self-tapping screws or welding. Decking and slab form are taken off in square feet measured to the inside faces of the perimeter walls.
- Total the columns on the quantity sheet. (See Figure 20.2). Convert linear feet of joists to tons.
- Do not add a waste allowance to the net quantities, since waste will be determined by the cost estimator.

Takeoff Demonstration

The High Roof Framing Plan and the Second Floor and Low Roof Framing Plan in Appendix A show the joist layout for our model administrative building. This information is required for taking off the open-web joists and metal decking. Refer to these figures throughout the procedure.

Step 1: High Roof

Joists

There are 4 bays using the same joists and same joist spacing:

9 (14K1) joists at 5′-0″ oc

The number of joists in one bay, where the spacing is 5′, is found using the formula:

$$\text{Number of joists} = \frac{\text{Bay width}}{\text{Joist spacing}} + 1$$

If joists are placed approximately 3′ from each parallel wall, and the width of the bay is 46′, the total number of joists in a bay will be:

$$\frac{46' - (2 \times 3')}{5'} + 1 = 9$$

Since each of the bays on the high roof are the same, we have 4 bays, each with 9 (14K1) joists. The spans will be:

2 bays at 27′-6″
1 bay at 22′-0″
1 bay at 23′-0″

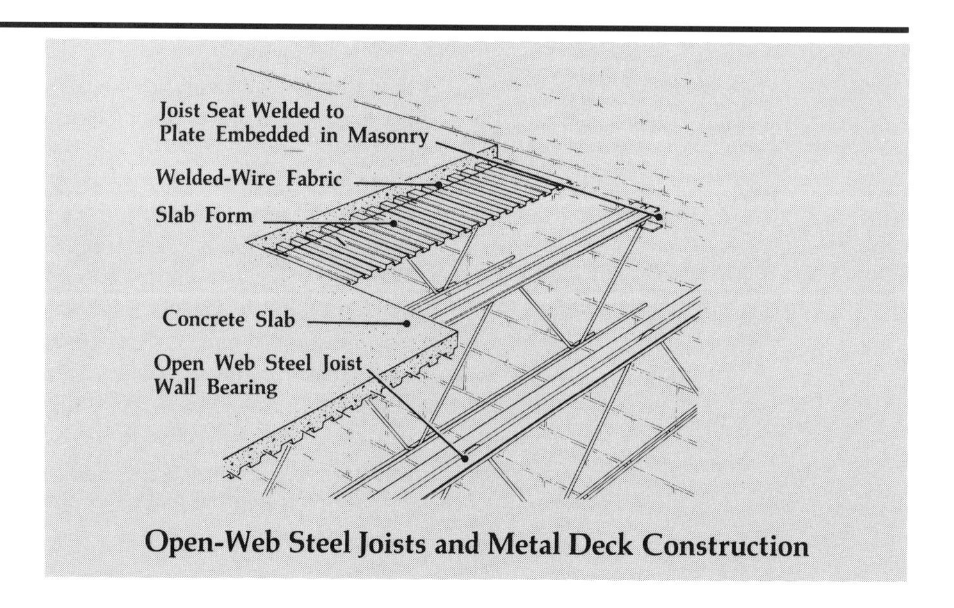

Figure 20.1 Open-Web Steel Joists and Metal Deck Construction

End Welds

One end of each joist will be welded to a steel beam. With 4 bays, 9 joists each, this comes to 36 end welds. Record this value in the column labeled "Welding."

Horizontal Bridging

Horizontal bridging is shown as one bar, top and bottom, in the middle of each span. The quantity is:

4 bays × 2 bars × 40′ = 320 lf

Decking

The galvanized metal deck should be measured to the inside of the perimeter walls. Deduct the 12″ thickness of parapet walls from the given outside dimensions of the building. Thus:

[101′ − (2 × 1′)] × [48′ − (2 × 1′)] = 99′ × 46′ = 4,554 sf

Step 2: Second Floor

Joists

In the northeast corner of the second floor there are 4 bays. In the first bay we find 24 (16K2) joists at 22′ long. The next bay contains 17 (16K2) joists at 22′ in length. In this bay there is an opening for stairs that requires a number of short joists: 3 (8K1) at 10′-4″ and 6 (8K1) at 6′. In the next two bays there are a total of 48 (16K2) joists at 27′-3′.

End Welds

For welding joist ends to steel beams, there is 1 weld for each joist. The total is:

24 + 17 + 3 + 6 + 24 + 24 = 98 end welds

Horizontal Bridging

The horizontal bridging for the first two bays is:

(47′ × 2) + (4′ × 2) + (10′ × 2) + (31′ × 2) = 184 lf

Horizontal bridging placed top and bottom at the center of each of the next two spans is:

2 bays × 2 bars × 47′ = 188 lf

Decking

Decking quantity is found as follows:

(48′ − 2′) × (100′− 2′) = 4,508 sf

Step 4: Low Roof

The section of roof along the south wall is 126′ long, with the joists spaced at 5′ oc and spanning approximately 30 lf′. The quantities for each item are listed below.

Joists: 25 (16K2) at 30′
End welds: 11 ea
Horizontal bridging: 120′ × 2 = 240 lf
Decking: 126′ × 29′ = 3,654 sf

The remaining roof area between column line B and D has 4 bays. The quantities are listed below.

Joists: 22 (16K2) at 27′-6″ and 22 (16K2) at 22′-0″
End welds: 45 ea
Horizontal bridging: 50′ × 2 × 4 bays = 400 lf
Decking: 100′ × 55′ = 5,500 sf

This completes the takeoff demonstration for open-web joists and metal decking. Chapter 21 examines the takeoff procedure for miscellaneous metal components.

Means® Forms
QUANTITY SHEET

PROJECT Admin. Bldg.
LOCATION Picacho, Ca.
TAKE OFF BY PC
ARCHITECT Bell & Bell
EXTENSIONS BY: ETW
SHEET NO. QS 20
ESTIMATE NO. 1017
DATE March 1989
CHECKED BY: NS

DESCRIPTION	NO	DIMENSIONS ℓ	SHORT JOISTS 8K1	UNIT	14K1 JOISTS	UNIT	16K2 JOISTS	UNIT	END WELDS	UNIT	HORIZ. BRIDG	UNIT	STEEL DECK 18GA	UNIT	STEEL DECK 28GA	UNIT
Open web joists & metal decking																
High Roof	9	23			207	LF			36	ea.	320	LF	4554	SF		
	9	22			198	LF										
	18	27.5			495	LF										
Second Floor	24	22					528	LF	98	ea.	188	LF			4508	SF
	17	22					374	LF								
short joists	3	10.33	31	LF												
" "	6	6	36	LF												
	48	27.33					1312	LF								
Low Roof	25	30					750	LF	11	ea.	240	LF	3654	SF		
	22	27.5					605	LF	45	ea.	400	LF	3500	SF		
	22	22					484	LF								
Total			67	LF	900	LF	4053	LF	190	ea.	1148	LF	13708	SF	4508	SF

Figure 20.2

Chapter 21
Miscellaneous Metal

There are two major classifications of metal work in the construction industry: *structural steel* and *miscellaneous metal*. Structural steel, as described in Chapter 19, refers to load bearing members made of steel that contribute to the "structure" of the building. Miscellaneous metal, on the other hand, are those ancillary pieces of iron work that are required around a building site: for example, pipe-guard posts, manhole covers and frames, manhole ladder rungs, metal stair nosings, and interior wall-hung stair railings with posts. Some of these items are embedded in concrete; others are bolted to wood or to other materials.

A single subcontractor is seldom responsible for both categories of metal work. The quantity estimator for the general contractor rarely takes off structural steel, since it is usually supplied by a subcontractor. But the quantity estimator will generally take off miscellaneous metal because even though it may be furnished by a subcontractor, it is almost always installed by the general contractor.

Miscellaneous metal is taken off for two reasons: (1) to provide a checklist for subcontractor quotations, and (2) to serve as the basis for estimating labor costs. The quantity estimator may choose to take off miscellaneous metal while taking off the bulk of the construction work (concrete, carpentry, and so forth). Or, he or she may go back through the drawings and details at a later date and perform an independent takeoff.

Takeoff Items

Our model administrative building contains the following items:

- Ladders
- Catch basin covers and frames
- Wall-hung exterior stair railing
- Exterior stair railing with posts

Each of these items is discussed below. Quantity Sheet 21 (Figure 21.1) shows how the quantity of each item is conveyed to the cost estimator.

Ladders

The building elevations in Appendix A show two exterior ladders, each 12′ high with hooks at the top of each ladder. List on the quantity sheet by number and length.

Catch Basin Covers and Frames

These items are shown on the site plan in Appendix A. The frame must be set into the concrete. Record the number and size on the quantity sheet.

Wall–hung Exterior Stair Railing

This type of stair railing is found on one side of the steps shown on the site plan. The quantity is taken off in linear feet.

Exterior Stair Railing with Posts

This type of railing, also shown on the site plan, is taken off in linear feet. Note that the sleeves will be set in concrete in order to hold the railing in place.

The information found in the drawings in Appendix A and recorded by the quantity estimator on the quantity sheets should be sufficient for a cost estimator to calculate the installation labor cost.

Next is Part III, "Miscellaneous Subtrades and Specialties." This section begins with a discussion of the takeoff procedures used for moisture and thermal control.

Means® Forms

QUANTITY SHEET

PROJECT Admin. Bldg.	SHEET NO. QS 21
LOCATION Picacho, Ca.	ESTIMATE NO. 1017
ARCHITECT Bell & Bell	DATE March 1989
TAKE OFF BY PC	EXTENSIONS BY: ETW
	CHECKED BY: NS

DESCRIPTION	NO.	DIMENSIONS				UNIT		UNIT		UNIT		UNIT
Miscellaneous Metal												
Ladder	2		12' LG.		2	ea.						
Catch basin frame & cover	2		30" ϕ		2	ea.						
Wall hung stair Railing	1	1¼" ϕ Galv.			6	LF						
Stair railing w/3 posts	1	1¼" ϕ Galv.			26	LF						
Post sleeves	6	1¼" ϕ			6	ea.						

Figure 21.1

Part III

Miscellaneous Subtrades and Specialties

Chapter 22

Moisture and Thermal Control

Moisture and thermal control involves the use of a wide variety of materials and methods to seal buildings from moisture and to limit penetration into the building of extreme heat or cold. In this chapter, the following three moisture/thermal construction trades will be discussed:

- Caulking
- Roofing
- Sheet metal

Caulking

Caulking is the process of applying mastic sealing compound between building materials to make the joint water- or airtight. A variety of caulking materials are available depending on the purpose and geographic location of the building. These materials offer climate protection ranging from the mild and semi-sheltered to the most extreme of outdoor exposures.

Caulking has become one of the high-technology trades and, if the required quantity is large enough, a subcontractor service. If the quantity of caulking in a project is relatively small and the technology fairly simple, caulking may be done by the general contractor's employees, and the takeoff performed by the general contractor's quantity estimator.

Guidelines for Takeoff

Guidelines have been established to enable the quantity estimator to perform the takeoff quickly and accurately. These are listed below.

- If cross-sectional dimensions are not given on the drawings, make a judgment, since the size of these areas will affect the cost estimate.
- Research and record on the quantity sheet each type of caulking material (butyl-based, polyurethane, polysulfide; one component, two component, and so forth).
- Indicate the locations of caulking (such as for windows and doors).
- Take off caulking in linear feet. Ignore fractions of a foot, and round any fractional amount to the next even foot. For instance, a measurement of 22′-3″ would be rounded up to 23′.
- Note scaffolding requirements.

Takeoff Demonstration

Project specifications supply instructions regarding the type of materials and methods of application. The drawings show the locations and sometimes the cross-sectional dimensions of the areas to be caulked.

The takeoff procedure of our model administrative building requires a complete search through all the drawings and details for places that require caulking. Take off, first, all areas that are clearly labeled and, second, those that evidently require caulking but are not labeled as such. For those areas that are not labeled, indicate on Quantity Sheet 22A (Figure 22.4, located at the end of this section) an *LS* (lump sum) allowance.

The following building elements require caulking:

- Parapet coping
- Windows and door jambs
- Windows and door heads
- Window sills
- Miscellaneous unlabeled caulking

Refer to the wall, window, and door sections for the location of all caulking. Note that scaffolding may be required for caulking that is located higher than 7′.

Step 1: Parapet Coping

Assume that polysulfide caulking will be required on both inside and outside sheet metal parapet flashing cap. It is given a dimension of 1/2″ × 1/2″. Note that the entire roof is surrounded by a parapet. The perimeter is 296′ for the high roof and 319′ for the low roof. Since there are two rows of caulking, the total quantity is:

615′ × 2 = 1,230 lf

Record this data on Quantity Sheet 22A.

Step 2: Windows and Door Jambs

Caulking of windows and door jambs consists of a single bead sized at 3/8″ × 1/2″. Find the total quantity of caulking by adding all the jambs (2 per opening) in the Window Schedule in Figure 18.3, and in the Door Schedule in Figure 18.2. This is illustrated in Figure 22.1.

Record the total quantity of caulking on Quantity Sheet 22A. The calculations in Figure 22.1 may also be recorded on the quantity sheet or kept with backup worksheets—whichever the quantity estimator prefers.

Step 3: Windows and Door Heads

The plans call for two beads of caulking sized 3/8″ × 3/4″ and 3/8″ × 3/8″. The total quantity of caulking is found by adding together the head widths of all the window and exterior doors in the schedules shown in Figures 18.2 and 18.3, and the head widths of the overhead door found on the East Elevation. This is shown in Figure 22.2.

Record the total quantity (186 lf) for each of the two caulking sizes on Quantity Sheet 22A.

Step 4: Window Sills

A section through the window sill shows one bead of caulking size 1/2″ × 3/4″. The quantity may be taken from the Window Schedule in Figure 18.3. The calculations are represented in Figure 22.3.

Record the total quantity of 143 lf on Quantity Sheet 22A.

Caulking-Window and Door Jambs				
Window	Jamb Height	Number of Jambs	Number of Openings	Linear Feet
A	3′	2	4	24
B	3′	2	4	24
C	3′	2	1	6
D	3′	2	2	12
E	4′	2	2	16
F	4′	2	1	8
G	5′	2	4	40
H	5′	2	3	30
I	5′	2	2	20
Door				
1	7′	2	1	14
2	7′	2	1	14
3	7′	2	1	14
4	7′	2	1	14
5	7′	2	1	14
9	7′	2	1	14
OH	9′	2	2	36
			Total	300

Figure 22.1

Caulking-Windows and Door Heads					
Windows	Width		Number Each		Linear Feet
A	4′	×	4	=	16
B	6′	×	4	=	24
C	5′	×	1	=	5
D	10′	×	2	=	20
E	6′	×	2	=	12
F	8′	×	1	=	8
G	4′	×	4	=	16
H	8′	×	3	=	24
I	9′	×	2	=	18
Doors (Wood & Metal)					
1	3.5′	×	1	=	3.5
2	3.5′	×	1	=	3.5
3	6.0′	×	1	=	6.0
4	3.5′	×	1	=	3.5
5	3.0′	×	1	=	3.0
9	3.5′	×	1	=	3.5
OH Door	10.0′	×	2	=	20.0
				Total	186

Figure 22.2

Step 5: Miscellaneous Unlabeled Caulking

In the drawings of a construction project there are likely to be many places that should receive caulking but are not shown or specified. This is a debatable item, as some contractors will not volunteer to caulk anything unlabeled or unspecified. If the quantity estimator receives no instructions on this point, he or she may supply an item for "miscellaneous caulking" and label the quantity *LS*, or lump sum.

Step 6: Scaffolding

When caulking is located higher than 7′ on the building, scaffolding may be required. Although scaffolding quantities are usually outside the scope of a quantity estimator's work, the scaffolding requirement should be noted on the quantity sheet as a cost factor.

Roofing

Roofing is the general term for the materials used on top of roof sheathing for waterproofing purposes. There is a wide variety of materials and methods for coating or covering roof structures to prevent the penetration of water into the structure. Our model administrative building uses one of the most common commercial roof coverings: the built-up roof. This is illustrated in Figure 22.5. Remember that the procedure used to take off this type of roofing may be used for other types of roofing as well.

It is important that the quantity estimator indicate on the quantity sheet the various layers, types of materials, methods of application, and associated items such as cant strips. Sheet metal is not included in the roofing takeoff, as it is customarily furnished and installed by sheet metal subcontractors. Sheet metal work must be closely coordinated with the roofing work, however, to ensure that the sealing of flashing is accomplished at the proper time.

Caulking-Window Sills

Window	Width		Number of Windows		Linear Feet
A	4′	×	4	=	16
B	6′	×	4	=	24
C	5′	×	1	=	5
D	10′	×	2	=	20
E	6′	×	2	=	12
F	8′	×	1	=	8
G	4′	×	4	=	16
H	8′	×	3	=	24
I	9′	×	2	=	18
				Total	143

Figure 22.3

Means® Forms

QUANTITY SHEET

SHEET NO. QS 22A

PROJECT Admin. Bldg.

ESTIMATE NO. 1017

LOCATION Picacho, Ca.

ARCHITECT Bell & Bell

DATE March 1989

TAKE OFF BY PC

EXTENSIONS BY: ETW

CHECKED BY: NS

DESCRIPTION	NO.	DIMENSIONS				UNIT		UNIT		UNIT		UNIT
Caulking												
Parapet Coping												
polysulfide ½" x ½"					1230	LF						
scaffold required						LS						
Window & Door Jambs												
polysulfide 3/8" x ½"					300	LF						
scaffold required @ windows						LS						
Window & Door Heads												
polysulfide (1) 3/8" x ¾"					186	LF						
(2) 3/8" x 3/8"					186	LF						
scaffold required @ windows						LS						
Window Sills												
polysulfide ½" x ¾"					143	LF						
scaffolding required upper windows						LS						
Miscellaneous Caulking						LS						

Figure 22.4

Guidelines for Takeoff

Guidelines have been established for taking off roofing. They are listed below.

- Define the specifications of the roofing for the cost estimator on the quantity sheets. The quantity sheet for our model building is labeled Quantity Sheet 22B (Figure 22.6), located at the end of this section.
- Calculate in square feet the main areas of each type of roofing, not including the quantity of material turned up at walls. Convert quantities from square feet to squares. Note that only main roofing areas are taken off in squares; associated items are taken off in other units of measurement, such as linear feet or square feet. One square equals 100 square feet. The final conversion to squares should be rounded, not to the next larger whole square, but to the next larger 100th of a square. Thus:

  7,853 sf ÷ 100 = 78.53 sq

- Round fractions to the next whole square foot. Thus:

  134.67′ × 58.3′ = 7,851.26 sf; round to 7,852 sf

- Take off any associated items that require separate unit cost estimating, such as cant strips, wall turn-ups, and walking deck material.

Takeoff Demonstration

Refer to the Roofing Plan in Appendix A. On our administrative building, we have a flat built-up roof with a parapet around the perimeter. Take off:

- Roofing
- Cant strips

Step 1: *Roofing*

The quantity of roofing on a flat roof is simply the surface area.

(130′ × 126′) − (100′ × 22′) = 14,180 sf or 141.80 squares.

There is no need for the quantity estimator to calculate the quantities of materials such as tar, insulation, felt, and gravel. The roofing contractor will determine these.

Figure 22.5

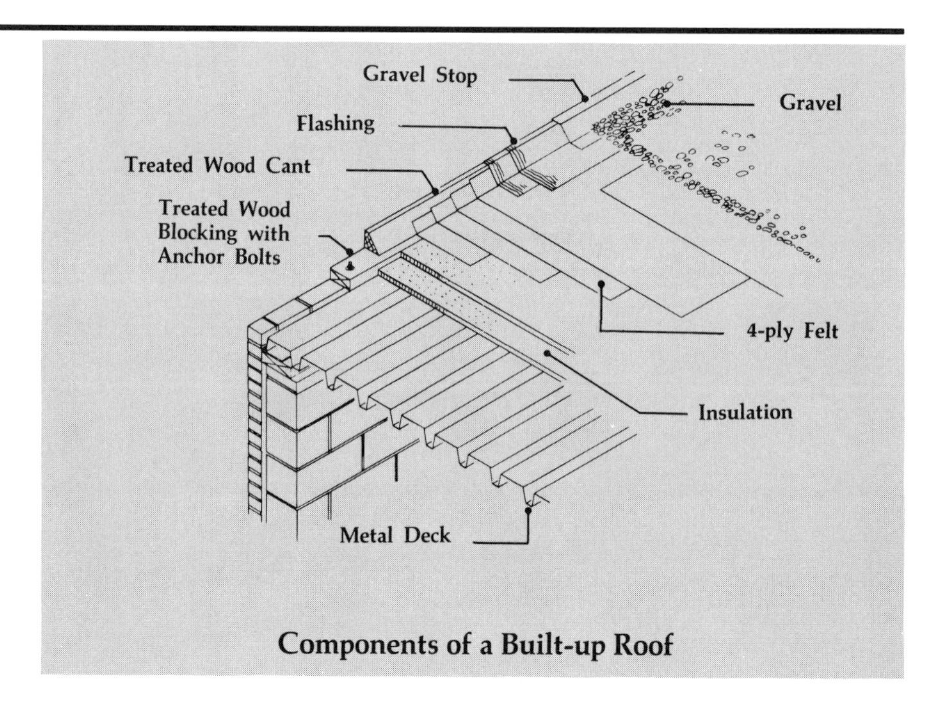

Components of a Built-up Roof

Step 2: Cant Strips

There is a cant strip (Figure 22.5) on the inside edge of all parapet walls.

$$2 \times (126' + 130') + 48' + 100' = 660 \text{ lf}$$

Note that we have used the outside measurements for convenience. This is well within our accuracy requirements.

Sheet Metal

Sheet metal is commonly used in buildings to seal out moisture and air. This is done by installing flashing over windows and doors, counterflashings at roofs, and copings (caps) on walls and parapet tops.

Sheet metal items sometimes come in stock shapes and sizes and require only on-site cutting, fitting, and installation. Other sheet metal items are custom-made in sheet metal shops. The need for custom work is the main reason why sheet metal is a highly specialized subcontract trade.

During the takeoff work the general contractor's quantity estimator must keep in mind the kind of information that sheet metal shop workers need to know for cost estimating. Such information includes kinds of materials, sizes, shapes, thicknesses (gauges), purposes, and locations in the building. Reference to drawing detail numbers is usually sufficient for identifying the locations of sheet metal items.

As a general rule, sheet metal is thinner than 10 gauge. Sheet metal subcontractors tend to exclude all metal in a project that is 10 gauge or thicker. The thicker material would be taken off by miscellaneous metal or structural steel contractors.

Takeoff Items

The following items are typically taken off for sheet metal:

- Parapet coping or cap
- Base flashing
- Reglets
- Gravel stop

Figure 22.7 is an example of a roof counterflashing. A reglet is a preformed strip of sheet metal embedded permanently in a wall to receive the upper edge of flashing. In our examples, the flashing details do not call for reglets or gravel stops. The quantity estimator should always review the roofing details to determine the requirements of the project.

Caulking at the reglet and sealing at the roofing are not always the responsibility of the sheet metal sub. Also, certain sheet metal items, such as heating and air conditioning work, are distinctly parts of other subcontract trades. The sheet metal items included in this section are those that are not taken off with other trades and are classified as "general sheet metal."

Stock items, such as reglets and gravel stops, are taken off in linear feet. Sheet metal flashing items under 6" wide are taken off in linear feet, while items more than 6" wide are taken off in square feet. Quantities may be rounded up to the next higher linear foot or square foot.

Takeoff Demonstration

Read the specifications and examine the plans and details. Begin with the parapet coping. Be sure to transfer all quantities to Quantity Sheet 22C (Figure 22.8), located at the end of this chapter.

Step 1: Parapet Coping or Cap

The parapet coping is specified to be aluminum, 0.019" thick. The length is the same as the parapet wall: 615 lf. The approximate expanded width is 24".

$$615' \times 2.0' = 1{,}230 \text{ sf}$$

Means® Forms

QUANTITY SHEET

SHEET NO. QS 22B

PROJECT Admin. Bldg. ESTIMATE NO. 1017

LOCATION Picacho, Ca. ARCHITECT Bell & Bell DATE March 1989

TAKE OFF BY PC EXTENSIONS BY: ETW CHECKED BY: NS

DESCRIPTION	NO.	DIMENSIONS				UNIT		UNIT		UNIT		UNIT
Roofing												
4 ply built-up roof w/gravel, #15 felt, hot mopped					14180	SF						
cant strip provide w/rough lumber					660	LF						
Traffic pads					14	ea.						

Figure 22.6

Step 2: Base Flashing

The base flashing is specified to be galvanized steel 20 ga. This flashing appears around the perimeters of both the high and the low roofs. Calculate the total length using the given dimensions on the plans, without deducting for wall thicknesses, as follows:

$48' + 100' + 48' + 100' + 48' + 22' + 30' + 126' + 85' + 56' + 55' = 718$ lf

The approximate expanded width of the base flashing is 24″. The total quantity is:

$718' \times 2.0' = 1{,}436$ sf

Step 3: Counterflashing

The roof counterflashing is specified to be galvanized steel 20 ga. Its length will be the same as the base flashing.

The approximate expanded width of the counterflashing is 24″ at the intersection of the low roof and the second floor, and 18″ everywhere else.

$615' \times 1.5' = 923$ sf of 18″
$103' \times 2.0' = 206$ sf of 24″

This concludes the discussion of moisture and thermal control. Chapter 23 examines the takeoff procedure for interior construction.

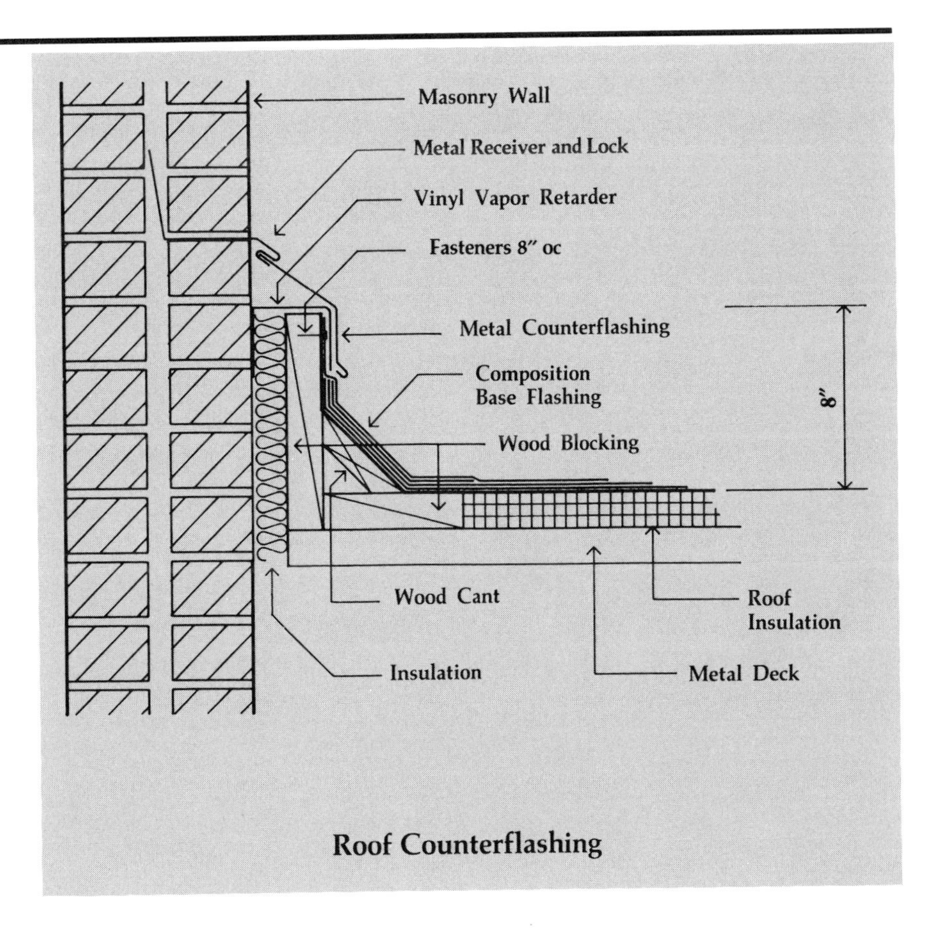

Roof Counterflashing

Figure 22.7

Means® Forms

QUANTITY SHEET

PROJECT Admin. Bldg.		SHEET NO. QS 22C
LOCATION Picacho, Ca.	ARCHITECT Bell & Bell	ESTIMATE NO. 1017
TAKE OFF BY PC	EXTENSIONS BY: ETW	DATE March 1989
		CHECKED BY: NS

DESCRIPTION	NO.	DIMENSIONS l	DIMENSIONS w		UNIT		UNIT		UNIT		UNIT
Sheet Metal Flashing											
parapet coping											
Alum., 0.019" thick		615	2	1230	SF						
(5 Bends)											
base flashing											
galv. steel, 20 ga.		718	2	1436	SF						
(2 bends)											
counter flashing											
galv. steel, 20 ga.											
(2 bends)		615	1.5	923	SF						
(4 bends)		103	2.0	206	SF						

Figure 22.8

Chapter 23

Interior Construction

Interior construction is used to describe those architectural trades that contribute to the usefulness, comfort, and aesthetic quality of a building's interior. Interior construction components include doors, partitions, wall finishes, ceilings, and flooring materials.

Interior Construction Trades

The following interior building elements are examined in this chapter:

- Wall finishes
- Ceilings
- Flooring
- Base trim

Wall Finishes

The three types of wall finishes used in our model building are:

- Gypsum board drywall
- Ceramic tile
- Wood paneling

Each of these is described below.

Gypsum Board Drywall

Drywall is a term used to describe a variety of factory-made sheet materials that are applied to walls and ceilings. Gypsum board so dominates this category of work that the terms *drywall* and *gypsum* board are practically synonymous. Gypsum board drywall is more economical than most other wall and ceiling covering materials, and takes less time to install, particularly compared to plaster.

Gypsum board is composed of a gypsum core sandwiched between two outer layers of tough paper. There are a number of different kinds of gypsum board, including backing board, foil-backed, fire-rated, and water resistant. Tongue-and-groove coreboard is also available for solid wall and shaft construction. A variety of accessories are available too, such as beads, screws, nails, and adhesives. Gypsum board comes in thicknesses ranging from 1/4″ to 5/8″ and in sizes of 2′ and 4′ wide to 16′ long. During takeoff, if no sheet sizes are given, assume that the standard size (4′ × 8′) is intended.

Gypsum board is taken off in square feet. This quantity includes all accessories such as nails or screws, tape, and tape compound. Different types of partition construction should be listed separately on the quantity sheets. There may be walls with studs of various widths including double studded and similar or dissimilar surface materials. Acoustical requirements vary, and wall systems are listed separately. Shaft work is usually of different construction from the surrounding partitions and will require separate listing and pricing.

Finally, a waste allowance is added to the net quantity, and a final adjustment is made to round out the total quantity to full sheet sizes (4′ x 8′, unless otherwise noted).

Gypsum board may or may not be sublet. The general contractor often makes an accurate cost estimate and then decides to either sublet or install the material using his or her employees.

Ceramic Tile

Ceramic tile is used as both a wall and a floor covering. Take off ceramic tile in square feet, keeping floor and wall requirements separate.

Wood Paneling

Wood paneling is manufactured in 4′ x 8′ sheets and installed by nailing or gluing in place. Take off wood paneling in square feet.

Ceilings

Ceiling systems fall into two main categories:

- Ceiling tiles applied directly to a backer
- Ceiling tiles applied to batts or boards which are installed on a suspension system

Tile materials can be mineral, glass, wood fibers, or metal pans with sound absorbing pads (called *acoustical tile*). These materials are taken off in square feet, with a 5% allowance for waste.

Flooring

Flooring includes the following three categories:

- Resilient flooring
- Carpeting
- Ceramic tile

Resilient Flooring

Resilient flooring refers to a wide spectrum of durable floor covering products such as vinyl tile and linoleum. The quantity estimator should specify the type of flooring required and list the quantity in square feet. (Note that vinyl tile and linoleum are not called for in our building and will not be taken off.)

Carpeting

Carpeting is taken off by the square foot and converted to square yards. If different grades of carpeting are specified, they should be listed separately.

Ceramic Tile

Ceramic floor tile is laid on the subfloor or concrete. The quantity estimator should specify whether it is *mud set* (set in mortar) or *thin set* (set using an adhesive).

Base Trim

Base trim or *coving* is the molding placed at the intersection of the wall and floor. Base trim is commonly made of wood, vinyl, or ceramic tile, and is taken off in linear feet.

Guidelines for Takeoff

Below are some guidelines for taking off interior construction.

- Read the specifications and note the different types of materials and methods of application.
- Examine the drawing details for thicknesses, layers, and accessories.
- Refer to the Finish Schedule (Figure 18.4) and proceed with the takeoff, room-by-room, as shown on Quantity Sheet 23 (Figure 23.1), located at the end of this chapter.
- Ignore openings that are less than 32 sf.
- Include a lump sum allowance for scaffolding when required.

Takeoff Demonstration

Refer to the floor plans shown in Appendix A. These plans show the length of the walls. The ceiling heights (wall heights) are shown on the Finish Schedule in Chapter 18, Figure 18.4. Use the given dimensions on the drawings and ignore wall thicknesses, keeping in mind that a waste allowance will be applied in the final quantity. Color or shade the Finish Schedule as each item is taken off.

Step 1: Walls and Ceilings

Begin the takeoff by calculating the quantity of wall and ceiling materials required for each room in our model building. Keep in mind that the takeoff method described in this chapter can be applied to most other types of wall materials, such as fiberboard and plywood.

First Floor

Room [101] : Room [101] includes the hall, and has no deductions for openings. There is a block wall that must be furred and insulated for 28′ on the north side. The block wall on the east side of the building will be wood paneled. It must be furred but does not need insulation.

The quantities for this room are shown below.

Furring and gypsum board: (55′ + 28′) × 9.5′ = 789 sf
Insulation: 28′ × 12′ = 336 sf (Note: it is 11.62′ from the floor to the bottom of the roof slab)
Ceiling area: 220 sf + 770 sf = 990 sf

Room [102] : Moving on to Room [102] , the north and west walls must be furred and insulated. The quantities are listed below.

Furring and gypsum board: (28′ + 55′) × 9.5′ = 789 sf
Insulation: (28′ + 55′) × 12′ = 996 sf
Ceiling area: 1,320 sf + 770 sf = 2,090 sf

Room [103] : Room [103] has outside walls on the west, south, east, and part of the north sides of the building. These walls will all receive furring and insulation. The block wall adjacent to Room [104] will receive furring but no insulation. The quantities for this room are as follows.

Furring and gypsum board: (30′ + 30′ + 126′ + 22′ + 48′) × 9.5′ = 2,432 sf
Insulation: 208′ × 12′ = 2,496 sf
Ceiling area: 126′ × 30′ = 3,780 sf

Room [104] : Room [104] has block walls on all four sides. The outside wall on the east side will receive furring and insulation. There are also 2 openings of more than 32 sf to deduct from this wall. (Note that the inside walls receive paint only and will be taken off by the painting subcontractor.) The quantities for this room are listed below.

Furring and gypsum board: (55′ × 10.38′) − (90′ × 2′) = 391 sf
Insulation: (55′ × 12′) − (90′ × 2′) = 480 sf
Ceiling area: 55′ × 48′ = 2,640 sf

Room [105] : Although Room [105] is a very small storage area, it takes just as much time to calculate as a large area. Two interior walls are gypsum board on metal lath. This quantity is shown below.

Gypsum board on metal lath: 17′ × 10′ = 170 sf

The remaining interior walls can be taken off with Room [106] . The exterior wall requires furring, insulation, and gypsum board, and will also be calculated with Room [106] . There is no ceiling in Room [105] .

Room [106] : Three of the walls of Room [106] are exterior walls and will require furring with insulation. The other wall will require furring only on the concrete block.

Furring with gypsum board: (96′ + 90′) × 10′ = 1,860 sf
Insulation: (48′ + 45′ + 45′) × 12′ = 1,656 sf
Ceiling area: (48′ × 45′) − 200 sf = 1,960 sf (200 sf for stairs and Room [105])
Patio: The aluminum soffit (ceiling) of the patio on the northwest corner of our building is:

45′ × 56′ = 2,520 sf

Second Floor

Rooms [201] *and* [202] : All exterior walls will have furring, insulation, and gypsum board. Interior walls have metal studs and gypsum board on both sides. In addition, there will be wood paneling in Room [201] (the Conference Room). The quantities for these two rooms are listed below.

Furring and gypsum board: (200′ + 96′) × 8′ = 2,368 sf
Insulation: 296′ × 10′ = 2,960 sf
Metal studs and gypsum board: (48′ + 48′ + 30′) × 8′ = 1,008 sf
Wood paneling: (90′ + 96′) × 8′ = 1,488 sf
Ceiling area: (for the entire second floor) 100′ × 48′ = 4,800 sf

Rooms [203] *and* [204] : Take off the quantity of ceramic tile needed for the walls in these rest rooms.

Ceramic tile: (24′ + 36′) × 4′ high = 240 sf

Step 2: Flooring

Next, take off the floors. Refer to the Finish Schedule in Figure 18.4. The calculations for the various flooring quantities of our model building are listed below.

Carpeting: (rooms [101] , [102] , [103] , [201] , and [202]) 3,080 sf + 3,780 sf + (4,800 sf − 200 sf) = 11,460 sf
Concrete: (rooms [104] , [105] , and [106]) 4,800 sf
Ceramic tile: (rooms [203] and [204] , the rest rooms) 18′ × 6′ = 108 sf

Step 3: Base Trim

Finally, take off the base trim. The calculations for each type of trim in our model building are shown below.

Wood trim: (rooms [101] and [201]) 48′ + 55′ = 103 lf
Vinyl trim: (rooms [101] , [102] , [103] , [104] , [105] , [106] , [201] , and [202]) 28′ + 83′ + 256′ + 206′ + 36′ + 186′ + 186′ + 208′ = 1,189 lf
Ceramic tile: (rooms [109] and [110]) 36′ + 24′ − 6 (2 doors) = 54 lf

This concludes the takeoff demonstration of interior construction. Chapter 24 examines the takeoff procedure for building specialties.

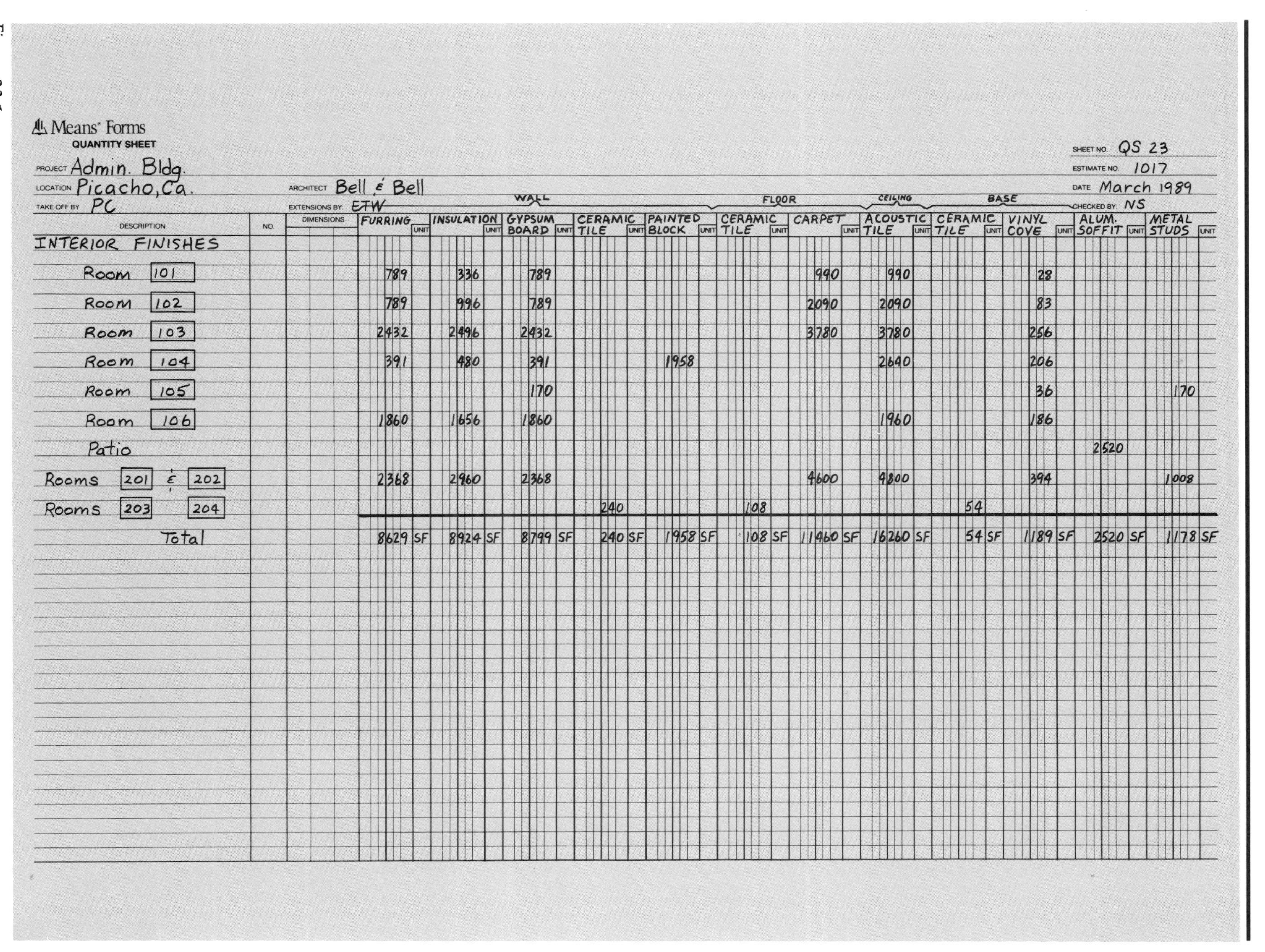

Means® Forms
QUANTITY SHEET

PROJECT Admin. Bldg.
LOCATION Picacho, Ca.
TAKE OFF BY PC
ARCHITECT Bell & Bell
EXTENSIONS BY: ETW
SHEET NO. QS 23
ESTIMATE NO. 1017
DATE March 1989
CHECKED BY: NS

DESCRIPTION	NO.	DIMENSIONS	WALL					FLOOR		CEILING	BASE			
			FURRING	INSULATION	GYPSUM BOARD	CERAMIC TILE	PAINTED BLOCK	CERAMIC TILE	CARPET	ACOUSTIC TILE	CERAMIC TILE	VINYL COVE	ALUM. SOFFIT	METAL STUDS
INTERIOR FINISHES														
Room 101			789	336	789				990	990		28		
Room 102			789	996	789				2090	2090		83		
Room 103			2432	2496	2432				3780	3780		256		
Room 104			391	480	391		1958			2640		206		
Room 105					170							36		170
Room 106			1860	1656	1860					1960		186		
Patio													2520	
Rooms 201 & 202			2368	2960	2368				4600	4800		394		1008
Rooms 203 204						240		108			54			
Total			8629 SF	8924 SF	8799 SF	240 SF	1958 SF	108 SF	11460 SF	16260 SF	54 SF	1189 SF	2520 SF	1178 SF

Figure 23.1

Chapter 24
Building Specialties

Building specialties are nonstructural items incorporated in and around a completed building which adapt the building to a particular use. The general contractor's quantity estimator takes these items off to determine their material and installation cost.

Takeoff Items

This chapter will discuss the takeoff procedure for the following building specialty items:

- Toilet partitions
- Bathroom accessories
- Window blinds
- Flag pole
- Office safe
- Accordion partitions
- Demountable partitions

The quantity estimator should examine the plans and specifications for building specialties and check them off as they are taken off. Refer to Quantity Sheet 24 (Figure 24.1), located at the end of this chapter, for an example of how these items are conveyed to the cost estimator.

Toilet Partitions

Toilet partitions should be identified by the type of material they are made of (such as marble, painted metal, stainless steel, or plastic laminate), by the method of installation (ceiling-hung, floor-anchored, or wall-hung), and by the size and number of doors.

The Second Floor Plan in Appendix A shows two restrooms. Each restroom has one toilet partition. The partition is a ceiling-hung panel and a door. The specifications require a painted metal door. This information should be recorded on the quantity sheet.

Bath Accessories

Our model project has two small restrooms. The specifications call for liquid soap dispensers, towel dispensers, robe hooks, mirrors, toilet tissue dispensers, toilet seat cover dispensers, and shelves. These items are listed on Quantity Sheet 24.

Window Blinds

The written specifications require that all windows on our model building have custom-made, solid-color window blinds constructed of horizontal, 2" aluminum slats. For sizes and quantities, see the window schedule in Chapter 18, Figure 18.3. Record the data on Quantity Sheet 24.

Flag Pole

The flag pole in the specifications is 35′ high, tapered aluminum, set in a concrete foundation. On Quantity Sheet 24 list "one each."

Wall Safe

The specifications call for a 4-hour-rated, 34″ × 20″ × 20″ wall safe. Record this on Quantity Sheet 24 as "one each."

Accordion Partition

An accordion partition divides the east end of Room [108] . The partition specifications require vinyl covering, 2 pounds per square foot. These partitions are full height and come complete with door frames and hardware.

From the dimensions in the First Floor Plan in Appendix A, the partition is shown to be 28′ wide and 9′-6″ high. On the quantity sheet list:

30′ × 9.5′ = 285 sf

Demountable Partitions

Demountable partitions are also shown on the First Floor Plan. Assume that they will be delivered to the job site in panels and crated. List the quantity in square feet.

The height of the panels is 6′. Since the ceiling is 9′-6″ high, there will be an open space over the top of the partitions. Vertical posts extending to the ceiling will be installed for rigidity.

Imagine that the specifications call for vinyl-clad drywall on two 1/2″ metal frames. When measuring quantities, do not deduct for door openings. Rather, count the number of doors as a separate cost item.

From both given dimensions and scaling, we find the total linear feet to be 121. Extend the quantity:

121′ × 6′ = 726 sf, 1 door

Record this data on Quantity Sheet 24.

Overhead Doors

Overhead doors are shown on the First Floor Plan and in the East Elevation in Appendix A. These are to be furnished and installed by a subcontractor. The specifications call for manually operated doors made of 24 gauge galvanized steel. Record this information on the quantity sheet as follows:

Overhead sectional steel doors: 9′H × 10′W, 2 each

This concludes the takeoff demonstration of building specialty items for our model administrative building. Chapter 25 provides a summary of the basic principles covered in this book.

Means® Forms

QUANTITY SHEET

SHEET NO. QS 24

PROJECT Admin. Bldg. — ESTIMATE NO. 1017

LOCATION Picacho, Ca. — ARCHITECT Bell & Bell — DATE March 1989

TAKE OFF BY PC — EXTENSIONS BY: ETW — CHECKED BY: NS

DESCRIPTION	NO.	DIMENSIONS w	DIMENSIONS h		UNIT		UNIT		UNIT		UNIT
Building Specialties											
Toilet partition – painted metal				2	ea.						
one panel – one door											
Bathroom Accessories											
liquid soap dispensers				2	ea.						
towel dispensers S.S. surf. Mtd				2	ea.						
robe hook S.S.				2	ea.						
mirror S.S. frame 24"x 24"				2	ea.						
toilet tissue dispenser											
S.S. single roll				2	ea.						
shelves S.S. 24" long				2	ea.						
toilet seat cover dispenser				2	ea.						
Window Blinds											
horiz. 2" Alum slats solid color											
A		4°	3°	4	ea.						
B		6°	3°	4	ea.						
C		5°	3°	1	ea.						
D		10°	3°	2	ea.						
E		6°	4°	2	ea.						
F		8°	4°	1	ea.						
G		4°	5°	4	ea.						
H		8°	5°	3	ea.						
I		9°	5°	2	ea.						
Flag Pole											
35' tapered alum. – set in conc.				1	ea.						
Wall Safe											
4 hr. 34"x 20"x 20" built into wall				1	ea.						
Accordion Partition				285	SF						
30'x 9'-6" vinyl covered											
include Frame & Hardware											
Demountable Partition				726	SF						
121'x 6'											
door with hardware				1	ea.						
Overhead Sectional Door				2	ea.						
9'x 10' 24 GA Steel Manual											

Figure 24.1

Chapter 25
Summary

It is customary in small- to medium-size construction companies for quantity takeoff and cost estimating to be done by the same person. In larger companies, however, it is not uncommon to find specialists who do nothing but take off quantities. This book presented quantity takeoff as performed by a specialist whose responsibility is to supply the cost estimator with all the information needed to estimate the cost of the project. The quantity estimator's goal is to compute *gross* quantities, that is, those quantities that must be purchased and handled, including waste allowances such as swelling, shrinkage, cutting, and damage.

The Quantity Estimator's Responsibilities

The quantity estimator's most important responsibility is to take off every item that has a cost value. A cost value refers to any labor, material, and equipment to be supplied and/or performed by the general contractor. The quantity estimator's greatest expertise lies in this area.

The quantity estimator's second responsibility is to take off any construction trades that are normally sublet, but are being performed, for whatever reason, by the general contractor's employees. Even though these subtrades may fall outside the quantity estimator's area of expertise, it is possible, after some practice, for the quantity estimator to become skilled in the takeoff of all trades.

The level of expertise that a quantity estimator develops depends largely on the demands his or her company makes. For instance, the quantity estimator can become very skilled in masonry, painting, lathing, plastering, and plumbing if the company repeatedly requests that he or she take off those trades.

Guidelines for Takeoff

Quantity estimating is not an exact science, but a degree of accuracy is assured by following these guidelines:

- The quantity estimator should take off certain building trades first, such as concrete work, proceed through all the structural trades, then take off finishing trades. Mass excavation and exterior (site) work may be taken off before, during, or after the major construction elements, whichever the quantity estimator prefers. Generally the quantity estimator should take off the trades, categories, and items of the general contractor's work before taking off any subtrades.

- A quantity estimator must set standards of precision in his or her work commensurate with the practical limitations that exist in cost estimating. In other words, use common sense. For instance, concrete, excavation, and gypsum board can be taken off straight through wall corners and small openings. Other materials, such as metal decking and acoustical tile should be taken off as accurately as possible. When taking off subtrades, the level of detail and precision will be influenced by the conditions, the reason for making a takeoff, the degree of dependence others will place on the quantities, and the time available to perform the takeoff.
- Anticipate the methods of construction that will be used in the field, such as trenching and backfilling configurations, material and design of concrete formwork, and procedures for casting and erecting precast concrete.
- The quantity estimator should develop a system for identifying items during the takeoff, such as referencing drawing detail numbers, grid lines, points of the compass, and so forth, and should proceed in an orderly manner—clockwise or counterclockwise, for instance.
- Use given dimensions on the drawings whenever possible, rather than scaling with a ruler.
- Whenever possible, round fractions to the next whole number.
- Add waste allowances based on calculations, reference data, and experience. Avoid guessing.
- Mark the drawings with colored pencils as the individual items are taken off.
- Select logical stopping points for breaks and interruptions.

Scheduling

In construction, like most other industries, time can be a critical factor. When reviewing his or her work load, the quantity estimator will either: (1) roughly schedule the amount of time required to perform a takeoff *if time is not a consideration*, or (2) roughly budget the *amount of time that is available* for the takeoff of individual trades. It is not always possible to devote an equal amount of time and care to all trades. Figure 25.1 shows a method of scheduling the takeoff when the quantity estimator has a relatively unlimited amount of time.

Open-ended Time Schedule

Trades	Time (Days) - - - - - - - - - - - - - - - - - - →
Mass Excavation	XXXXXXX
Concrete	XXXXXX
Masonry	XXXXX
Rough Carpentry	XXXXXX
Finish Carpentry	XX
Miscellaneous Metal	X
Moisture and Thermal Control	XXXXXXXXX
Interior Construction	XXXXXX
Building Specialties	XX

Figure 25.1

In this example, the total time allotted for takeoff depends on the size and complexity of the project and the number and complexity of the subtrades. This schedule begins on the Day 1 of the takeoff and moves forward over the number of days actually needed to perform a proper takeoff of all trades.

It is not often that a quantity estimator is fortunate enough to have such an *open-ended schedule*. More likely, a quantity estimator is working under time constraints, and would employ the *fixed time schedule*.

In fixed time schedules, time is limited by: (1) bid deadlines, and (2) commitments to other projects. This schedule is determined by establishing a designated future fixed date and working backward to Day 1 of the takeoff. Notice that the fixed time schedule is nearly the same as the open-ended time schedule in that priority is given to those trades that are the general contractor's direct responsibility. What time remains is divided among the subtrades on a priority basis. Figure 25.2 illustrates a fixed time schedule.

The construction trades discussed in this book are those applicable to the model administrative building used to demonstrate the takeoff. Obviously there are other trades that merit discussion that could not very well have been demonstrated using this particular building example. However, the guidelines used in this book may be applied, with some variation, to most other trades.

This concludes the discussion and demonstration of traditional quantity takeoff procedures for the general contractor. Part IV, "New Technology," brings the quantity estimator into the computer age. Chapter 26, "Electronic Takeoff," examines the latest technology used to perform quantity takeoff.

Fixed Time Schedule

Trades	Available Time (Days) ------------------------➤	Cut-off Date
Mass Excavation	XXXXX	
Concrete	XXXXX	
Masonry	XXXX	
Rough Carpentry	XXXXXX	
Finish Carpentry	XX	
Miscellaneous Metal	X	
Moisture and Thermal Control	XX	
Interior Construction	XXXX	
Building Specialties	X	

Figure 25.2

Part IV

New Technology

Chapter 26
Electronic Takeoff

Consider all that the quantity estimator must do to perform a takeoff like the one demonstrated in this book. First, the quantity estimator must consult the plans for dimensions and, using a variety of complex formulas and a calculator, find the quantity of each item in a building composed sometimes of thousands of items. Next, each quantity must be carefully transferred to a spread sheet and the columns of numbers totaled. Finally, the quantity estimator adds a waste allowance to certain quantities, and then converts quantities from the units in which they were measured to the units in which they are purchased. If the dimensions for certain items are not given in the plans or specs, the quantity estimator must scale the drawing—in addition to performing all of the calculations and conversions! For large or complex structures, this entire procedure can be extremely time-consuming, and the potential for error is enormous.

Within the past decade, however, tools have become available for automating the takeoff process, or performing the takeoff electronically. In electronic takeoff, information from architectural plans and drawings is "read" by an electronic sensing or "digitizing" device (either a pen-like stylus or a "mouse," depending on the system), and input into a microcomputer which then calculates the length, area, or volume of the individual items based on the location of and distance between points. What would normally take the quantity estimator an hour or more to calculate, can be done in a fraction of that time with less potential for error using this high-tech takeoff method.

Advantages of Electronic Takeoff

There are several advantages to using electronic takeoff. First, it is faster—as much as 50 to 70 percent faster—than manual takeoff procedures. As described in Chapter 1, there are three stages in the bidding process: *quantity takeoff, cost estimating*, and *bidding*; with the quantity takeoff being the most time-consuming stage of the total bidding process. This relationship is shown in Figure 26.1.

Electronic takeoff reduces the time spent on this aspect of bid preparation, thereby speeding up the entire bidding process. The sooner the bid package is completed, the more time a construction firm has for preparing new bids. In other words, a company that reduces its quantity takeoff time by 50 percent, increases the number of bids that can be produced by 50 percent. The more bids that are prepared, the greater a firm's chances of winning contracts and increasing its revenue.

A second advantage of electronic takeoff is that it can be more accurate than manual methods. Twenty to thirty percent of all errors made during the estimating process are calculation errors. Electronic takeoff virtually eliminates calculation errors by relegating this task to a computer. Furthermore, for those linear dimensions that must be scaled, the electronic digitizing device is far more precise than the traditional scales and planimeters used by quantity estimators performing takeoff manually.

A third advantage of electronic takeoff is consistency. In those companies that employ more than one quantity estimator, the individual style of each quantity estimator may determine whether the estimate is high or low. By automating the process, a firm can be sure that its estimates will be consistent, regardless of who prepares them.

Fourth, because electronic takeoff systems combine hardware (equipment) and software systems (programs that run the equipment), all information that is derived from the takeoff can be stored and quickly revised or adjusted for later use. For instance, after finding the total quantity of lumber needed for a particular building, that list can later be adapted by the contractor for use as a materials purchase list.

Finally, electronic takeoff can be used for most types of building construction. In spite of this broad applicability, however, only 10 to 15 percent of all construction firms in this country perform their quantity estimates using electronic devices. This is surprising, considering that the vast majority of construction firms—both large and small—use computers for routine administrative functions, like bookkeeping and payroll, that do not, by themselves, contribute to the firm's bottom line.

Types of Electronic Takeoff Systems

Electronic takeoff can be performed using the following three systems:

- Sonic digitizer
- Electromagnetic digitizing table
- Digitizing using a mouse

The following sections describe these three methods in detail.

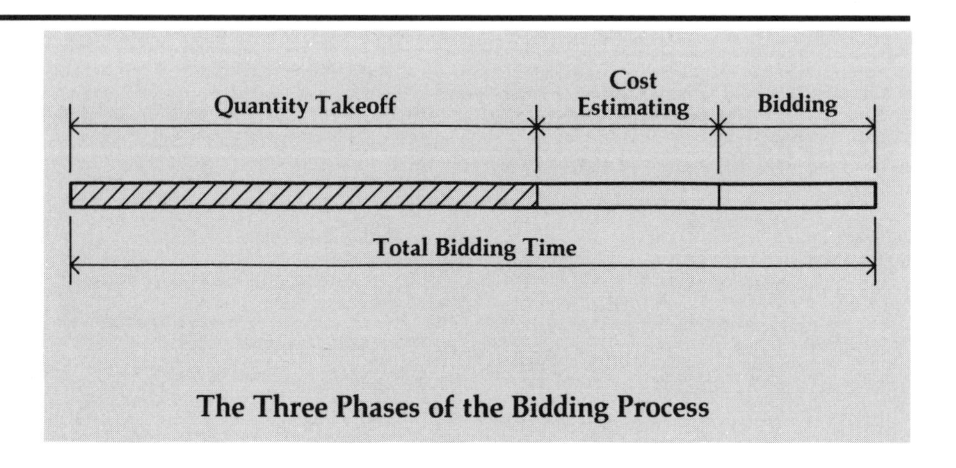

The Three Phases of the Bidding Process

Figure 26.1

Sonic Digitizer

A sonic digitizer uses sound to measure distance. This device is composed of two banks of microphones in a lightweight, aluminum L-frame assembly. The quantity estimator lays the drawings between the microphones and taps a stylus on the end points of the item to be measured. The microphones pick up the sounds, register their location, and record this information in the computer. The computer, in turn, calculates the distance between the points and uses this information to compute linear, area, and volume quantities. Figure 26.2 illustrates this device.

Introduced in 1981, the sonic digitizer was the first type of electronic takeoff device available for general use. It is a portable system; the linear microphones fold up and can be carried from site to site, reassembled on any flat surface, and hooked up to any of a number of microcomputer models.

The sonic digitizer is useful for simple takeoffs such as linear dimensions. Unfortunately, this device is less accurate for more complex "reads" or irregular shapes. Additionally, this device is sensitive to interference, which can result in inaccuracies. For instance, if the quantity estimator accidently places a pencil within the sonic field, the microphones will record the location of the pencil. Background noise can also interfere with the takeoff.

As happens with new technology, the sonic digitizer has become somewhat obsolete. Within the past few years, the sonic digitizer has been replaced by simpler and more reliable devices, such as the electromagnetic digitizing table, described in the next section.

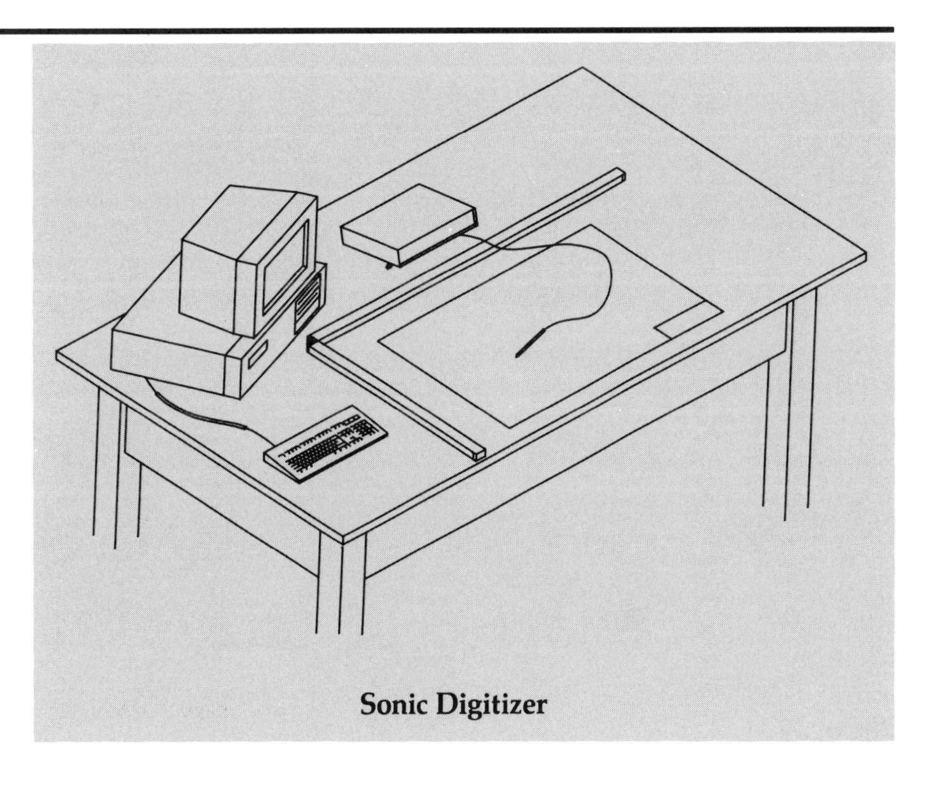

Figure 26.2

Sonic Digitizer

Electromagnetic Digitizing Table

The electromagnetic digitizing table was introduced in 1983 as an alternative to the sonic digitizing device. Beneath the surface of this table is a copper wire grid capable of measuring 1,000 points per inch. The drawings are placed on the table, and the scale is entered into the computer. The stylus is connected to the computer terminal and contains a magnetic tip so that when it is touched to various points on the drawings, the table registers these points as X and Y coordinates and transfers this information to the computer. The computer uses these coordinates to calculate the length, area, or volume of the item on the drawing. See Figure 26.3.

This system is also capable of taking off cut-and-fill quantities by comparing existing and proposed contour lines from the site plan, calculating the total cubic yards of cut and fill, and generating a report and a matrix indicating the volume.

The electromagnetic digitizing table is faster and more reliable than the sonic digitizer. In fact, of the construction firms currently using electronic devices for quantity takeoff, the vast majority are using the electromagnetic digitizing table. Unlike the sonic digitizer, however, the electromagnetic digitizing table is not a portable system. Because of its size, it cannot be carried from site to site.

R.S. Means Company, Inc. produces a software package for quantity takeoff using the electromagnetic digitizing table. This software package, called *GALAXY*, is essentially an electronic data entry program designed for use with *ASTRO*, Means' estimating program. Quantities from the drawings are transferred directly from the digitizing board to the computer using the *GALAXY* program. Once entered,

Figure 26.3

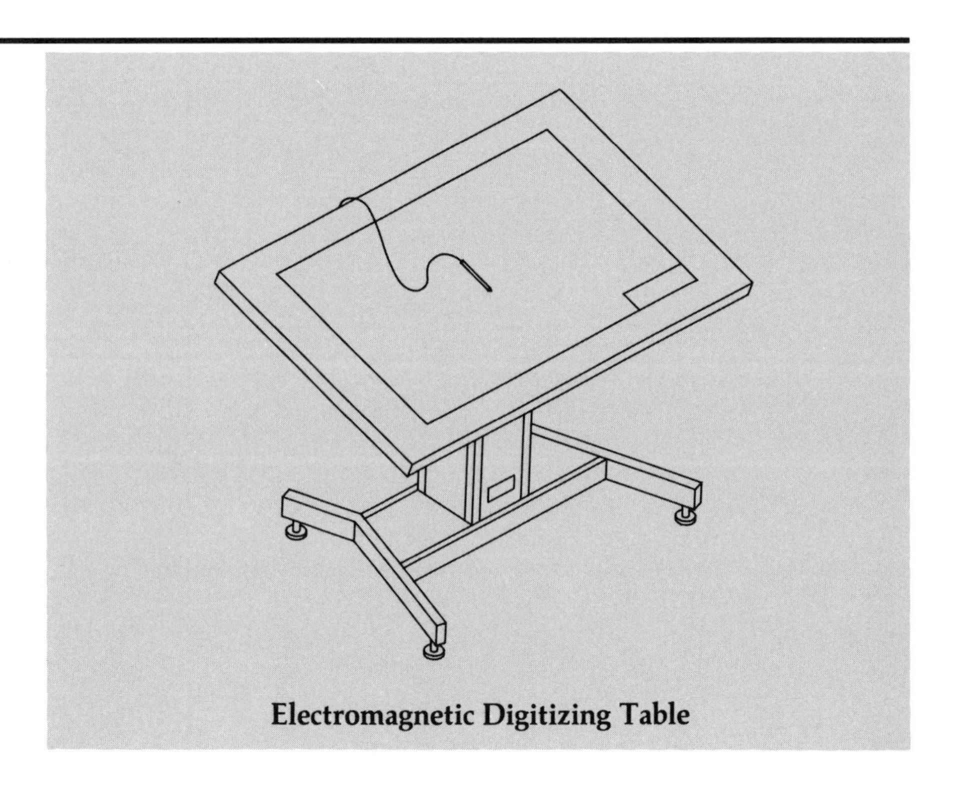

Electromagnetic Digitizing Table

ASTRO supplies the item description and costs from the Means cost data base or from a user-created cost data file. Once the quantity and corresponding cost code are entered, *ASTRO* calculates the extension. The cost item is then added to a project data file. When the takeoff is complete, the results can be printed in any of over 20 standard report formats. Two reports that are used quite often are the *Job Summary Report* (Figure 26.4) and the *Itemized Job Report* (Figure 26.5).

The *Job Summary Report* provides the cost of the job, including a percentage markup, based on the 16 divisions of the CSI Code. The *Itemized Job Report* is an itemized estimate; every item on the quantity estimate is listed by description, cost, and unit of measurement.

The *ASTRO* system alone can generate these reports, but without the *GALAXY* takeoff program, all of the quantities in these reports would have to be calculated manually and keyed into the computer by hand. Of those construction firms currently using electromagnetic digitizing hardware, a large percentage have chosen Means' *GALAXY* program for their software.

Digitizing Using a Mouse

The third and newest method of electronic takeoff utilizes an electronic mouse. The mouse, which is connected to a computer, is moved over various points on the plans. The quantity estimator presses a button on the mouse and the coordinates are registered and used by the computer to calculate dimensions and quantities. Figure 26.6 illustrates this device.

Professionals in both the construction and the computer industries see this device as the wave of the future, since it eliminates the need for additional hardware (microphone banks or a digitizing board), yet offers the estimator a comparable level of accuracy. Furthermore, the mobility of this device enables every computer to become a potential takeoff center.

R.S. Means Company, Inc. currently offers a software package called *PULSAR* that, at present, is used as a project management tool and performs estimating and scheduling functions. Means is currently incorporating a takeoff function into its *PULSAR* software package for use with both the electromagnetic digitizing table and the mouse.

Electronic takeoff systems have changed dramatically since their introduction less than 10 years ago. What has not changed is the need for properly trained and educated estimators. Electronic takeoff systems will never replace the quantity estimator, but they will enable the estimator to utilize his or her time more efficiently by spending less time scaling drawings and crunching numbers, and more time estimating.

NO. A-102 UNBURDENED JOB REPORT SUMMARY 01:11:19 PAGE 1

PROJECT : Means R & D Building
ARCHITECT : John Roth
QUANTITIES: gfk

LOCATION : Kingston, MA
OWNER : R.S. Means Co., Inc.
ENTERED BY: gfk

NO.	DIVISION	MANHOURS	MATERIAL	LABOR	EQUIP	SUB CONTRACT
1	GENERAL REQUIREMENTS	4	135	90	0	4723
2	SITEWORK	593	829	9676	8547	163
3	CONCRETE	33	14878	665	41	0
4	MASONRY	1838	577651	34170	193	0
5	METALS	87	2180	1735	0	0
6	WOOD & PLASTICS	45	725	1120	39	0
7	MOISTURE PROTECTION	187	5376	3713	0	0
9	FINISHES	77	809	1878	0	0
15	MECHANICAL	41	29913	845	0	0
16	ELECTRICAL	26	200	580	0	0
	JOB TOTAL	2931	632696	54472	8820	4886

	Rate	MATERIAL	LABOR	EQUIP	SUB CONTRACT	Total
SALES TAX	5.50%	34798				
MATERIAL MARK-UP	7.00%	44289				
LABOR MARK-UP	35.00%		19065			
EQUIPMENT MARK-UP	10.00%			882		
SUBCONTRACTOR MARK-UP	9.00%				440	
		711783	73537	9702	5326	
TOTAL BEFORE PROFIT						800348
PROFIT	15.00%					120052
BOND	0.02%					160
JOB TOTAL PROFIT & BOND INCLUDED						$ 920560

USER-DEFINED MARKUPS

Figure 26.4

NO. A-102	UNBURDENED ITEMIZED JOB REPORT	01:20:12 PAGE 1

PROJECT : Means R & D Building
ARCHITECT : John Roth
QUANTITIES: gfk

LOCATION : Kingston, MA
OWNER : R.S. Means Co., Inc.
ENTERED BY: gfk

4 MASONRY

4.1 MORTAR & MASONRY ACCESSORIES

DESCRIPTION					CREW	QUANTITY	UNIT	M/H	MATERIAL	LABOR	EQUIP	TOTAL	SUB
LINE NO.		TAG											
ASMBLY#	RENUMBER1	RENUMBER2	PER1	PER2									
CONTROL JOINT, PVC 4" AND WIDER WALL													
041 200 0050 00 M					BRIC1	272.50	L.F.	0.013	1.20	0.27	0.00	1.47	
04-1200	BLD W	PLAN 12	98%	112%				3.63	327.00	72.30	0.00	399.30	
GROUTING CAVITY WALL 2" SPACE, .167∂C∂F/∂S∂F, PUMPED													
041 300 0500 00 M					D4	2725.00	S.F.	0.016	0.36	0.28	0.07	0.71	
04-1200	BLD W	PLAN 12	98%	112%				43.60	981.00	756.46	192.79	1930.25	
WALL TIES FOR BRICK VENEER GALV. CORRG 7/8" X 7", 24 GAGE													
041 700 0010 00 M					BRIC1	54.50	C	0.762	3.10	15.16	0.00	18.26	
04-1200	BLD W	PLAN 12	98%	112%				41.52	168.95	826.32	0.00	995.27	
					SUB TOTAL :			89	1477	1655	193	3325	0

4.2 BRICK MASONRY

DESCRIPTION					CREW	QUANTITY	UNIT	M/H	MATERIAL	LABOR	EQUIP	TOTAL	SUB
LINE NO.		TAG											
ASMBLY#	RENUMBER1	RENUMBER2	PER1	PER2									
BRICK VENEER 4" THICK RUNNING BOND													
042 560 0010 00 U					D2	5450.00	S.F.	0.200	1.68	3.75	0.00	5.43	
04-1200	BLD W	PLAN 12	98%	112%				1090.00	9156.00	20432.54	0.00	29588.54	
WASHING BRICK, SMOOTH BRICK													
042 680 0010 00 M					BRIC1	5450.00	S.F.	0.014	0.04	0.28	0.00	0.32	
04-1200	BLD W	PLAN 12	98%	112%				77.86	218.00	1549.36	0.00	1767.36	
					SUB TOTAL :			1168	9374	21982	0	31356	0

Figure 26.5

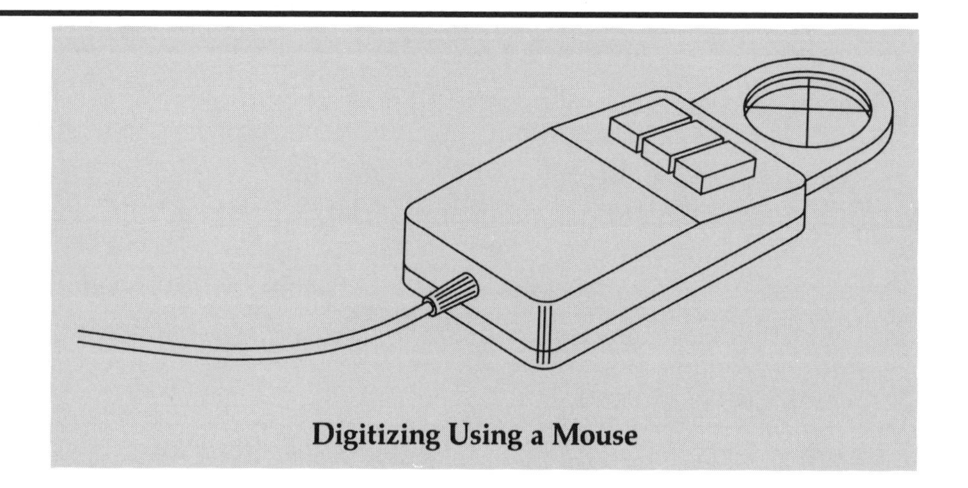

Figure 26.6

Digitizing Using a Mouse

Part V

Appendix

Appendix

Table of Contents

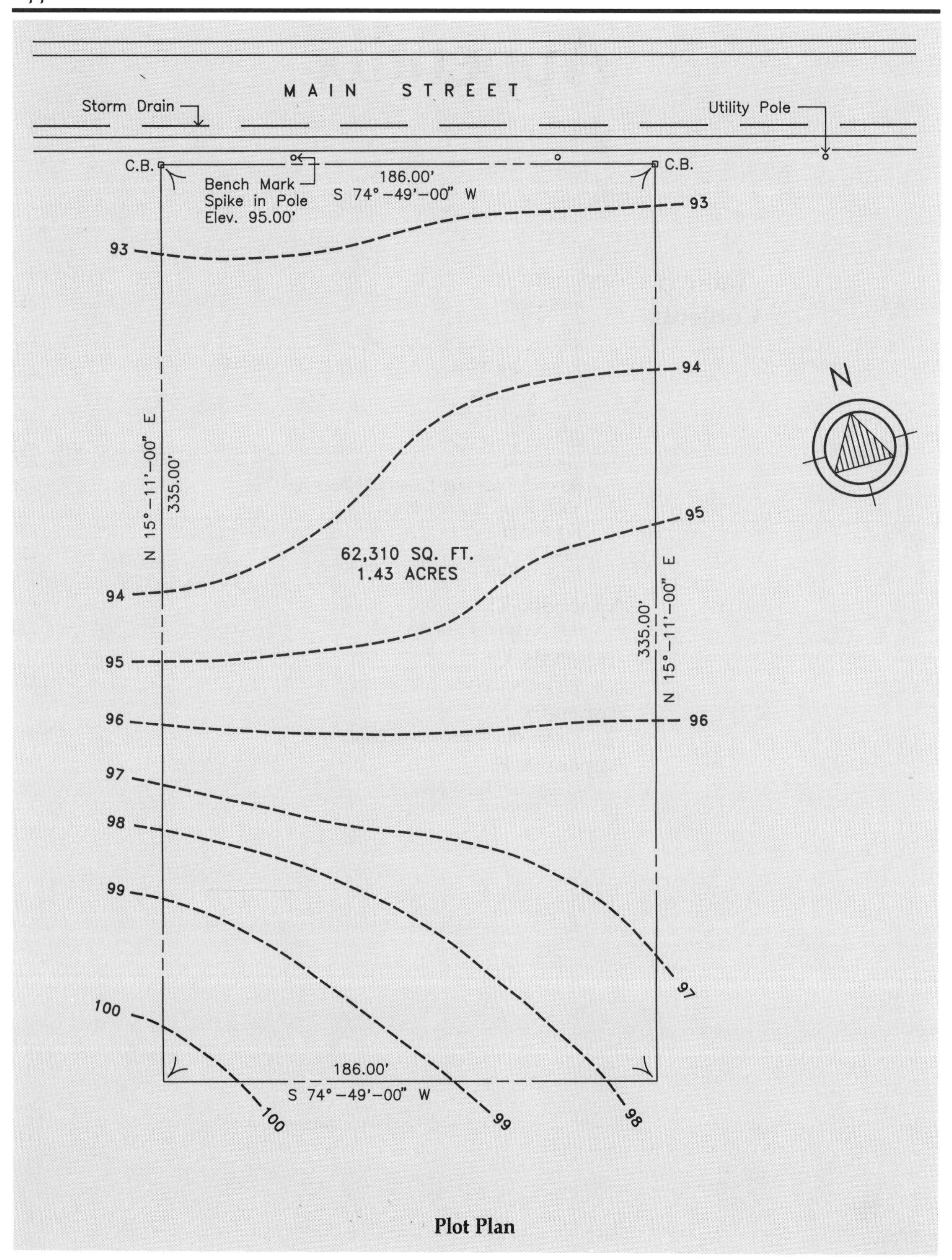
MAIN STREET
Storm Drain
Utility Pole
C.B.
C.B.
Bench Mark
Spike in Pole
Elev. 95.00'
186.00'
S 74° -49'-00" W
N 15° -11'-00" E
335.00'
62,310 SQ. FT.
1.43 ACRES
335.00'
N 15° -11'-00" E
186.00'
S 74° -49'-00" W
93
94
95
96
97
98
99
100
N

Plot Plan

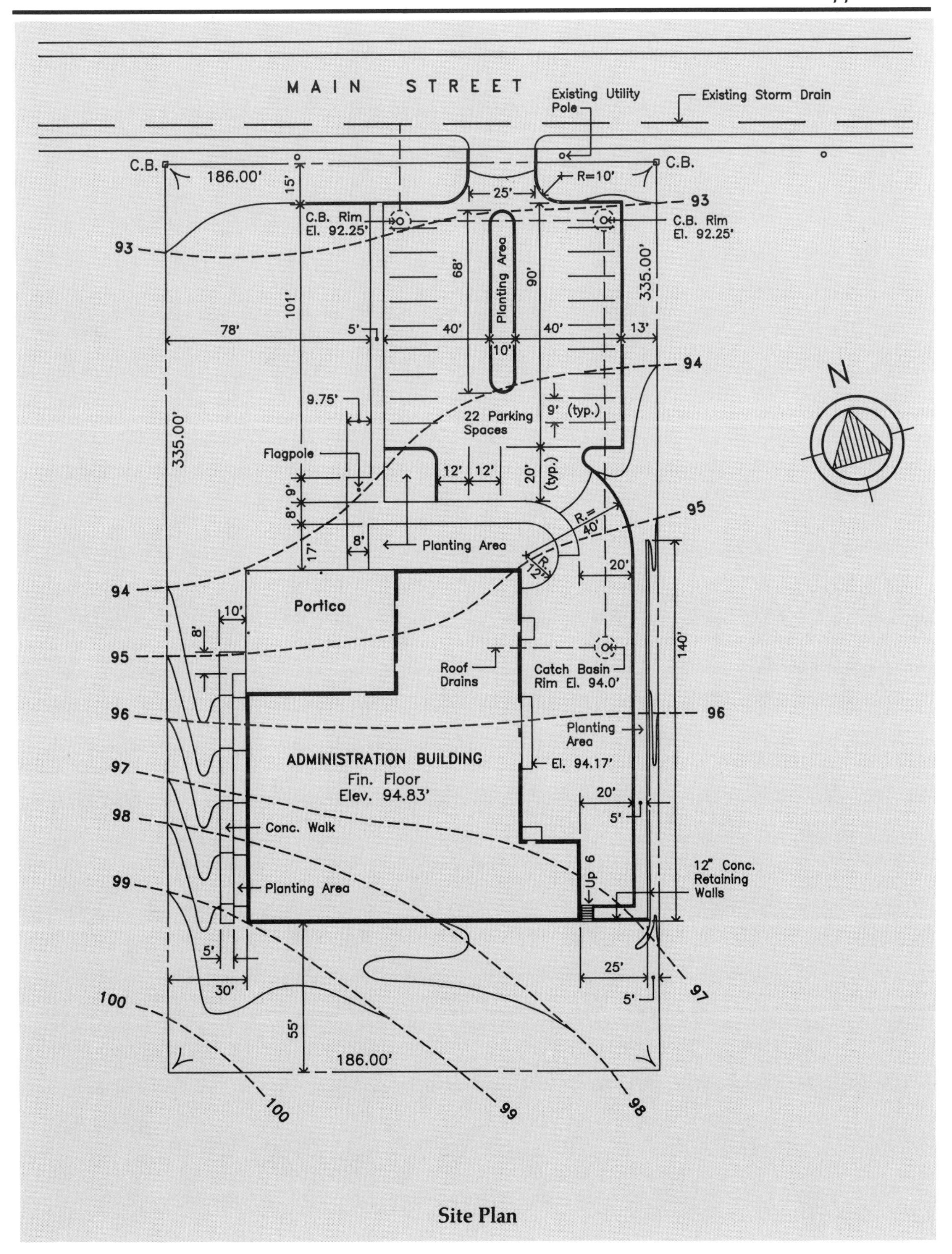
MAIN STREET
Existing Utility Pole
Existing Storm Drain
C.B.
C.B.
186.00'
15'
25'
R=10'
93
C.B. Rim El. 92.25'
C.B. Rim El. 92.25'
93
68'
Planting Area
90'
335.00'
101'
78'
5'
40'
10'
40'
13'
94
N
9.75'
22 Parking Spaces
9' (typ.)
335.00'
Flagpole
12'
12'
20' (typ.)
9'
8'
8'
R.= 40'
95
Planting Area
17'
R. 12'
20'
94
Portico
10'
8'
140'
95
Roof Drains
Catch Basin Rim El. 94.0'
96
96
Planting Area
ADMINISTRATION BUILDING
Fin. Floor Elev. 94.83'
El. 94.17'
97
20'
98
Conc. Walk
5'
Up 6
12" Conc. Retaining Walls
99
Planting Area
5'
25'
30'
5'
97
100
55'
186.00'
100
99
98

Site Plan

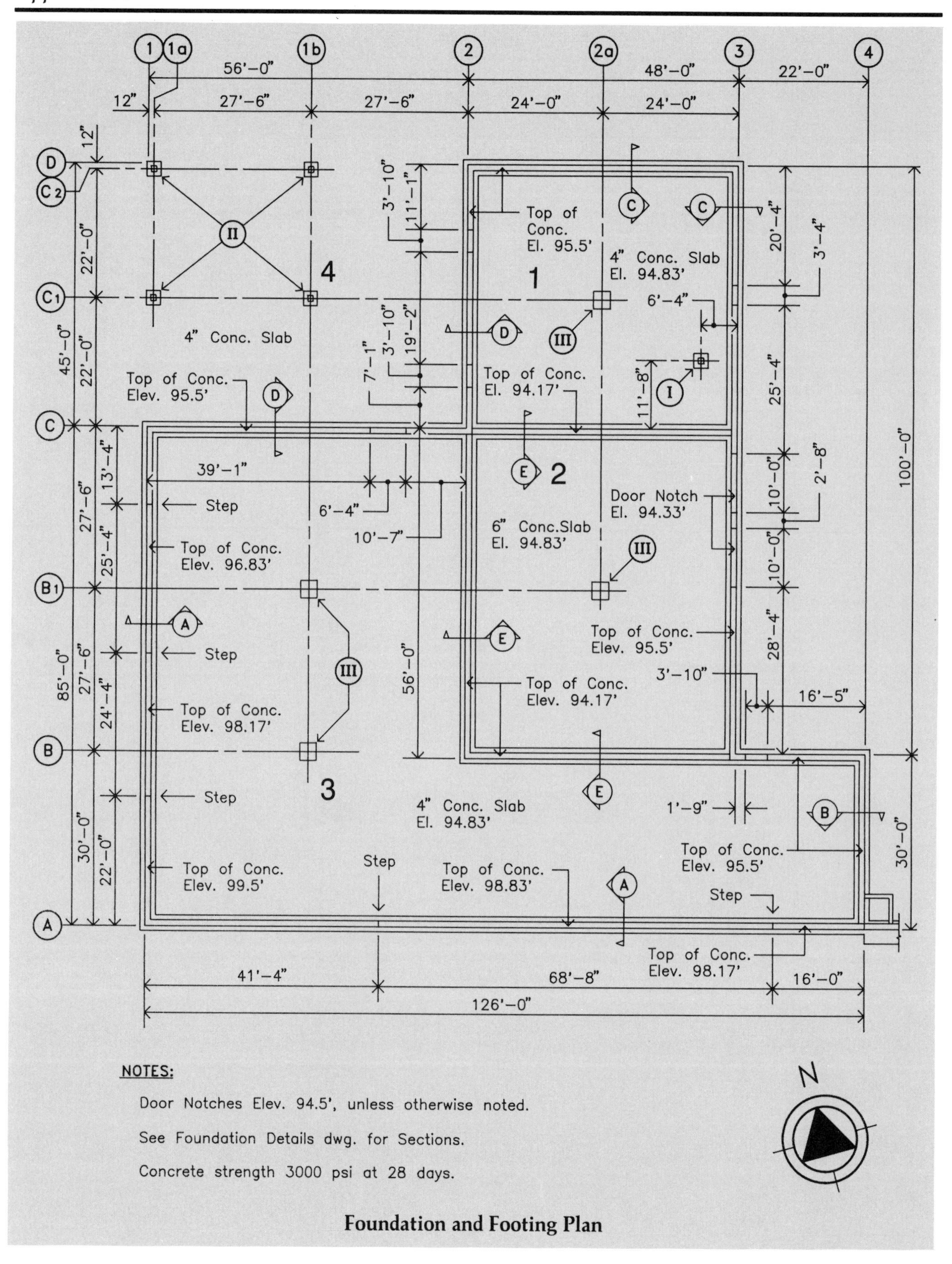

Foundation and Footing Plan

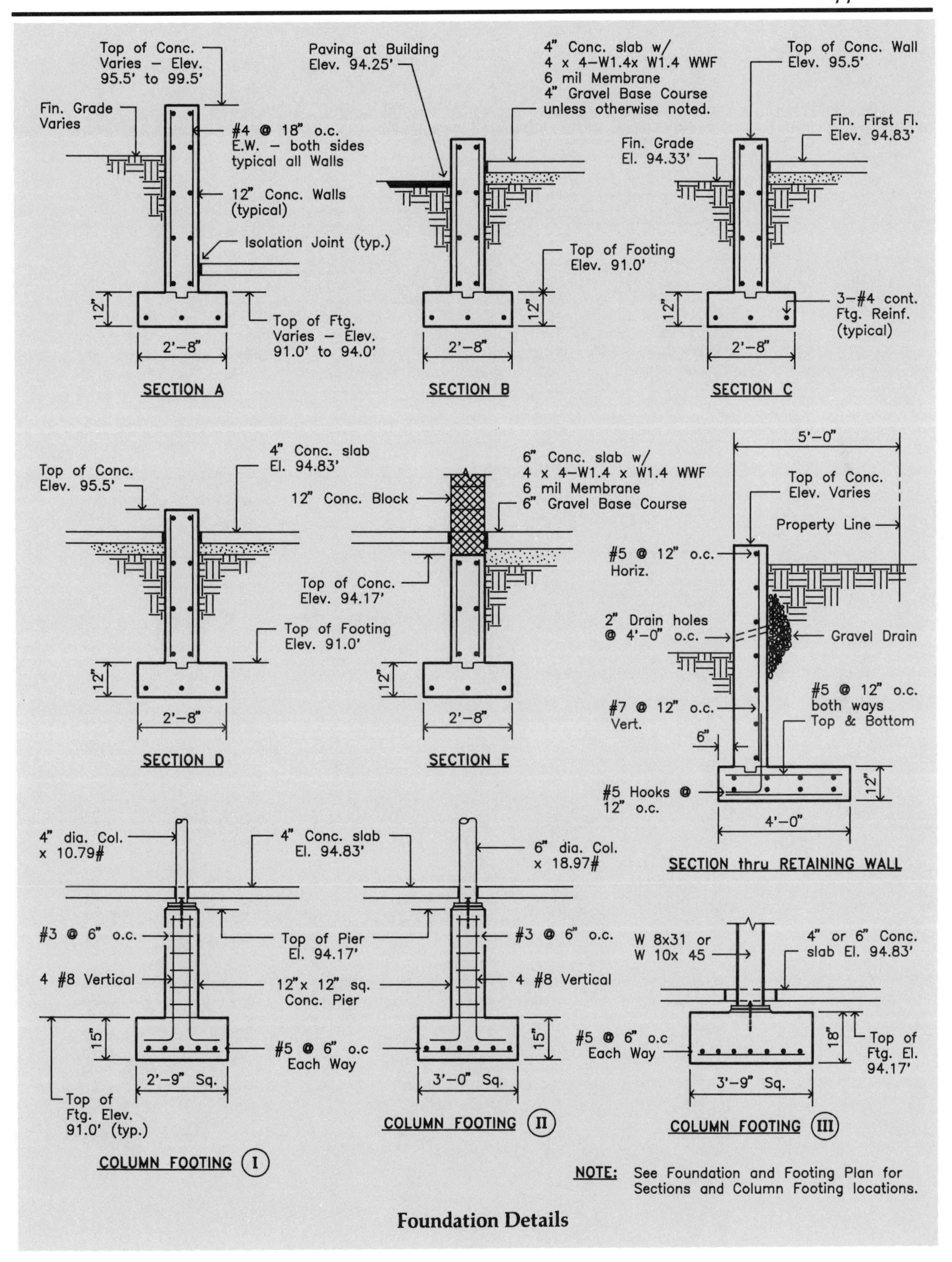

Foundation Details

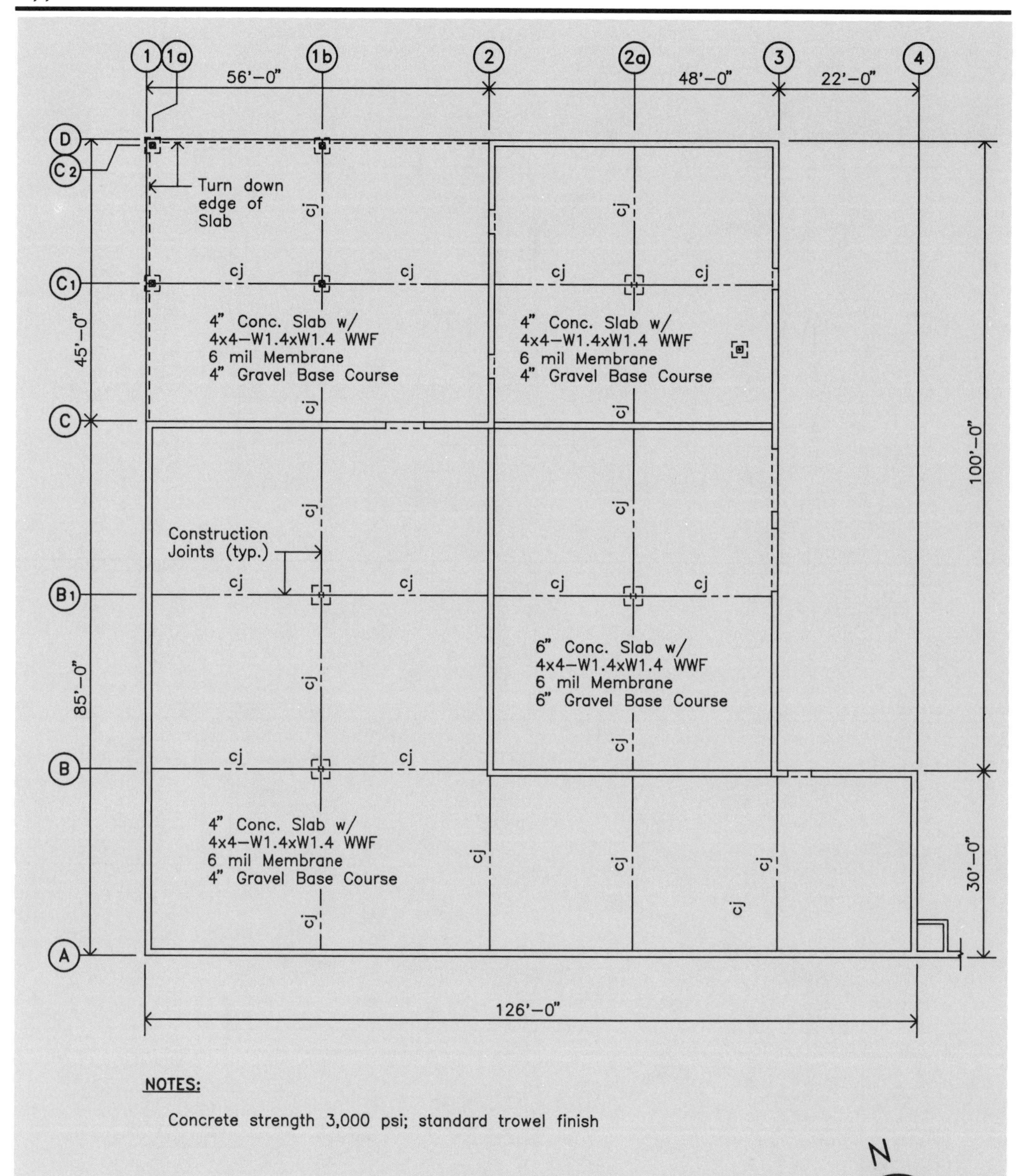

Slab on Grade Plan

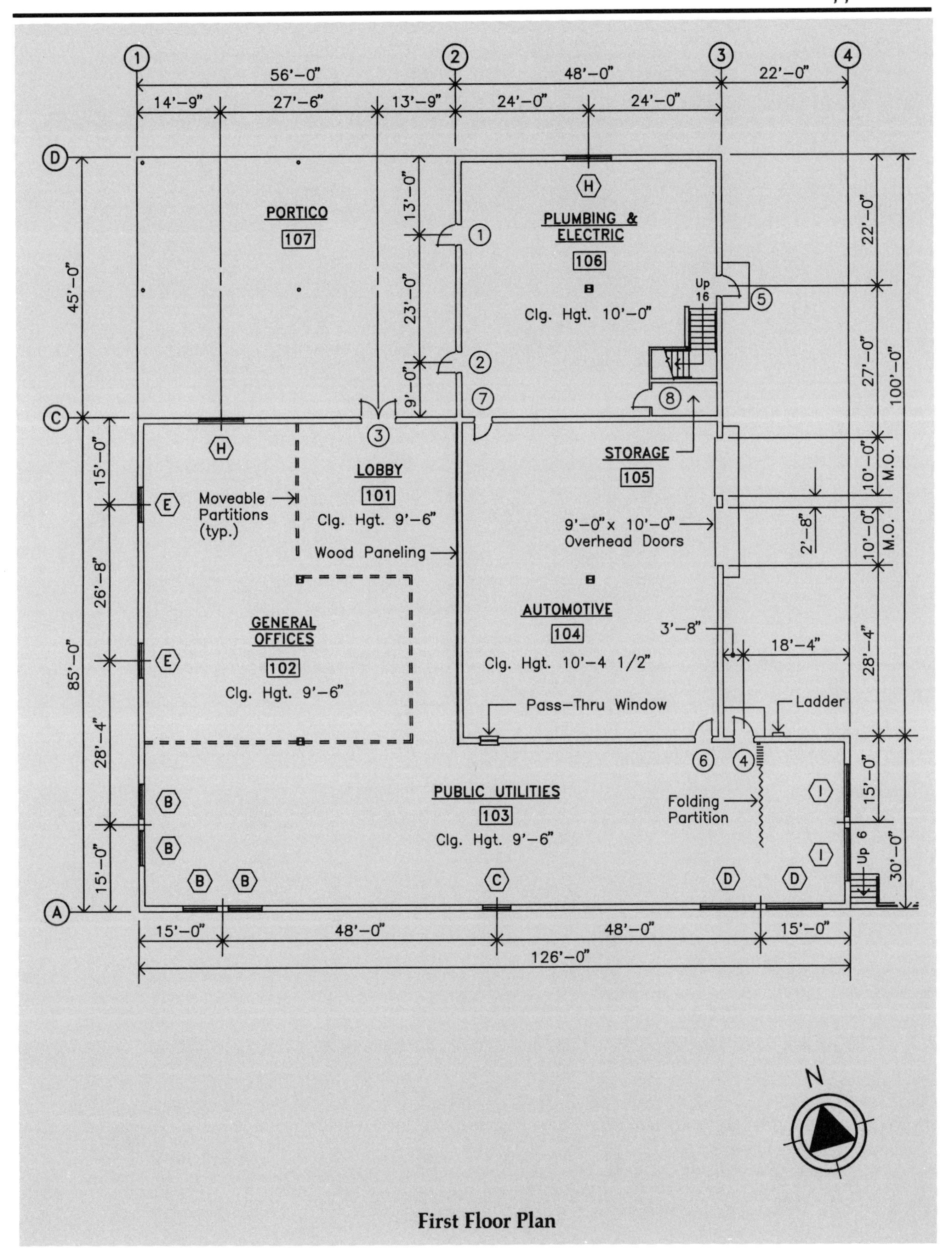

First Floor Plan

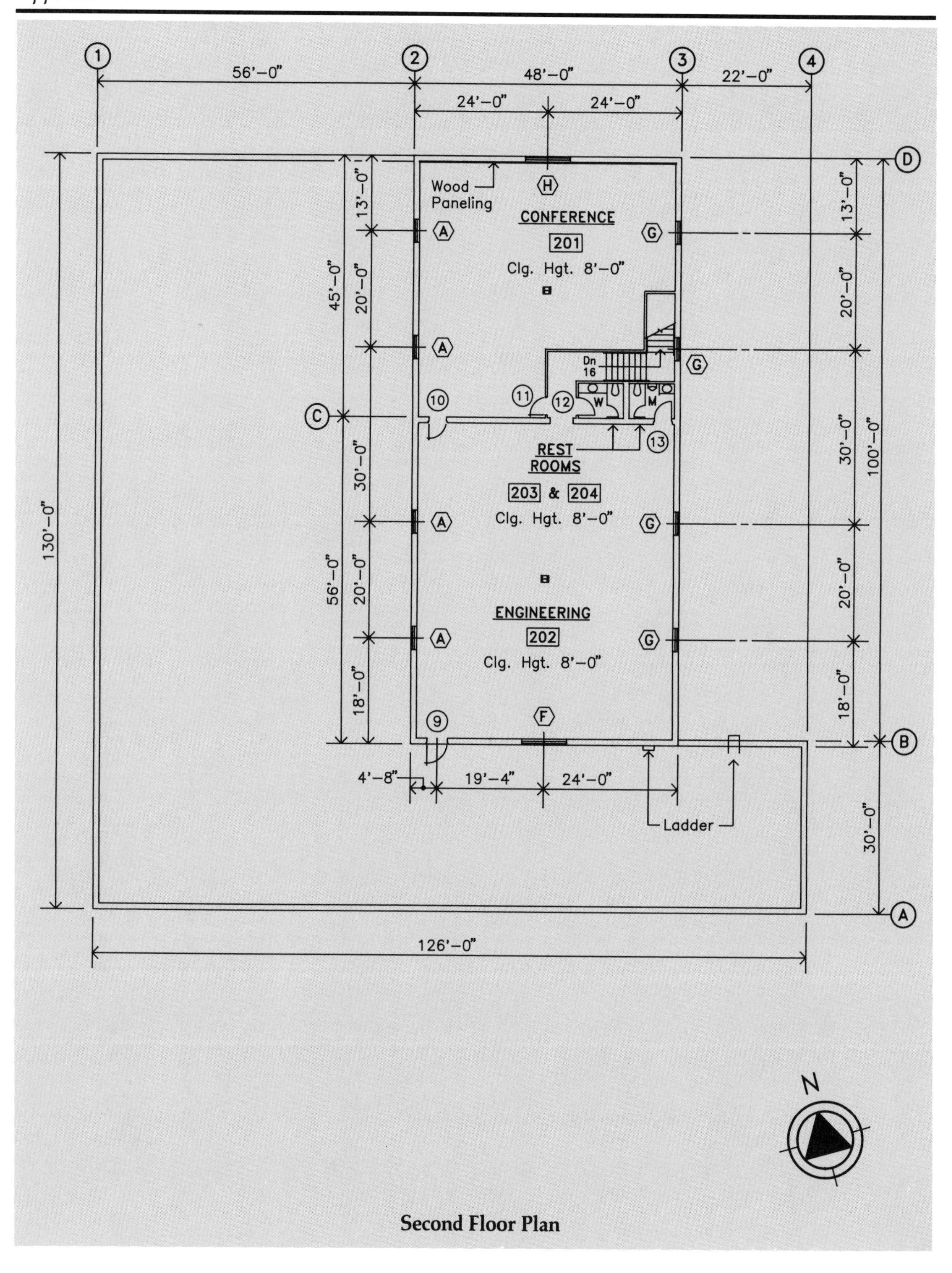

Second Floor Plan

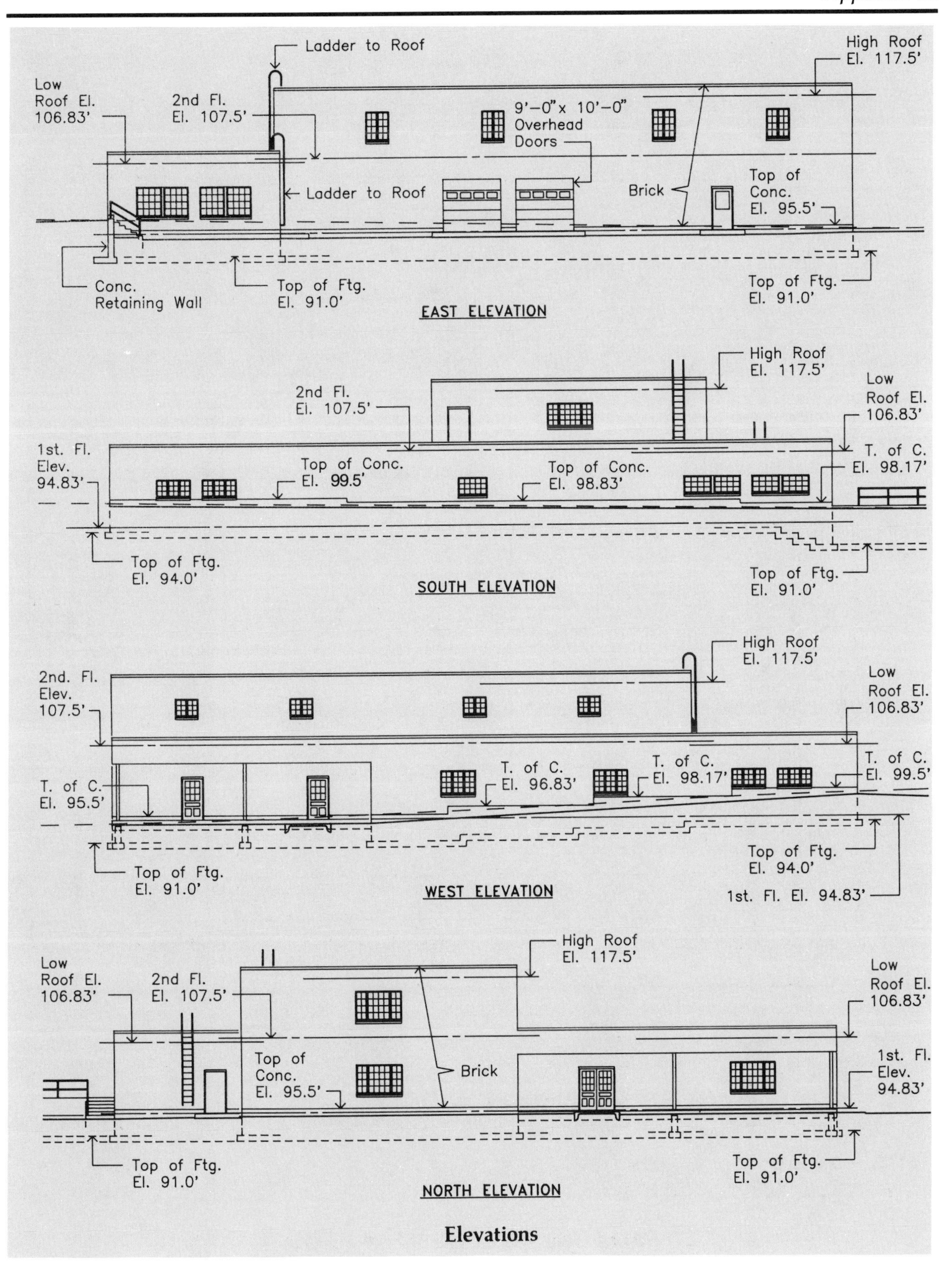
Ladder to Roof
High Roof
El. 117.5'
Low
Roof El.
106.83'
2nd Fl.
El. 107.5'
9'–0" x 10'–0"
Overhead
Doors
Ladder to Roof
Brick
Top of
Conc.
El. 95.5'
Conc.
Retaining Wall
Top of Ftg.
El. 91.0'
Top of Ftg.
El. 91.0'
EAST ELEVATION
High Roof
El. 117.5'
Low
Roof El.
106.83'
2nd Fl.
El. 107.5'
1st. Fl.
Elev.
94.83'
Top of Conc.
El. 99.5'
Top of Conc.
El. 98.83'
T. of C.
El. 98.17'
Top of Ftg.
El. 94.0'
Top of Ftg.
El. 91.0'
SOUTH ELEVATION
High Roof
El. 117.5'
2nd. Fl.
Elev.
107.5'
Low
Roof El.
106.83'
T. of C.
El. 96.83'
T. of C.
El. 98.17'
T. of C.
El. 99.5'
T. of C.
El. 95.5'
Top of Ftg.
El. 94.0'
Top of Ftg.
El. 91.0'
WEST ELEVATION
1st. Fl. El. 94.83'
High Roof
El. 117.5'
Low
Roof El.
106.83'
2nd Fl.
El. 107.5'
Low
Roof El.
106.83'
Top of
Conc.
El. 95.5'
Brick
1st. Fl.
Elev.
94.83'
Top of Ftg.
El. 91.0'
Top of Ftg.
El. 91.0'
NORTH ELEVATION

Elevations

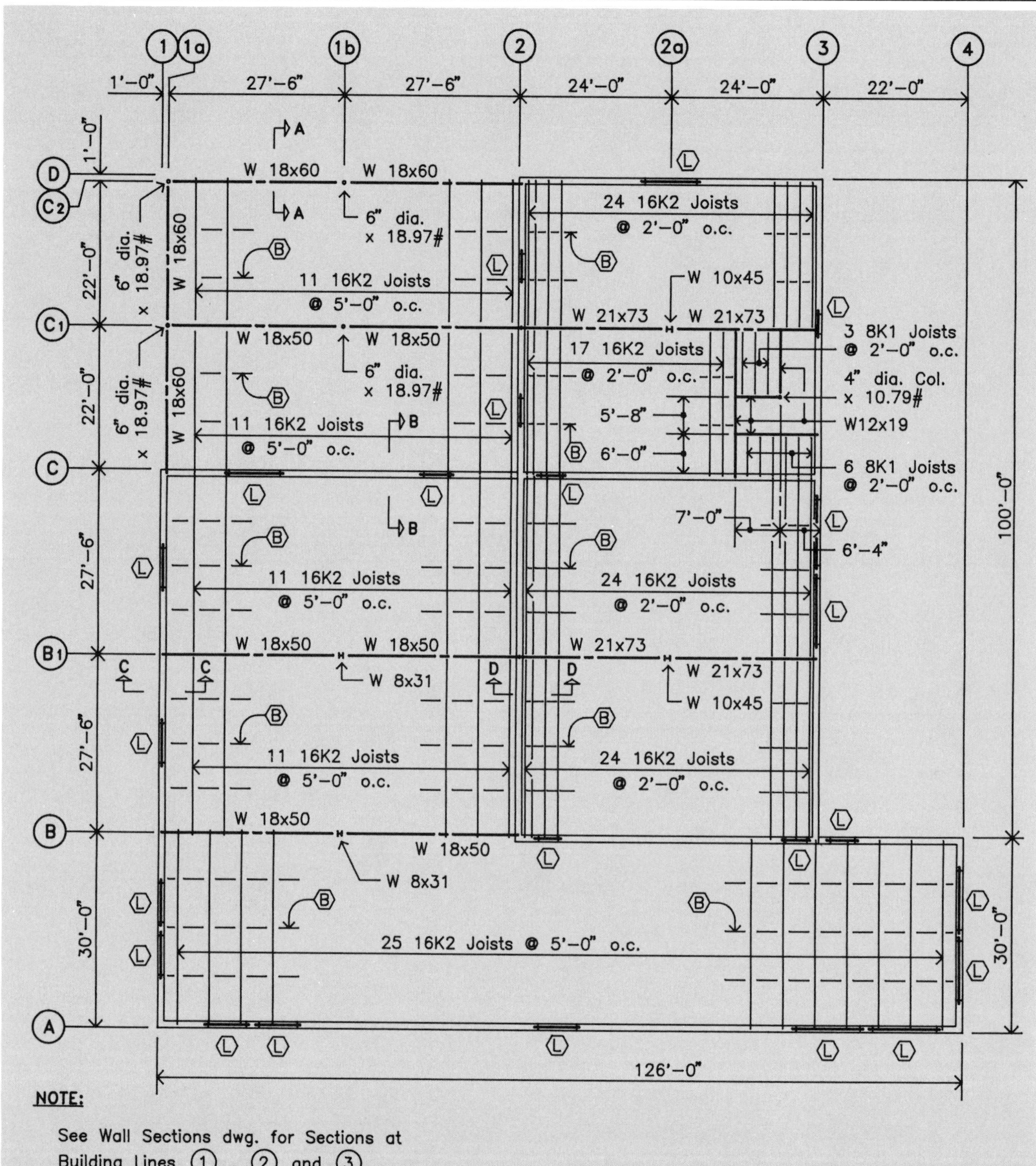

NOTE:

See Wall Sections dwg. for Sections at Building Lines ①, ② and ③.

See Wall Details dwg. for Sections A–A, B–B, C–C, and D–D.

All Structural Steel members to be ASTM A36.

Ⓑ = Horizontal Bridging, Top and Bottom.

Ⓛ = Lintel, Window or Door.

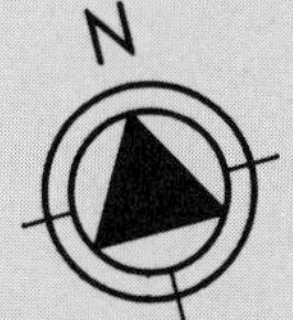

Second Floor and Low Roof Framing Plan

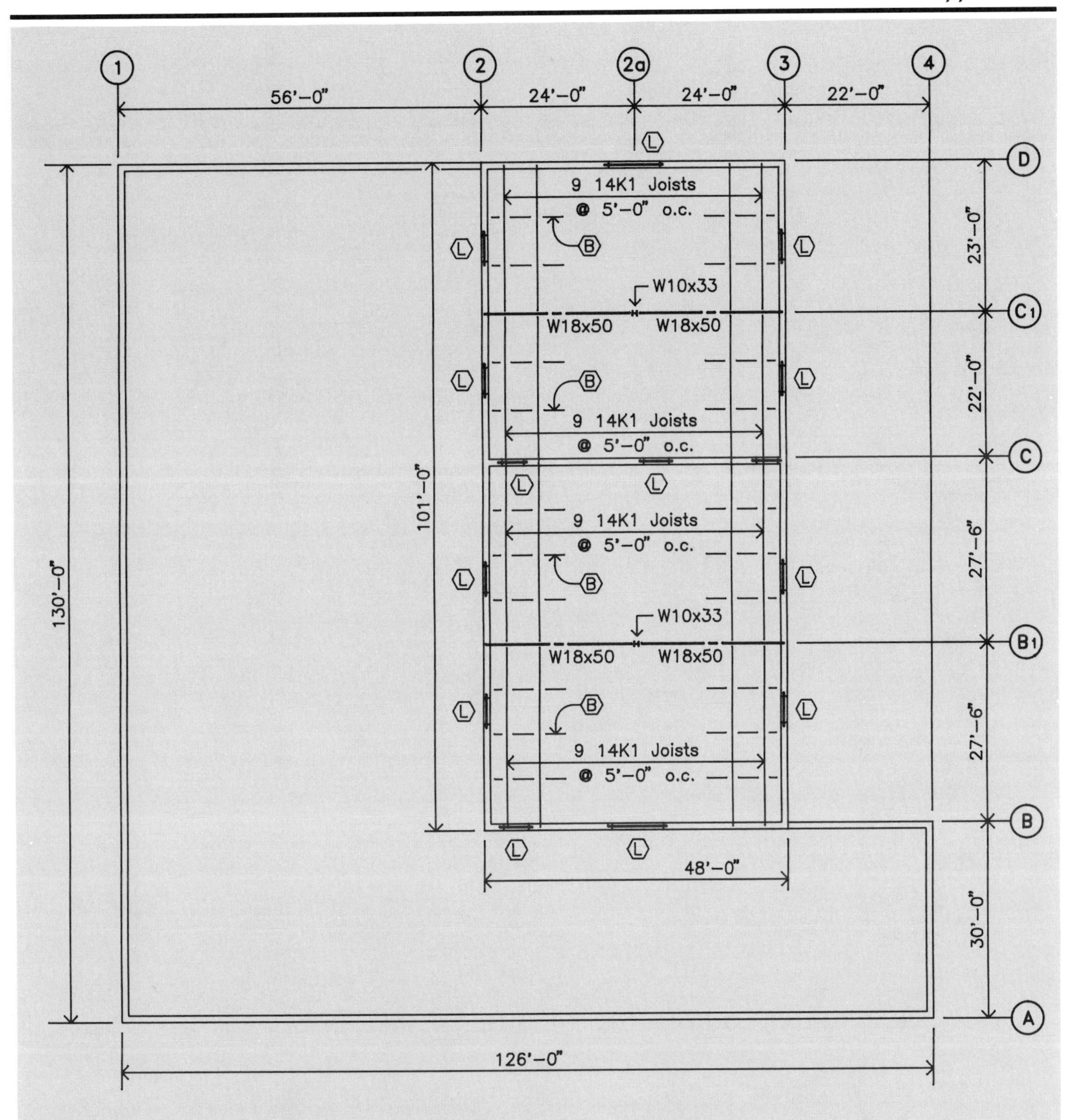

NOTE:

See Wall Sections dwg. for Sections at Building Lines (2) and (3).

All Structural Steel members to be ASTM A36.

(B) = Horizontal Bridging, Top and Bottom.

(L) = Lintel, Window or Door.

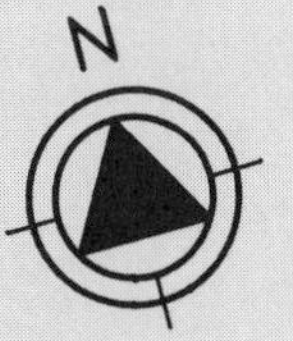

High Roof Framing Plan

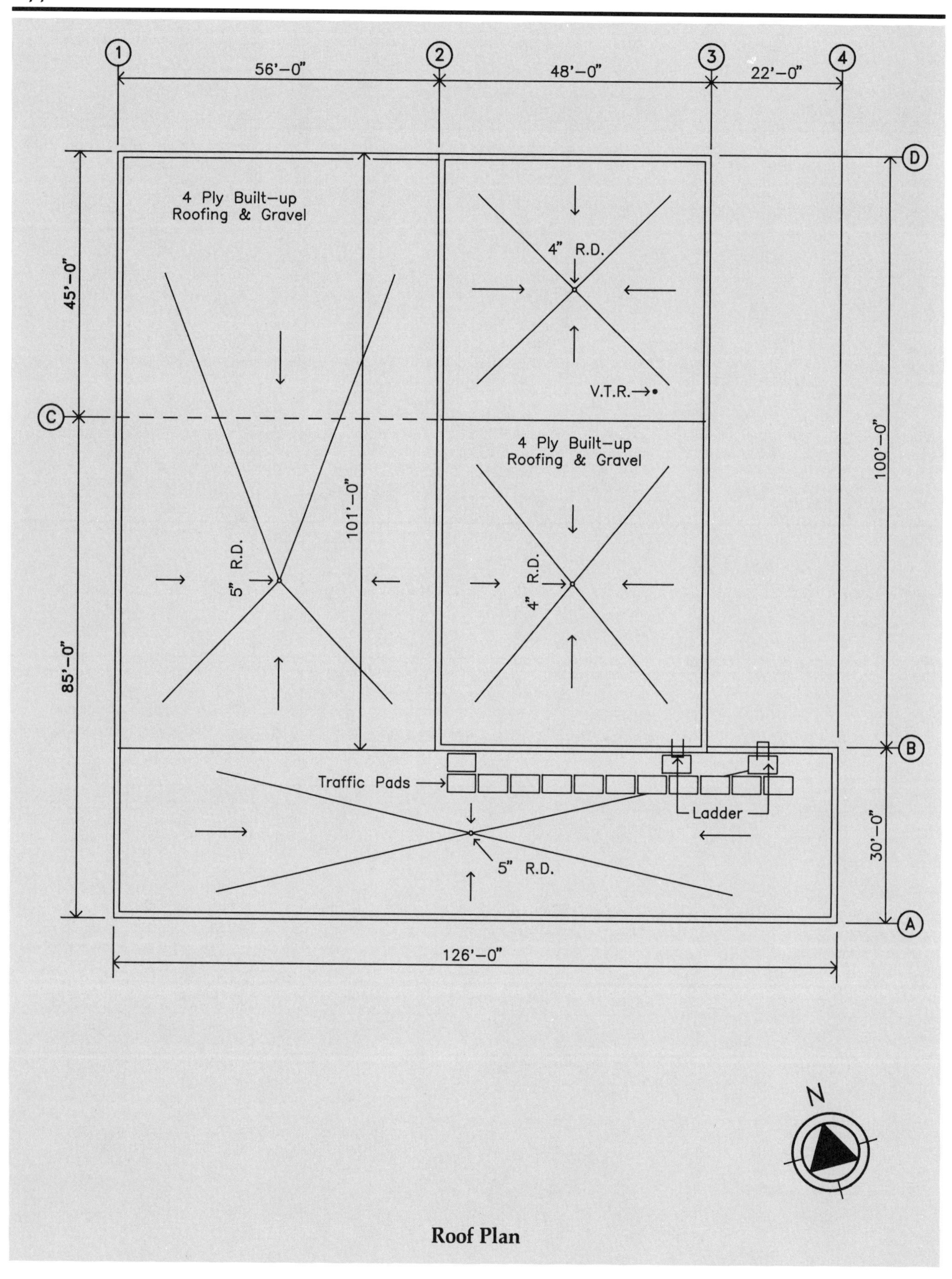

1
2
3
4
56'–0"
48'–0"
22'–0"
D
C
B
A
45'–0"
85'–0"
101'–0"
100'–0"
30'–0"
126'–0"
4 Ply Built–up Roofing & Gravel
4 Ply Built–up Roofing & Gravel
4" R.D.
V.T.R.
5" R.D.
4" R.D.
Traffic Pads
Ladder
5" R.D.
N

Roof Plan

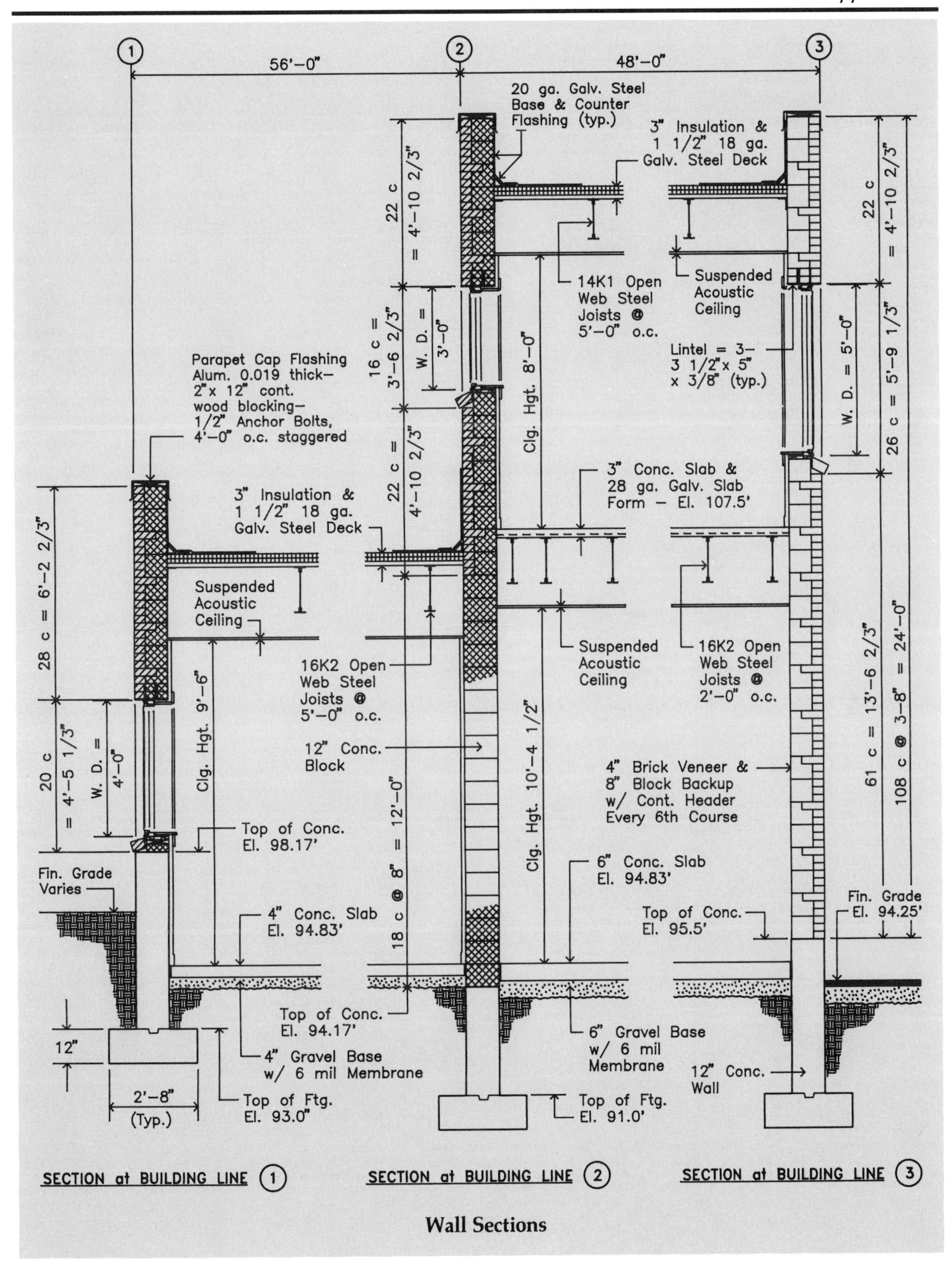

Wall Sections

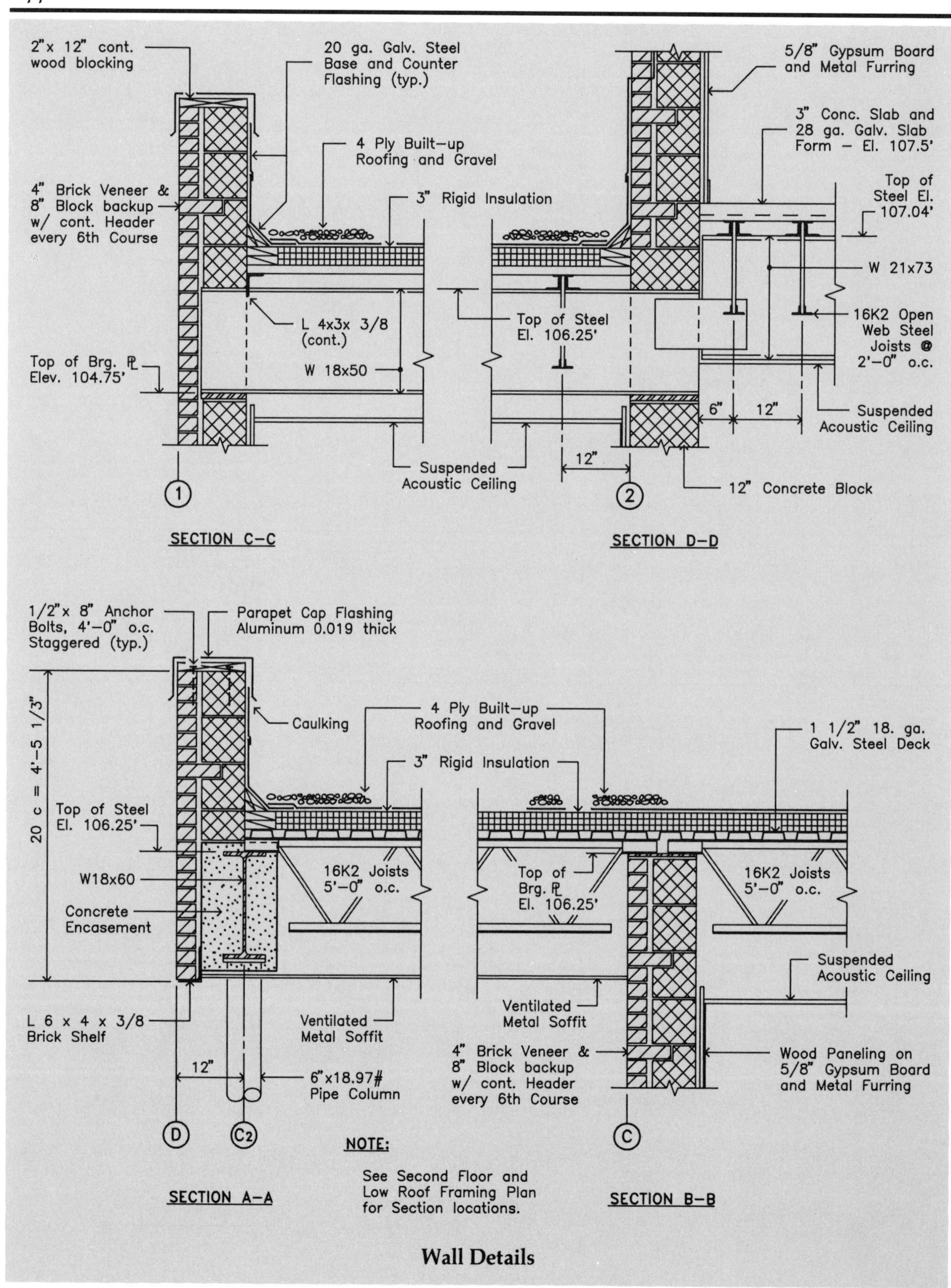

Wall Details

Abbreviations and Symbols

Construction professionals vary somewhat in the way they abbreviate terms commonly used in the industry. The following is a list of abbreviations and symbols accepted by many professionals. Periods have been omitted except when needed for clarity.

A

A&E	architect and engineer
ab	anchor bolt
al (alum)	aluminum
appr	approximate
arch.	architect

B

bd	board
BF	backfill
bf	board feet
bft	bottom of footing
bg	below grade
bldg	building
blk	block
bm	beam
bot	bottom

C

c. in.	cubic inch
cab	cabinet
carp	carpenter
cb	concrete block
cf	cubic feet
CIP	cast-in-place
cir	circle
circum	circumference
clg	ceiling
col	column
conc	concrete
cont	continuous
const	construction
contr	contractor
cr rk	crushed rock
cy	cubic yard

D

d	penny
d	depth
ded	deduct
deg	degree
demo	demolition
det	detail
diam	diameter
dim	dimension
disp	disposal
dp	deep
dr	door
drg	drawing
ds	downspout

E

ea	each
El. (elev)	elevation
elec	electrical
engr	engineer
equip	equipment
ex (excav)	excavation
exist'g	existing
exp	expansion
ext	exterior

F

fg	finish grade
fin	finish
flr	floor
foun	foundation
ft	feet
ftg	footing

G

ga	gauge
galv	galvanize
glu-lam	glue-laminated
gr	ground
grd	grade
gyp	gypsum

H

h (ht)	height
hc	hollow core
hdwe	hardware
hdwd	hardwood
horiz	horizontal
hr	hour

I

in	inch
insul	insulation
int	interior

J

jst	joist
jt	joint

L

l	length
lab	labor
lam plas	laminated plastic
lb	pound
ld	load
lf	linear feet
lg	long
lin	linear
LS	lump sum

M

mach	machine
mat'l	material
max	maximum
mb	machine bolt
MBF	thousand board feet
meas	measure
mech	mechanical
membr	membrane
met	metal
manuf	manufacture
mhr	man-hour
min	minute
misc	miscellaneous
mnfr	manufacturer

N

no.	number
NTS	not to scale

O

oc	on center

P

P&P	point and patch
perim	perimeter
pg	paint grade
pl	panel
plbg	plumbing
plt	plate
pr	pair
prec	precast
ptg	painting
pt'n	partition

Q

QS	quantity sheet

R

r	radius
R&G	rub and grind
ran	random
rebar	reinforcing steel
ref	reference
reinf	reinforcing steel
req'd	required
rm	room

S

s. in.	square inch
sc	solid core
sec	second
sec.	section
sf	square feet
sh met	sheet metal
sht	sheet
sim	similar
specs	specifications
sq	square
ss	stainless steel
std	standard
stl	steel
struc	structural
susp	suspended
sym	symmetrical

T

temp	temperature
tf	top of footing
thk	thick
t/o	takeoff
tot	total
trds	trades
typ	typical

U

uon	unless otherwise noted

V

vert	vertical

W

w	width
wdw	window
wp	waterproof
wt	weight

X

X thk	extra thickness

Y

yd	yard
yr	year
&	and
≐	approximately
∅	diameter
%	percent
±	plus-or-minus
⧠	square foot
w/	with

Suggested Waste Allowances

Soil (shrinking/swelling)	
Crushed rock/gravel	15%
Sand	20%
Silt	22%
Loam (average soil)	24%
Decomposed granite	25%
Clay	26%
Concrete	
Footing (formed)	4–10%
Footings (poured against earth)	10–30%
Foundation walls (formed)	11%
Walls above grade (formed)	3–6%
Slabs on grade	6–12%
Columns	15%
Beams	10%
Suspended slabs	8%
Stairs	15%
Lumber	
Heavy timbers	4%
Light framing	8%
Plywood	
Roof or floor	3%
Walls	5%
Gypsum Board	
Ceilings	4%
Walls	6%
Reinforcing Steel	
Welded wire fabric on slabs	8%
Large walls	10%
Small walls	12%
Suspended slabs	14%
Footings	18%
Columns and beams	20%

Tables of Proportionate Quantities

Flat Roof Framing

Joist Size	Inches on Center	Board Feet per Square Foot of Roof Area	Nails Lbs. per MBM
2″ x 6″	12″	1.17	10
	16″	.91	10
	20″	.76	10
	24″	.65	10
2″ x 8″	12″	1.56	8
	16″	1.21	8
	20″	1.01	8
	24″	.86	8
2″ x 10″	12″	1.96	6
	16″	1.51	6
	20″	1.27	6
	24″	1.08	6
2″ x 12″	12″	2.35	5
	16″	1.82	5
	20″	1.52	5
	24″	1.30	5
3″ x 8″	12″	1.82	5
	16″	1.82	5
	20″	1.52	5
	24″	1.30	5
3″ x 10″	12″	2.94	4
	16″	2.27	4
	20″	1.90	4
	24″	1.62	4

Pitched Roof Framing

Rafters Including Collar Ties, Hip and Valley Rafters, Ridge Poles								
	Spacing Center to Center							
	12 Inches		16 Inches		20 Inches		24 Inches	
Rafter Size	Board Feet per Square Foot of Roof Area	Nails Lbs. per MBM	Board Feet per Square Foot of Roof Area	Nails Lbs. per MBM	Board Feet per Square Foot of Roof Area	Nails Lbs. per MBM	Board Feet per Square Foot of Roof Area	Nails Lbs. per MBM
2″ x 4″	.89	17	.71	17	.59	17	.53	17
2″ x 6″	1.29	12	1.02	12	.85	12	.75	12
2″ x 8″	1.71	9	1.34	9	1.12	9	.98	9
2″ x 10″	2.12	7	1.66	7	1.38	7	1.21	7
2″ x 12″	2.52	6	1.97	6	1.64	6	1.43	6
3″ x 8″	2.52	6	1.97	6	1.64	6	1.43	6
3″ x 10″	3.13	5	2.45	5	2.02	5	1.78	5

Hip and Valley Rafter Ratios

Ratios of Hip or Valley Length to Run of Common Rafter for Various Slopes					
Roof Slope			Roof Slope		
Rise	Run	Ratio	Rise	Run	Ratio
3	12	1.4361	9	12	1.6008
4	12	1.4530	10	12	1.6415
4.5	12	1.4631	11	12	1.6853
5	12	1.4743	12	12	1.7321
6	12	1.5000	13	12	1.7815
7	12	1.5298	14	12	1.8333
8	12	1.5635	15	12	1.8875

Roof Slope Ratios

Ratios of Rafter Length to Run for Various Slopes

Rise	Run	Ratio	Rise	Run	Ratio
3	12	1.0308	9	12	1.2500
4	12	1.0541	10	12	1.3017
4.5	12	1.0680	11	12	1.3566
5	12	1.0833	12	12	1.4142
6	12	1.1180	13	12	1.5366
7	12	1.1577	14	12	1.5366
8	12	1.2019	15	12	1.6008

Cross Bridging

Cross Bridging—Board Foot per Square Foot of Floors, Ceiling or Flat Roof Area, Nails—Pounds per MBM of Bridging

		1″ x 3″		1″ x 4″		2″ x 3″	
Joist Size	Spacing	Bd. Ft.	Nails	Bd. Ft.	Nails	Bd. Ft.	Nails
2″ x 8″	12″	.04	147	.05	112	.08	77
	16″	.04	120	.05	91	.08	61
	20″	.04	102	.05	77	.08	52
	24″	.04	83	.05	63	.08	42
2″ x 10″	12″	.04	36	.05	103	.08	71
	16″	.04	114	.05	87	.08	58
	20″	.04	98	.05	74	.08	50
	24″	.04	80	.05	61	.08	41
2″ x 12″	12″	.04	127	.05	96	.08	67
	16″	.04	108	.05	82	.08	55
	20″	.04	94	.05	71	.08	48
	24″	.04	78	.05	59	.08	39
3″ x 8″	12″	.04	160	.05	122	.08	84
	16″	.04	127	.05	96	.08	66
	20″	.04	107	.05	81	.08	54
	24″	.04	86	.05	65	.08	44
3″ x 10″	12″	.04	146	.05	111	.08	77
	16″	.04	120	.05	91	.08	62
	20″	.04	.02	.05	78	.08	52
	24″	.04	83	.05	63	.08	42

Siding

Type of Siding	Size	Exposure	Board Feet per Square Foot of Wall Area	Lbs. Nails MBM of Siding — Stud Spacing 16″	20″	24″
Plain Bevel Siding	1/2″ x 4″	2-1/2″	1.60	17	13	11
		2-3/4″	1.45			
	1/2″ x 6″	4-1/2″	1.33	11	9	7
		4-3/4″	1.26			
		5″	1.20			
	1/2″ x 8″	6-1/2″	1.23	8	7	6
		7″	1.14			
Plain Bevel Bungalow Siding	5/8″ x 8″	6-1/2″	1.23	14	11	9
		7″	1.14			
	5/8″ x 10″	8-1/2″	1.18	16	13	11
		9″	1.11			
	3/4″ x 8″	6-1/2″	1.23	14	11	9
		7″	1.14			
	3/4″ x 10″	8-1/2″	1.18	16	13	11
		9″	1.11			
	3/4″ x 12″	10-1/2″	1.14	14	11	9
		11″	1.09			
Drop or Rustic Siding	3/4″ x 4″	3-1/4″	1.23	27	22	18
	3/4″ x 6″	5-1/16″	1.19	18	15	12
		5-3/16″	1.17			

Furring

Size	Board Foot per Square Foot of Wall Area — Spacing Center to Center 12″	16″	20″	24″	Lbs. Nails per MBM of Furring
1″ x 2″	.18	.14	.11	.10	55
1″ x 3″	.28	.21	.17	.14	37

Wallboard

Includes Fiber Board, Gypsum Board and Plywood, Used as Underflooring, Sheathing, Plaster Base, or as Drywall Finish					
Factors		Nail			
Used for Underflooring, Sheathing and Plaster Base	Used for Exposed Dry Wall Finish	Pounds of Nails per 1,000 Sq. Ft. of Wallboard — Joist, Stud, or Rafter Spacing 12″	16″	20″	24″
1.05	1.10	7	6	5	4

Floor Framing

Floor Joists				Blocking Over Main Bearing	
Joist Size	Inches on Center	Board Feet per Square Foot of Floor Area	Nails Lbs. per MBM	Board Feet per Square Foot of Floor Area	Nails Lbs. per MBM Blocking
2″ x 6″	12″	1.28	10	.16	133
	16″	1.02	10	.03	95
	20″	.88	10	.03	77
	24″	.78	10	.03	57
2″ x 8″	12″	1.71	8	.04	100
	16″	1.36	8	.04	72
	20″	1.17	8	.04	57
	24″	1.03	8	.05	43
2″ x 10″	12″	2.14	6	.05	79
	16″	1.71	6	.05	57
	20″	1.48	6	.06	46
	24″	1.30	6	.06	34
2″ x 12″	12″	2.56	5	.06	66
	16″	2.05	5	.06	47
	20″	1.77	5	.07	39
	24″	1.56	5	.07	29
3″ x 8″	12″	2.56	5	.04	39
	16″	2.05	5	.05	57
	20″	1.77	5	.06	45
	24″	1.56	5	.06	33
3″ x 10″	12″	3.20	4	.05	72
	16″	2.56	4	.07	46
	20″	2.21	4	.07	36
	24″	1.95	4	.08	26

Board Sheathing and Subflooring

Type	Size	Diagonal: Board Feet per Square Foot of Area	Lbs. Nails per MBM Lumber — Joist, Stud, or Rafter Spacing: 12″	16″	20″	24″
Surface 4 Sides (S4S)	1″ x 4″	1.22	58	46	39	32
	1″ x 6″	1.18	39	31	25	21
	1″ x 8″	1.18	30	23	19	16
	1″ x 10″	1.17	35	27	23	19
Tongue and Groove (T&G)	1″ x 4″	1.36	65	51	43	36
	1″ x 6″	1.26	42	33	27	23
	1″ x 8″	1.22	31	24	20	17
	1″ x 10″	1.20	36	28	24	19
Shiplap	1″ x 4″	1.41	67	53	45	37
	1″ x 6″	1.29	43	33	28	23
	1″ x 8″	1.24	31	24	20	17
	1″ x 10″	1.21	36	28	24	19

Board Sheathing and Subflooring

Type	Size	Right Angles: Board Feet per Square Foot of Area	Lbs. Nails per MBM Lumber — Joist, Stud, or Rafter Spacing: 12″	16″	20″	24″
Surface 4 Sides (S4S)	1″ x 4″	1.19	60	47	40	33
	1″ x 6″	1.15	40	31	26	22
	1″ x 8″	1.15	30	23	20	17
	1″ x 10″	1.14	36	28	24	19
Tongue and Groove (T&G)	1″ x 4″	1.32	66	52	44	36
	1″ x 6″	1.23	43	33	28	23
	1″ x 8″	1.19	32	24	21	17
	1″ x 10″	1.17	37	29	24	20
Shiplap	1″ x 4″	1.38	69	55	46	38
	1″ x 6″	1.26	44	34	29	24
	1″ x 8″	1.21	32	25	21	17
	1″ x 10″	1.18	37	29	25	20

Ceiling Joists

Joist Size	Inches on Center	Board Feet per Square Foot of Ceiling Area	Nails Lbs. per MBM
2″ x 4″	12″	.78	17
	16″	.59	19
	20″	.48	19
2″ x 6″	12″	1.15	11
	16″	.88	13
	20″	.72	13
	24″	.63	13
2″ x 8″	12″	1.53	9
	16″	1.17	9
	20″	.96	9
	24″	.84	9
2″ x 10″	12″	1.94	7
	16″	1.47	7
	20″	1.21	7
	24″	1.04	7
3″ x 8″	12″	2.32	6
	16″	1.76	6
	20″	1.44	6
	24″	1.25	6

Exterior Wall Stud Framing

		Studs Including Corner Bracing		Horizontal Bracing Midway Between Plates	
Stud Size	Inches on Center	Board Feet per Square Foot of Ext. Wall Area	Lbs. Nails per MBM of Stud Framing	Board Feet per Square Foot of Ext. Wall Area	Lbs. Nails per MBM of Bracing
2″ x 3″	16″	.78	30	.03	117
	20″	.74	30	.03	97
	24″	.71	30	.03	85
2″ x 4″	16″	1.05	22	.04	87
	20″	.98	22	.04	72
	24″	.94	22	.04	64
2″ x 6″	16″	1.51	15	.06	59
	20″	1.44	15	.06	48
	24″	1.38	15	.06	43

Partition Stud Framing

Studs Including Sole and C Plates				Horizontal Bracing in All Partitions		Horizontal Bracing in Bearing Partitions Only	
Stud Size	Inches on Center	Board Feet per Square Foot of Partition Area	Lbs. Nails per MBM of Stud Framing	Board Feet per Square Foot of Partition Area	Lbs. Nails per MBM of Stud Framing	Board Feet per Square Foot of Partition Area	Lbs. Nails per MBM of Stud Framing
2″ x 3″	12″	.91	25	.04	145	.01	145
	16″	.83	25	.04	111	.01	111
	20″	.78	25	.04	90	.01	90
	24″	.76	25	.04	79	.01	79
2″ x 4″	12″	1.22	19	.05	108	.02	108
	16″	1.12	19	.05	87	.02	87
	20″	1.05	19	.05	72	.02	72
	24″	1.02	19	.05	64	.02	64
2″ x 6″	16″	1.02	19			.04	59
	20″	1.29	16			.04	48
	24″	1.22	16			.04	43
2″ x 4″ Staggered	8″	1.69	22				
3″ x 4″	16″	1.35	17				
2″ x 4″ 2″ Way	16″	1.08	19				

Geometric Formulas

1

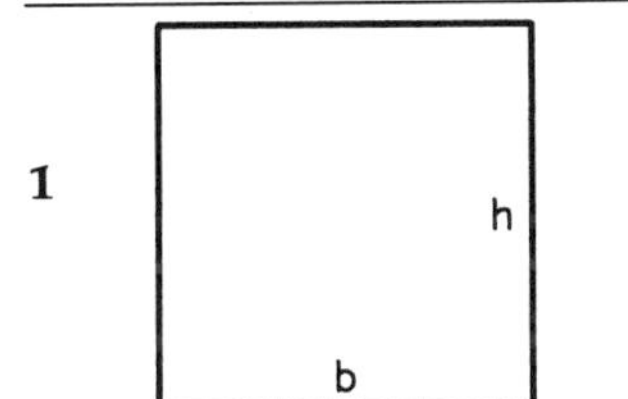

Square
Area = $h \times b$
Perimeter = $2 \times (b + h)$

2

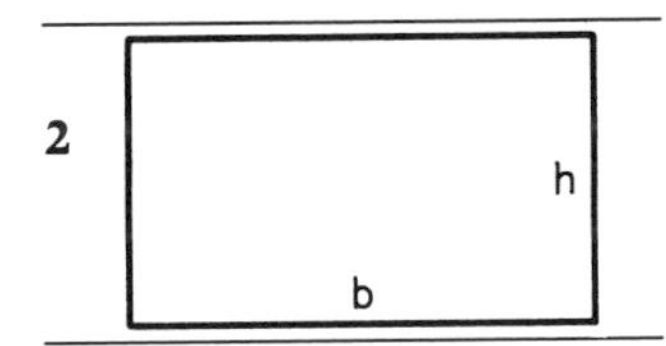

Rectangle
Area = $h \times b$
Perimeter = $2 \times (b + h)$

3

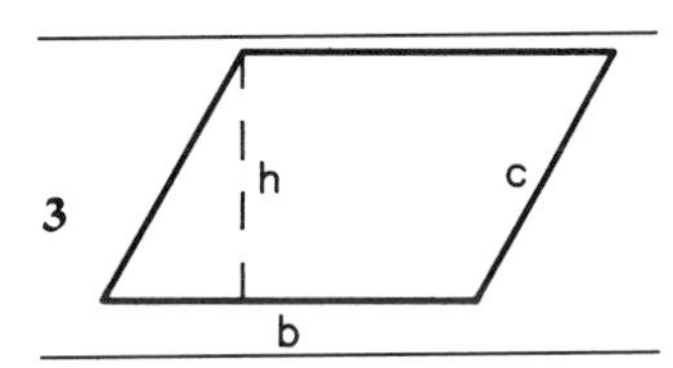

Parallelogram
Area = $h \times b$
Perimeter = $2 \times (b + c)$

4

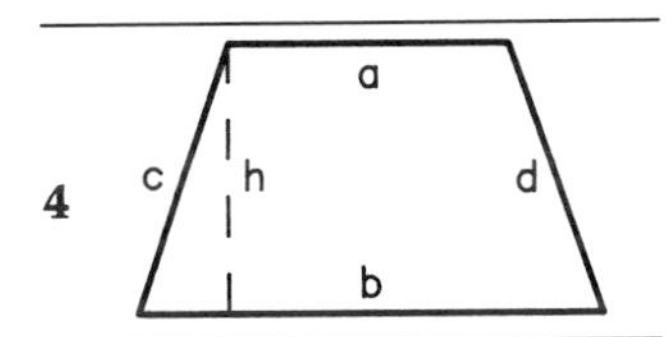

Trapezoid
Area = $\frac{(a + b)h}{2}$
Perimeter = $a + b + c + d$

5

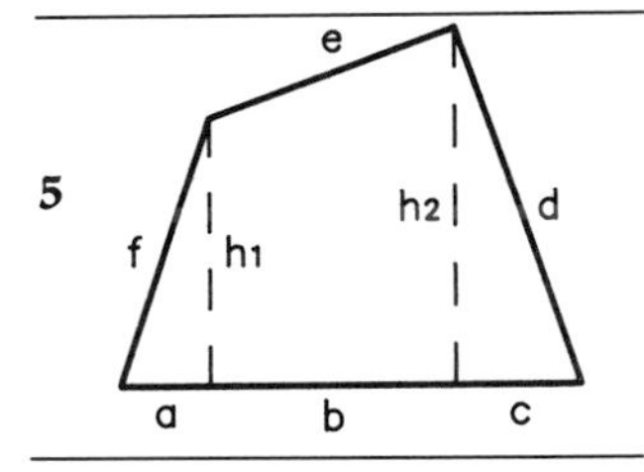

Trapezium
Area = $\frac{b(h_1 + h_2) + ah_1 + ch_2}{2}$
Perimeter = $a + b + c + d + e + f$

6

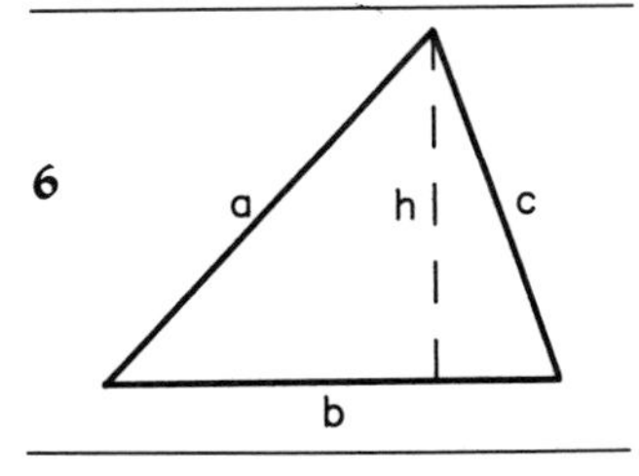

Triangle
Area = $\frac{bh}{2}$
Perimeter = $a + b + c$

7

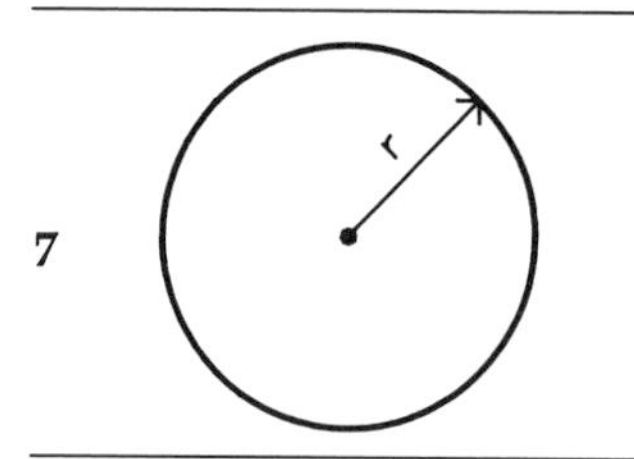

Circle

Area $= \pi r^2$ ($\pi = 3.1416$)

Perimeter (circumference) $= 2\pi r$

8

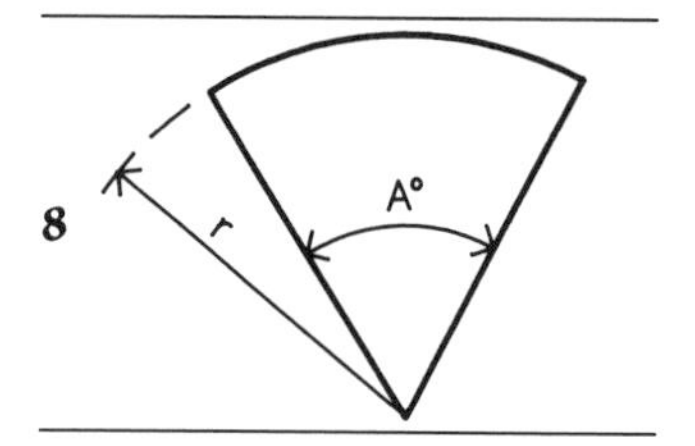

Segment of a Circle

Area $= \pi r^2 \dfrac{A°}{360}$

9

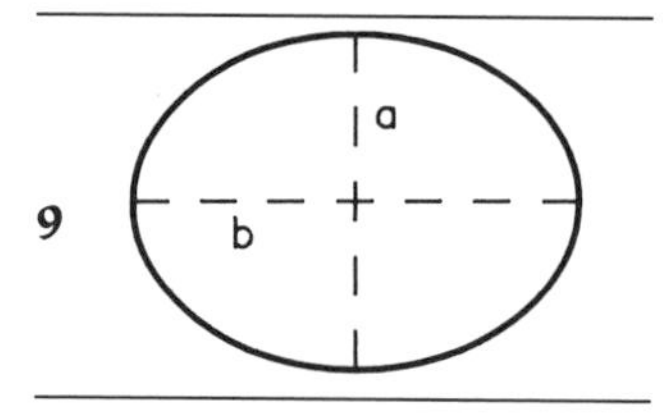

Ellipse

Area $= 0.7854ab$

10

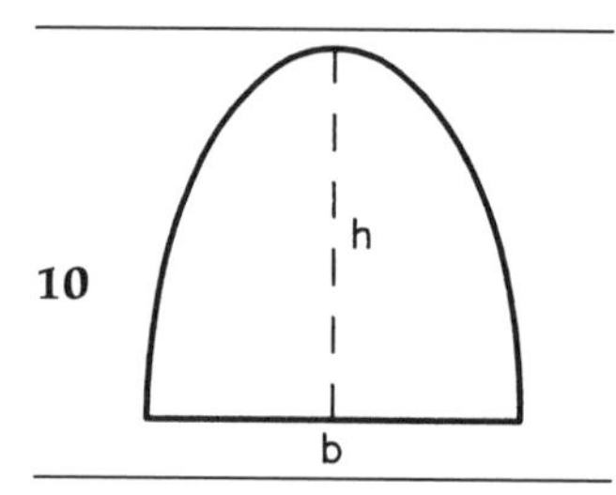

Parabola

Area $= \dfrac{2bh}{3}$

11

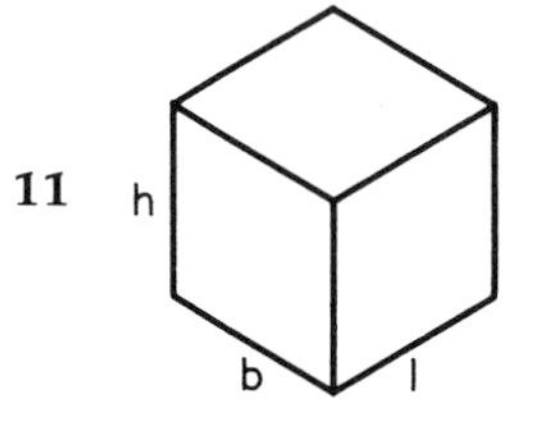

Cube or Block

Volume $= bhl$

Surface Area $= 2bh + 2lh + 2bl$

12

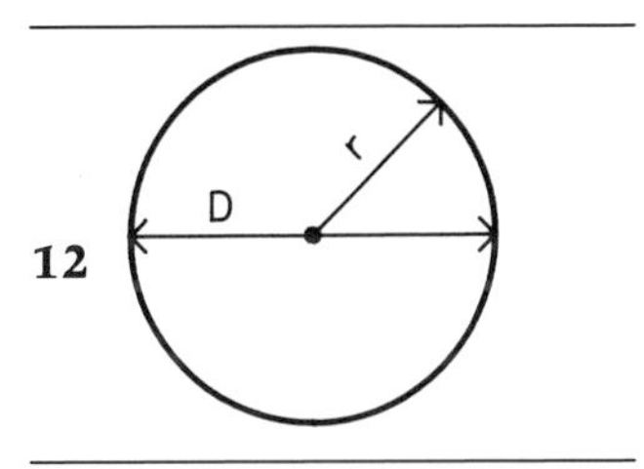

Sphere

Volume = $0.5236\ D^3$

Surface Area = $4\pi r^2$ $(\pi = 3.1416)$

13

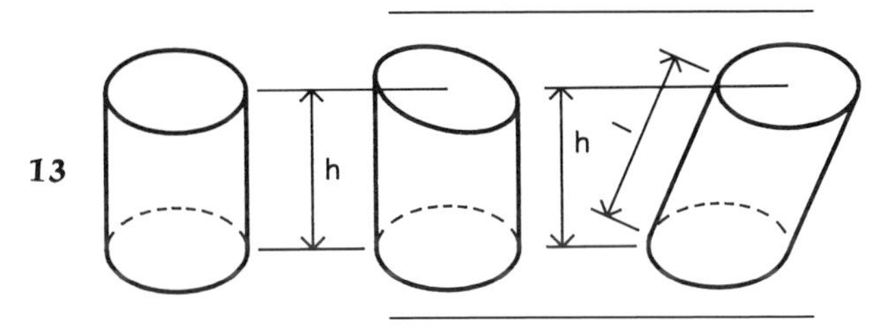

Cylinder, Slant Top, or Oblique

Volume = Area of Base × h

Surface Area = Perimeter × Slant Height (l)

14

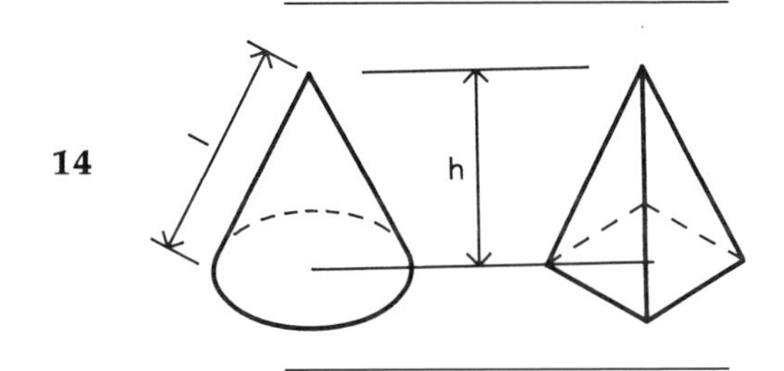

Cone or Pyramid

$$\text{Volume} = \frac{\text{Area of Base} \times h}{3}$$

Surface Area = Perimeter of Base × Slant Height (l)

15

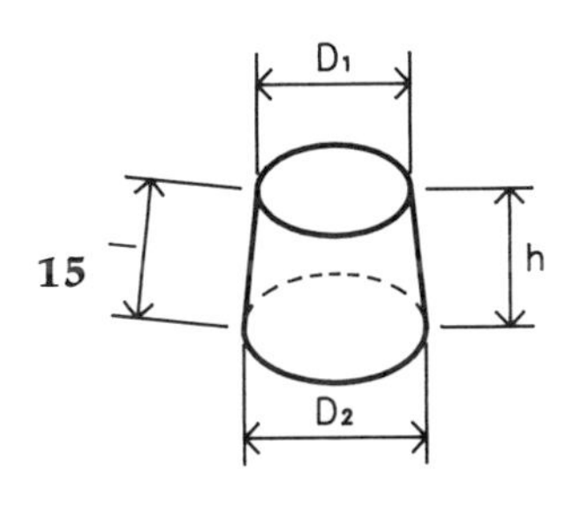

Frustrum of a Cone

Volume =

$$\frac{D_1 + D_2 + (\text{Area of Top} + \text{Area of Base}) \times h \times 0.7854}{3}$$

$${}^{*}\text{Surface Area} = \frac{(D_1 + D_2)l}{2}$$

*Excludes Top & Base Areas

Index

D

E

F

Q

R

S